AN INTRODUCTION TO THE

Calculus of Variations

AN INTRODUCTION
TO THE
Calculus of Variations

BY

L. A. PARS
President of Jesus College, Cambridge

H·E·B

HEINEMANN
LONDON

Heinemann Educational Books Ltd
LONDON MELBOURNE TORONTO
SINGAPORE CAPE TOWN
AUCKLAND IBADAN
HONG KONG

J. E. LITTLEWOOD
amicitiae et admirationis ergo

First published 1962
Reprinted 1965

Published by Heinemann Educational Books Ltd
48, Charles Street, London W.1

Printed in Northern Ireland at The Universities Press, Belfast

Preface

For many years I have felt the need of an introduction, in the English tongue, to the Calculus of Variations; this book is designed to meet that need. My aim has been to provide a clear and rigorous exposition of the fundamental theory, without losing sight of the practical applications—in geometry and dynamics and physics. I hope that this contact with the concrete applications will illuminate the theory for the reader whose interests are mainly in the direction of pure analysis, and also that it will make the book more useful to the reader whose interests lie more in the direction of mathematical physics. A theoretical exposition, entirely divorced from applications, might appear somewhat arid and forbidding, especially to the physicist. A book consisting mainly of applications to problems of mathematical physics, with scant attention to the logical basis of the theory, would be unattractive to the pure mathematician. I have tried to steer a middle course between these extremes.

I have chosen, after some hesitation, to exhibit the theory in terms of the Riemann integral rather than the Lebesgue integral, though I digress occasionally to point out how the theory would be modified in the alternative choice. To defend the choice of the Riemann integral it would be almost sufficient to point out that this was the choice made by so great an authority as Bliss in his important and scholarly book (3).* The gain in generality that would follow from using the Lebesgue integral is not substantial in the early stages, and I believe that the choice of the Riemann integral will make the book useful to a wider circle of readers.

One source of embarrassment in some branches of analysis, and especially in the Calculus of Variations, arises from the choice of notation. One often meets formulae which are in themselves ambiguous (though no doubt the interpretation can be clarified by careful reference to the context) and this is undoubtedly a source of real difficulty to students. For this reason I have taken special care with the notation, particularly in the early chapters, occasionally even at the risk of appearing pedantic.

The book is definitely introductory and makes no claim to cover the whole subject; if it made any approach to completeness it would

* The numbers refer to the short bibliography on p. 347.

be many times larger than it is. Inevitably, since the scope is limited, some readers would prefer an enlargement of the treatment of this topic or of that, according to their particular tastes and interests. But I hope that the book will give to the non-specialist a good insight into the fundamental ideas of the subject, a good working knowledge of the relevant techniques, and an adequate starting-point for further study and research into those regions of the subject not dealt with here.

When one sets out to determine the precise scope of an introduction to the Calculus of Variations, a little reflexion shows that the crucial question arises from the problem of Lagrange; should the book contain a proof of the Multiplier Rule or not? So far as I know, no easy proof of the Multiplier Rule has been found. On the other hand, it is an extremely powerful and versatile result, and, though it is not easy to establish, it is quite easy to use.

The decision to go just so far as to include a proof of the Multiplier Rule (for normal arcs only) more-or-less determines the scope of the book. The "ordinary" problem, with one independent variable (as contrasted with the "parametric" problem) is treated fairly fully, and the investigation is carried far enough to include a proof of the fundamental sufficiency theorem, first for the plane problem (with one dependent variable) and then for the spatial problem (with n dependent variables). Euler's Rule for the isoperimetrical problem, and the Multiplier Rule for the problem of Lagrange, are established, but only so far as necessary conditions. The parametric problem (for plane curves only) is treated rather less intensively than the ordinary problem, but the work is carried far enough to establish the fundamental sufficiency theorem, and to solve completely Newton's famous problem of the solid of revolution of least resistance.

Some of the examples chosen as illustrations in the early stages may appear at first sight somewhat trivial and artificial. But this is merely because each example has been chosen to illuminate a particular point of logic, and to do so concisely, without lengthy calculations.

A number of topics that fall outside the chosen domain are of great interest and importance. The specialist will notice the absence of sufficient conditions for the isoperimetrical problem and for Lagrange's problem, of any discussion of the abnormal cases in the Multiplier Rule, of the existence theorem of Hilbert, and of the Hamilton-Jacobi theory. I have given very little space to the theory of the second variation, but the importance of this topic in the history of the subject persuaded me that it should not be omitted altogether.

The last chapter is devoted to problems with multiple integrals. It is an open question whether this topic should be included or not. The case against it is that the line of development for multiple integrals differs sharply from that for problems with one independent variable, and it must be admitted that the unity of the book is somewhat impaired by including problems of this class. However, I felt that the subject was too important to be passed over in silence, and indeed that there would be some readers for whom it would be the most interesting chapter in the book. The last chapter involves a higher standard of sophistication, and demands a somewhat larger mathematical equipment, than the rest of the book; it presupposes some knowledge of point-set theory, of harmonic functions, and of Fourier series. This chapter is of necessity largely concerned with Dirichlet's principle. Of the various known attacks on this rather difficult subject I have chosen a modification of Poincaré's *méthode de balayage.*

I have included a short collection of illustrative examples, which I hope will be helpful, and a short Bibliography.

Like all workers in this field, I owe much to the great and encyclopaedic treatise of Bolza (**4**), which has been for half a century the standard work of reference, and I have already mentioned the important book by his disciple, Bliss (**3**). The smaller introductory book of Bliss (**2**) is an admirable exposition of the earliest stages—indeed a model of what an elementary text-book should be. The work of Courant has been helpful, both generally, and more particularly in the chapter on multiple integrals (**7**). Finally I must mention my indebtedness to the late Prof. G. H. Hardy; I never, alas, had the opportunity of attending his lectures on the Calculus of Variations, but I had many conversations on the subject with him which were helpful and illuminating.

There are many friends who have helped me with advice at various stages of the work, and I wish to record my thanks to them, in particular to Dr. Sheila M. Edmonds, Miss M. E. Grimshaw, Mr. A. E. Ingham, Dr. J. C. P. Miller, Dr. W. B. Pennington, and Dr. F. Smithies; to Dr. C. T. C. Wall for his careful reading of the proofs and for many helpful suggestions; and especially to Prof. J. E. Littlewood, to whom I dedicate this book.

L. A. Pars

Jesus College, Cambridge

Contents

CHAPTER I

Introduction

1.1 The fundamental problem

The fundamental problem of the Calculus of Variations is as follows. The real numbers X, Y, $\overline{X}$, $\overline{Y}$ are prescribed, and $X < \overline{X}$. The function $F(x, y, z)$ is a given function of the three independent variables x, y, z. We consider a set of functions $\varphi(x)$, called the *admissible functions* (of which the precise definition is given below) each of which has the value Y at X and the value $\overline{Y}$ at $\overline{X}$,

$$\varphi(X) = Y, \qquad \varphi(\overline{X}) = \overline{Y}. \tag{1.1.1}$$

The problem is to find among the admissible functions one that minimizes the integral

$$I = \int_X^{\overline{X}} F\{x, \varphi(x), \varphi'(x)\}\, dx. \tag{1.1.2}$$

With each admissible function $\varphi(x)$ is associated the number I. If we think of φ as the independent variable, I is a *functional*, i.e. a numerical-valued function of φ.

It is natural, and usual, to interpret the problem geometrically; indeed, many of the most famous problems are geometrical in origin. We take rectangular axes Ox, Oy in a plane, and consider the end-point A with coordinates (X, Y), and the end-point B with coordinates $(\overline{X}, \overline{Y})$. Instead of speaking of the admissible functions $\varphi(x)$ we now speak of the *admissible curves* K,

$$y = \varphi(x), \tag{1.1.3}$$

where the functions $\varphi(x)$ are as before. The problem is to find among the admissible curves (all of which join A to B) one that minimizes the integral I.

We sometimes write the integral (1.1.2) in the form

$$I = \int_K F(x, y, y')\, dx, \tag{1.1.4}$$

and sometimes in the form

$$I = \int_X^{\overline{X}} F(x, y, y')\, dx, \tag{1.1.5}$$

it being understood in (1.1.5) that the integral is taken along the curve K (1.1.3), so that the symbols y, y' in (1.1.5) stand for $\varphi(x)$, $\varphi'(x)$. We speak of the ordered pair (x, y) (or $\{x, \varphi(x)\}$) as a *point* of the curve, of y' (or $\varphi'(x)$) as the *slope* of the curve at the point (x, y), and of the ordered triple (x, y, y') (or $\{x, \varphi(x), \varphi'(x)\}$) as an *element* of the curve.

1.2 Notation

For a function $\psi(x)$ of a single variable x we shall usually denote the derived function, if it exists, by $\psi'(x)$. For a function of several variables we shall usually denote the partial derivatives, if they exist, by suffixes. Thus if $\psi(x, \alpha)$ is a function of the two independent variables x, α, we denote the partial derivative with respect to α by $\psi_\alpha(x, \alpha)$; in particular

$$\left\{\frac{\partial}{\partial \alpha}\psi(x, \alpha)\right\}_{\alpha=0}$$

is written $\psi_\alpha(x, 0)$. Similarly if $f(x, y, z)$ is a function of three independent variables x, y, z we denote the partial derivative with respect to y by $f_y(x, y, z)$, and so on. For the second derivatives, f_{yz} means $(f_y)_z$, i.e. $\partial^2 f/\partial z\, \partial y$, and similarly for higher derivatives. Particular care is needed with the derivatives of the function $F(x, y, z)$ which appears in (1.1.2) and (1.1.4) and (1.1.5). In (1.1.4) and (1.1.5) the integrand was written $F(x, y, y')$, but the derivatives are to be found as though the symbols x, y, y' represented independent variables (although $\varphi'(x)$ is known when $\varphi(x)$ is prescribed). Thus $F_{yy'}(x, y, y')$ means that we calculate the derivative $\partial^2 F/\partial z\, \partial y$ of the function $F(x, y, z)$, and put y' for z after differentiation.

An exception occurs when we are dealing with a function $\psi(x, \alpha, \beta, \ldots)$ where the arguments are x and a number of parameters $\alpha, \beta, \ldots$ We usually denote the partial derivative with respect to x by $\psi'(x, \alpha, \beta, \ldots)$ rather than $\psi_x(x, \alpha, \beta, \ldots)$. The notation $\psi_\alpha'(x, \alpha, \beta, \ldots)$ means $\psi_{\alpha x}(x, \alpha, \beta, \ldots)$, i.e. $\partial^2\psi/\partial x\, \partial\alpha$.

If $\mathscr{D}$ is the domain (open interval) $X < x < \overline{X}$ we say that $\psi(x)$ belongs to the class C_1 in $\mathscr{D}$ if it possesses a continuous derivative $\psi'(x)$ at all points of $\mathscr{D}$; we usually write $\psi \in C_1$ in $\mathscr{D}$. Similarly we say that $\psi \in C_n$ in $\mathscr{D}$ if $\psi(x)$ possesses a continuous nth derivative $\psi^{(n)}(x)$ at all points of $\mathscr{D}$.

Sometimes we wish to extend this nomenclature to the closed interval $\mathscr{F} = \{x\colon\ X \leqslant x \leqslant \overline{X}\}$. We say that $\psi \in C_1$ in $\mathscr{F}$ if $\psi'(x)$ exists and is continuous in $\mathscr{F}$, where the derivatives at the interior points are defined as usual, but the derivatives at the end-points are one-sided derivatives. Thus the existence of $\psi'(X)$ for example means that

$$\{\psi(X+h)-\psi(X)\}/h$$

tends to a finite limit, which we call $\psi'(X)$, as $h \to 0$ *through positive values*. Similarly $\psi \in C_n$ in $\mathscr{F}$ if $\psi^{(n)}(x)$ exists and is continuous in $\mathscr{F}$, the derivatives at the end-points being one-sided derivatives. We shall sometimes denote the closed interval $\mathscr{F}$, $X \leqslant x \leqslant \overline{X}$, by $[X,\overline{X}]$.

It should be noticed that if $\psi \in C_1$ in $\mathscr{F}$, we can extend the interval of definition, to the left of X and to the right of $\overline{X}$, so that $\psi \in C_1$ in a domain properly containing $\mathscr{F}$. For example we could define $\psi(x)$ for $x < X$ by the formula

$$\psi(X)+(x-X)\psi'(X),$$

and similarly for $x > \overline{X}$. In a similar way, if $\psi \in C_n$ in $\mathscr{F}$, we can find a domain properly containing $\mathscr{F}$ in which $\psi \in C_n$. In this case we could define $\psi(x)$ for $x < X$ by the formula

$$\psi(X)+(x-X)\psi'(X)+\frac{1}{2!}(x-X)^2\psi''(X) + \ldots + \frac{1}{n!}(x-X)^n\,\psi^{(n)}(X),$$

and similarly for $x > \overline{X}$.

This device is important in the Calculus of Variations for the following reason. In the fundamental problem described in §1.1 the end-points were fixed. But frequently in the sequel we shall wish to compare the value of the integral taken along the original curve from A to B with its value along a neighbouring curve from A' to B', and the range of integration $(X', \overline{X}')$ for the new curve may not be the same as the range $(X, \overline{X})$ for the old. Now it is often convenient to think of the new curve as produced from the original by *contemporaneous variations*, i.e. by variations in which each point on the original curve moves parallel to Oy, to the point with the same value of x on the new curve. If part of the range $(X', \overline{X}')$ lies outside $(X, \overline{X})$ we cannot produce the new curve from the original by contemporaneous variations. But we can do so if we accept the convention that a curve may be extended beyond its original range (in whatever class C_r is appropriate to the particular problem) by the device mentioned. (The adjective 'contemporaneous' arises from problems of mathematical physics in which the independent variable x represents the time.)

The notation C_r is also used for functions of several variables, though here we shall usually confine its use to a domain (an open connected set). Thus we say that $f(x, y, z)$ belongs to the class C_1 in R if the first partial derivatives f_x, f_y, f_z exist and are continuous in the domain R of 3-dimensional Euclidean space. More generally, we say that $f \in C_n$ in R if all the partial derivatives of order n exist and are continuous in R. In virtue of a fundamental theorem, if $f \in C_n$ in R we can change the order of the differentiations in any derivative of order r, $r \leqslant n$, without changing the value. In particular, if $f \in C_2$ in R,

$$f_{yz} = f_{zy}, \qquad f_{zx} = f_{xz}, \qquad f_{xy} = f_{yx},$$

at all points of R.

1.3 Conditions assumed in the fundamental problem

We return to the fundamental problem enunciated in §1.1. The function $F(x, y, z)$ which appears in the integrand is assumed to be a function of a simple type. Explicitly, we assume that $F(x, y, z) \in C_4$ in an appropriate domain R of the (x, y, z)-space. This will suffice for all purposes, and indeed, for most of the theory developed in this book, it is more than enough. We shall usually assume that the domain R is *z-convex*, i.e. R is such that, if (x, y, z_1) and (x, y, z_2) lie in R, then so also does (x, y, z_3) if z_3 is any number between z_1 and z_2. The domain R is not necessarily bounded; for example it may be the whole real space, or the half-space $y > 0$, or the slab $x_1 < x < x_2$.

Next, we must define the admissible functions $\varphi(x)$. Actually we have tacitly assumed some properties of these functions already; we have in fact assumed that $\varphi(x)$ is defined uniquely in the (closed) interval $[X, \overline{X}]$, that $\varphi'(x)$ exists at least almost everywhere in $[X, \overline{X}]$, and that for each φ the integral I has a well-defined value.

We now turn to the precise definition of the admissible functions. The admissible functions are the real-valued functions $\varphi(x)$ satisfying the following conditions:

(i) $\varphi(x)$ is defined in the interval $[X, \overline{X}]$ and belongs to a prescribed class κ,

(ii) various choices are possible for the class κ, but in every case each member $\varphi(x)$ of κ is a uniform (one-valued) continuous function, and $\varphi'(x)$ exists almost everywhere in $[X, \overline{X}]$,

(iii) $\varphi(X) = Y$, $\varphi(\overline{X}) = \overline{Y}$, and all the elements $\{x, \varphi(x), \varphi'(x)\}$ lie in R (so the integrand in I is defined at least almost everywhere in $[X, \overline{X}]$),

(iv) the class κ is such that for each $\varphi(x)$ in κ the integral I has a well-defined value.

Now the choice of the class κ is at our disposal (subject to the conditions imposed in (ii) and (iv)) and the subsequent development of the theory will depend upon the choice we make. Let us consider some of the possibilities:

(*a*) We might choose for κ the class C_2, so that $\varphi'(x)$, $\varphi''(x)$ exist and are continuous. Each admissible curve has a continuously turning tangent (which is never vertical) and a continuously varying curvature. (For our immediate purpose we are concerned with the closed interval $[X, \overline{X}]$, and it will suffice if the right-hand derivatives exist at X and the left-hand derivatives at $\overline{X}$, as explained in §1.2.)

(*b*) We might choose for κ the class C_1, so that $\varphi(x)$ has a continuous derivative. The geometrical significance is that each admissible curve has a continuously turning tangent.

(*c*) We might choose for κ the class of functions $\varphi(x)$ for which $\varphi'(x)$ is piecewise continuous. This means that $\varphi(x)$ is continuous, and that the range $[X, \overline{X}]$ can be divided into a finite number of segments by dividing points x_r,

$$X = x_0 < x_1 < x_2 \ldots < x_{n-1} < x_n = \overline{X},$$

such that in each segment $[x_{r-1}, x_r]$, taken closed, $\varphi(x) \in C_1$. In this case $\varphi'(x)$ exists at all points of $[X, \overline{X}]$ except at the points x_r, and at each of these points (for $r = 1, 2, \ldots, (n-1)$) $\varphi'(x_r - 0)$ and $\varphi'(x_r + 0)$ are finite and unequal, where $\varphi'(x_r - 0)$ and $\varphi'(x_r + 0)$ denote the one-sided derivatives to left and to right at x_r. We shall say that such functions belong to the class D_1. If $\kappa \equiv D_1$ the admissible curves have continuously turning tangents except at a finite number of corners.

In cases (*a*), (*b*) and (*c*), the integral can be interpreted as a Riemann integral.

(*d*) We can choose for κ a still wider class of functions. At first sight we might be tempted to take for κ the class of continuous functions for which $\varphi'(x)$ exists almost everywhere. Actually this goes too far, and does not, as we shall see, provide a useful and satisfying theory. To obtain such a theory we must restrict the discussion to absolutely continuous functions. For absolutely continuous functions $\varphi(x)$ is continuous, $\varphi'(x)$ exists almost everywhere, and $\varphi(x)$ is the integral of $\varphi'(x)$. The integral is interpreted as a Lebesgue integral.

The choice we shall make in this book, as a general rule, is (*c*),

$$\kappa \equiv D_1,$$

though we shall occasionally digress to point out how the theory is modified if we make a different choice. Thus, in general, the admissible curves will be built up of arcs with continuously turning tangents, and there is a corner where one of these arcs joins the next.

One other point may be noticed here for the sake of completeness. The condition (iii) requires that the elements of the admissible curves lie in R, and this implies that they are interior points of R, since R is open. But occasionally we shall wish to consider the value of I for a curve some of whose elements are frontier points of R. For such a curve the permissible variations are restricted by the requirement that the elements of the varied curve do not lie outside R. In practice the commonest case is that in which the element of the curve at an end-point lies on the frontier of R; but occasionally also we shall encounter curves for which all the elements of a finite arc lie on the frontier of R. The exceptional character of these examples will be sufficiently evident, and they will not give rise to any serious embarrassment.

1.4 The geodesic problem

One of the elementary problems of the Calculus of Variations is the *geodesic problem*, the problem of finding the (plane) curve of minimum length joining A to B.

To begin with, let us consider a simple special case. Let A be the origin (0, 0) and B the point (1, 0), and let us consider the *ordinary* problem in which the curves admitted to competition have the form $y = \varphi(x)$. We wish to find among the curves K given by $y = \varphi(x)$, where $\varphi(x)$ belongs to the prescribed class κ, and $\varphi(0) = \varphi(1) = 0$, a curve K_0 which minimizes the integral

$$I = \int_0^1 \sqrt{(1 + y'^2)}\, dx. \tag{1.4.1}$$

The solution is simple. Whichever of the choices mentioned in §1.3 we made for κ, the minimizing curve K_0 is the segment, from $x = 0$ to $x = 1$, of the straight line $y = 0$. For K_0 the value of I is 1, for any other admissible curve, $I > 1$.

But this is by no means a complete solution of the geodesic problem. For one thing, the class of curves admitted to competition (when we deal with the ordinary problem) depends on the orientation of the axes chosen; in the simple case we have considered, Ox was taken in the direction AB. For another, all the curves considered so far have the form $y = \varphi(x)$, where $\varphi(x)$ is a single-valued function of x. Interpreted geometrically, this means that the curves considered lie wholly in the strip $X \leqslant x \leqslant \overline{X}$, and each curve cuts any line $x = \xi$, where $X < \xi < \overline{X}$, in precisely one point.

To free ourselves from these restrictions, we turn to the so-called *parametric problem*, in contrast with the *ordinary problem* considered hitherto. We now deal with curves expressed in the form

$$x = \varphi(t), \qquad y = \psi(t), \qquad (T \leqslant t \leqslant \overline{T}) \tag{1.4.2}$$

where

$$\varphi(T) = 0, \qquad \psi(T) = 0, \qquad \varphi(\overline{T}) = 1, \qquad \psi(\overline{T}) = 0. \tag{1.4.3}$$

As before, we have taken the axis Ox along AB; it will be noticed that, in the parametric problem, this choice involves no loss of generality.

To make the problem precise, we must state to what class of functions $\varphi(t)$ and $\psi(t)$ belong. For example, following the same line of thought as in §1.3, we might impose the conditions (*a*) that $\varphi(t)$ and $\psi(t)$ are of class C_2, or (*b*) of class C_1, or (*c*) that $\varphi(t)$ and $\psi(t)$ are continuous, with piecewise continuous derivatives $\dot{\varphi}(t)$ and $\dot{\psi}(t)$, or (*d*) that $\varphi(t)$ and $\psi(t)$ are only absolutely continuous. In each case we impose the additional restriction that $\dot{\varphi}(t)$ and $\dot{\psi}(t)$ do not vanish simultaneously; thus

$$[\dot{\varphi}(t)]^2 + [\dot{\psi}(t)]^2 > 0 \tag{1.4.4}$$

for all t in $[T, \overline{T}]$ for which $\dot{\varphi}(t)$ and $\dot{\psi}(t)$ exist. If $\varphi(t)$ and $\psi(t)$ are restricted to be of class C_1, this means that curves with cusps are excluded.

The solution of the geodesic problem, i.e. to find the minimizing curve for

$$I = \int_T^{\overline{T}} \sqrt{\{\dot{\varphi}(t)^2 + \dot{\psi}(t)^2\}}\, dt, \tag{1.4.5}$$

is the same whichever choice we make. The straight line segment AB is still the curve of minimum length. To prove this, we have only to notice that

$$\int_T^{\overline{T}} \sqrt{(\dot{\varphi}^2 + \dot{\psi}^2)}\, dt \geqslant \int_T^{\overline{T}} |\dot{\varphi}|\, dt \geqslant 1. \tag{1.4.6}$$

The length I has the value 1 if $\psi(t) = 0$ for all t in $[T, \overline{T}]$ and if $\varphi(t)$ increases steadily from 0 to 1 as t increases steadily from T to $\overline{T}$; in all other cases $I > 1$.

In the parametric problem, the choice (*b*) gives curves with continuously turning tangents; in (*c*) the curves may have a finite number of corners.

For the present we shall be concerned with the ordinary, not the parametric problem, and (as already mentioned) we shall usually take $\kappa \equiv D_1$, so that the admissible curves are curves which have continuously turning tangents except at a finite number of corners.

1.5 Absolute minima

We turn from the special case of the geodesic problem to the general problem

$$I = \int_X^{\bar{X}} F\{x, \varphi(x), \varphi'(x)\}\, dx, \tag{1.5.1}$$

where $\varphi(x)$ belongs to the prescribed class κ. We can use the same symbol κ to denote also the class of admissible curves $y = \varphi(x)$, and the dual usage will not give rise to any embarrassment. We denote the curve $y = \varphi(x)$ by K. I is a numerical-valued function of the function φ, or of the curve K, and we consider how this functional

$$I = I(K) \tag{1.5.2}$$

behaves for $K \in \kappa$.

There are three possibilities, all of which will appear frequently in the sequel.

(i) It may happen that $I(K)$ is not bounded below for $K \in \kappa$, and no minimum exists.

(ii) It may happen that $I(K)$ *is* bounded below for $K \in \kappa$. We denote the infimum (greatest lower bound) by m. Then two cases arise:

(*a*) The infimum is attained, i.e. there exists a curve K_0 belonging to κ such that

$$I(K_0) = m. \tag{1.5.3}$$

Then

$$I(K) \geqslant I(K_0) \tag{1.5.4}$$

if $K \neq K_0$, and the integral has an absolute minimum when $K = K_0$. If there is no other curve in the class κ for which I has the value m, so that

$$I(K) > m \tag{1.5.5}$$

for $K \neq K_0$, we may say that I has a *proper* absolute minimum at K_0.

(*b*) The infimum is not attained. There is no curve K in the class κ for which $I(K)$ has the value m. We know of course that there are curves K for which $I(K)$ has a value exceeding m by as little as we please. It may happen that the infimum *is* attained by a curve not belonging to κ.

An example of (*a*), where a proper absolute minimum is attained, has already been encountered in the geodesic problem. As a simple illustration of (*b*) we may take the following. Let A be (0, 0) and let B be (1, 0), let κ be the class C_1, and let

$$I = \int_0^1 (y'^2 - 1)^2 \, dx. \qquad (1.5.6)$$

It is evident that $m = 0$, and that this value is not attained by any curve in the class C_1. But the value is attained by curves of class D_1, in fact by any curve (such as those shown in the figure) for which $y' = \pm 1$ except at the corners.

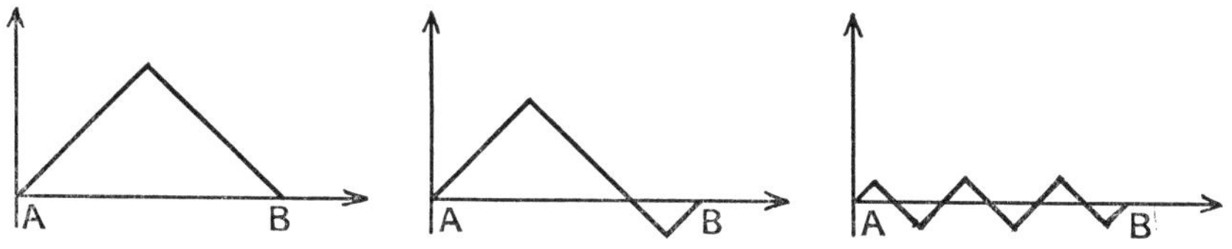

Fig. 1.5

As another example of (*b*) we consider a problem of a somewhat different type from those previously considered, namely one in which the curves admitted to competition are subject to an additional restriction. Let us consider the geodesic problem for the same end-points as in §1.4 (A is (0, 0) and B is (1, 0)) when all the curves admitted to competition have the same tangent at A. (The tangent at A is not along AB nor perpendicular to AB.) If κ is the class of curves of class C_1 with the prescribed tangent at A, it is clear that $m = 1$, and that no curve belonging to κ has length 1. In this example however, unlike the previous example, the infimum for curves of class C_1 with the given tangent at A is not attained even if we extend the class of admitted curves to include curves of class D_1 with the given tangent at A.

1.6 The rounding argument

The example (1.5.6) illustrates an important observation. If Γ is a curve of class D_1 joining A to B, and ε is a given positive number, we can find a curve K of class C_1, joining A to B, such that $I(K)$ lies between $I(\Gamma) - \varepsilon$ and $I(\Gamma) + \varepsilon$. This is spoken of as *the rounding argument*. The theorem is almost evident. (To construct a formal proof for the case when Γ has a single corner at $x = x_0$, we replace the part of Γ in the range $(x_0 - \eta, x_0 + \eta)$ by a curve of class C_1 touching Γ at $x_0 - \eta$ and at $x_0 + \eta$; the cubic curve will suffice. We can choose η so small that

(1.6.1) $$|I(K) - I(\Gamma)| < \varepsilon.)$$

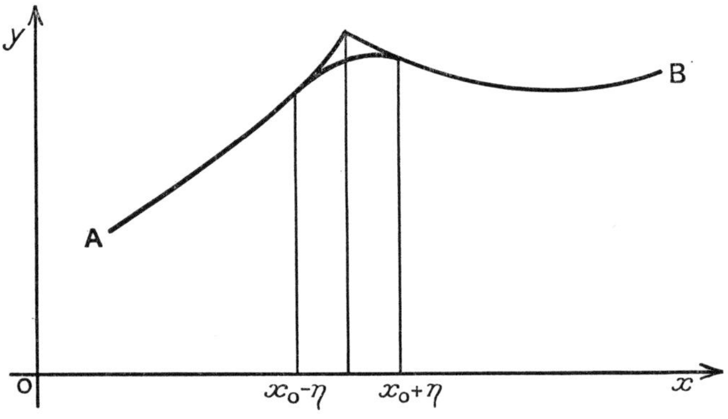

Fig. 1.6

An important deduction follows at once from the rounding argument; a curve K_0 of class C_1 cannot furnish a minimum in the class C_1 if there is a curve Γ of class D_1 for which

(1.6.2) $$I(\Gamma) < I(K_0).$$

To prove this, suppose that

(1.6.3) $$I(\Gamma) = I(K_0) - 2\varepsilon,$$

where $\varepsilon > 0$. We now find, by the rounding argument, a curve K of class C_1 such that

(1.6.4) $$I(K) < I(\Gamma) + \varepsilon = I(K_0) - \varepsilon < I(K_0).$$

Thus K_0 does not minimize I in the class C_1.

It follows that, if K_0 minimizes I in the class C_1, it also minimizes I in the class D_1.

If we take $\kappa \equiv D_1$, so that curves with corners are admitted to competition, a minimizing curve with a corner is called a *discontinuous solution*. The adjective discontinuous refers of course to y', not to y.

1.7 Relative minima: strong and weak variations

The notion of a relative minimum is already familiar in the ordinary theory of maxima and minima of functions of one, or of several, variables.

In the geodesic problem we found a minimizing curve K_0 for which I has a smaller value than for any other admissible curve; in this case there exists a proper absolute minimum. But sometimes we shall be concerned with a curve K_0 which gives to I a relative minimum, i.e. the inequality

$$I(K_0) \leqslant I(K) \tag{1.7.1}$$

holds, not for all curves K in the prescribed class κ, but for all those curves K of the class κ which lie in a neighbourhood of K_0.

To make this more precise, we introduce the notion of a *variation* (or, strictly speaking, a *contemporaneous variation*). When we transfer our attention from a curve K_0, $y = \varphi_0(x)$, to a neighbouring curve K, $y = \varphi(x)$, we speak of the change in the ordinate y for a given x as the *variation* of y, and we denote it by δy,

$$\delta y = \varphi(x) - \varphi_0(x). \tag{1.7.2}$$

Similarly we speak of the change in the slope y' for a given x as the *variation* of y', and we denote it by $\delta y'$,

$$\delta y' = \varphi'(x) - \varphi_0'(x). \tag{1.7.3}$$

We notice, for future reference, that

$$\delta y' = \frac{d}{dx}\,\delta y. \tag{1.7.4}$$

Sometimes we shall be concerned with curves K in the neighbourhood of a given curve K_0 which are such that the variation δy is small, but the variation $\delta y'$ is unrestricted, and then we speak of a *strong* variation. And sometimes we shall be concerned with curves K which are such that the variations δy and $\delta y'$ are both small, and then we speak of a *weak* variation. The notion of a strong variation involves smallness in the change of ordinate, but no restriction on the change of slope. The notion of a weak variation implies *less variation* than does a strong variation; it involves smallness both in the change of ordinate and in the change of slope.

We shall say that the curve K_0, $y = \varphi_0(x)$, joining A to B, provides a strong relative minimum for the integral I if it provides a minimum in the sub-class of admissible curves $y = \varphi(x)$ for which $|\delta y| < \varepsilon$, i.e.

(1.7.5) $$|\varphi(x) - \varphi_0(x)| < \varepsilon, \qquad (X \leqslant x \leqslant \overline{X})$$

for some positive ε. On the other hand, we shall say that K_0 provides a weak relative minimum if it provides a minimum in the sub-class of admissible curves for which $|\delta y| < \varepsilon$ and $|\delta y'| < \varepsilon$, i.e.

(1.7.6) $$|\varphi(x) - \varphi_0(x)| < \varepsilon, \qquad |\varphi'(x) - \varphi_0'(x)| < \varepsilon, \quad (X \leqslant x \leqslant \overline{X})$$

for some positive ε. It is clear that an absolute minimum is *a fortiori* a strong relative minimum, and that a strong relative minimum is *a fortiori* a weak relative minimum.

One observation about weak variations should be made at this point. We said above that a weak variation is one in which both δy and $\delta y'$ are small; but in fact it suffices to say that a weak variation is one in which $\delta y'$ is small, since smallness in $\delta y'$ implies smallness in δy. To prove this we have, from (1.7.4),

(1.7.7) $$\delta y(x) = \int_X^x \delta y'(t)\, dt,$$

since $\delta y(X) = 0$; hence if $|\delta y'| < \eta$,

(1.7.8) $$|\delta y| < (\overline{X} - X)\eta,$$

which establishes the result. We can say that a strong variation is one in which δy is small, and a weak variation is one in which $\delta y'$ is small.

The effects of strong and of weak variations are strikingly different. We can illustrate this fact by reference to the geodesic problem already discussed. Let us consider the ordinary (not the parametric) problem, with curves $y = \varphi(x)$, and let $\kappa \equiv D_1$, so that the curves considered may have a finite number of corners. We shall see that, for weak variations from the minimizing curve K_0, the length I only alters slightly: for strong variations the length alters substantially: and if $\delta y'$ is unbounded the increase of length can be unbounded, even though δy is restricted to be arbitrarily small. To prove these statements, taking the terminal points A and B to be $(0, 0)$ and $(1, 0)$ as before, we consider three types of variation as follows. (The original curve K_0 is $y = 0$, so in this problem $\delta y = y$ and $\delta y' = y'$.)

(i) If $|y'| < \varepsilon$, which implies $|y| < \varepsilon$,

(1.7.9) $$I = \int_0^1 \sqrt{(1 + y'^2)}\, dx < \sqrt{(1 + \varepsilon^2)},$$

and

(1.7.10) $$\delta I = I(K) - I(K_0) < \sqrt{(1 + \varepsilon^2)} - 1 < \varepsilon^2.$$

Thus in a weak variation in which $|\delta y| < \varepsilon$ and $|\delta y'| < \varepsilon$, the increase of length δI is less than ε^2.

(ii) For the curves shown in Fig. 1.7*a*, derived from an isosceles triangle of height $\frac{1}{2}\tan\beta$ by successively halving the height and doubling the number of triangles, $|y'| = \text{constant} = \tan\beta$, and all the curves have the same length $\sec\beta$. But $|y| \to 0$ uniformly in [0, 1] as $n \to \infty$, for in the nth curve $|y| \leqslant (\tan\beta)/2^n$. We can observe the same phenomenon in Fig. 1.7*b*, where again $I = \sec\beta$, and this time $|y| \leqslant (\tan\beta)/(2n)$, and again $|y| \to 0$ uniformly in [0, 1] as $n \to \infty$.

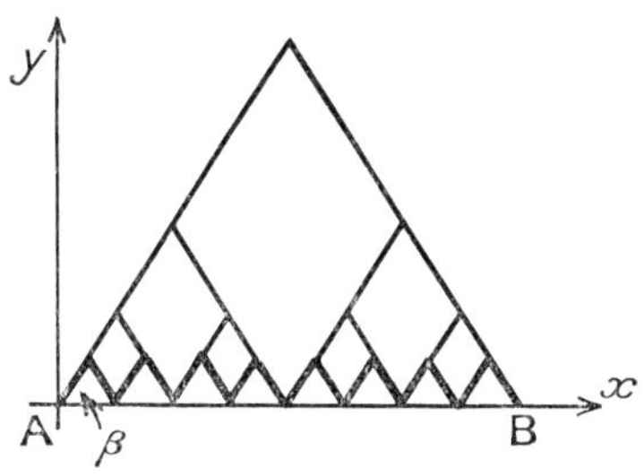

Fig. 1.7*a*

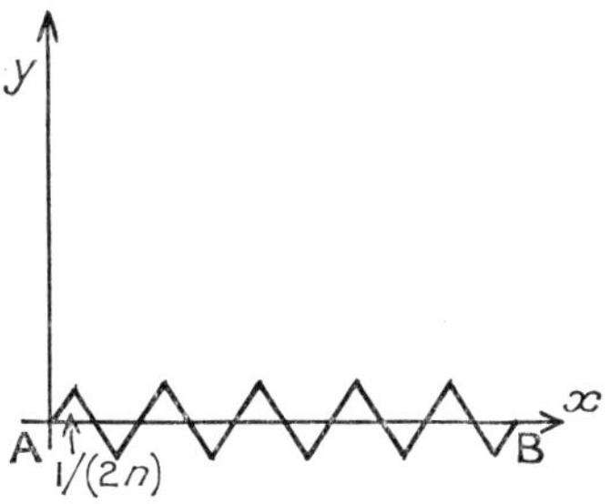

Fig. 1.7*b*

(iii) For the curve

(1.7.11) $$y = a \sin r\pi x,$$

where r is a positive integer, and a is positive, the length is

(1.7.12) $$I = \int_0^1 \sqrt{(1 + y'^2)}\, dx = \int_0^1 \sqrt{(1 + r^2\pi^2a^2\cos^2 r\pi x)}\, dx$$
$$> r\pi a\int_0^1 |\cos r\pi x|\, dx = r\pi a \,.\, 2r\int_0^{1/2r} \cos r\pi x\, dx = 2ar.$$

If now we take

(1.7.13) $$a = \frac{1}{n}, \qquad r = n^2,$$

where n is a positive integer, we have

(1.7.14) $$I > 2n,$$

and $I \to \infty$ with n. On the other hand

(1.7.15) $$|y| \leqslant \frac{1}{n},$$

and $|y| \to 0$ uniformly in [0, 1]. We have here a strong variation in which the maximum δy is arbitrarily small and δI is arbitrarily large.

1.8 Minima, maxima, stationary values

So far we have spoken only of minima, absolute or relative. The theory of maxima presents no essentially new feature, since a maximizing curve for the integrand F is a minimizing curve for $-F$, and we follow the traditional pattern of the subject by taking the finding of a minimizing curve as the standard problem.

Consider for a moment the ordinary theory of minima and maxima of a function $f(x)$ of a single variable x. We assume that $f(x)$ is of class C_2. If the function has a relative minimum at x_0, $f'(x_0) = 0$; this is the familiar first-order necessary condition. But the condition is by no means sufficient. If $f'(x_0) = 0$, $f(x)$ may have a relative minimum at x_0, or a relative maximum, or merely a stationary value which is neither a minimum nor a maximum. For example $f'(0) = 0$ for $f(x) = x^2, -x^2, x^3$, and the point $x = 0$ gives a minimum for the first function, a maximum for the second, and a stationary value which is neither a minimum nor a maximum for the third.

A similar situation arises in the Calculus of Variations. The classical approach to the subject sets out by finding a first-order condition which is satisfied by any curve giving a weak relative minimum to I. But the condition is only a necessary condition, not a sufficient condition, even for a weak relative minimum. A curve which satisfies it may give a relative minimum, or a relative maximum; or it may give merely a stationary value (in the sense that, if $|\delta y|$ and $|\delta y'|$ are both less than ε, then δI is $o(\varepsilon)$). The finding of sufficient conditions requires further analysis.

But one important point should be noticed at once. In some variational principles of mathematical physics the essential point is that the solution of the physical problem gives a stationary value to the integral concerned, and it is usually irrelevant whether this stationary value is a minimum or a maximum or neither. In this context the first-order conditions alone usually suffice for the solution of the problem.

1.9 Historical

Two problems of the Calculus of Variations were known in ancient Greece, the geodesic problem (§1.4) and the classical isoperimetrical problem, i.e. the problem of finding among the closed curves of given length the one that encloses the greatest area. But these are isolated appearances, and few other references to the subject seem to have emerged until comparatively recent times. The history of the subject since the time of Newton can be conveniently divided into four periods.

(i) One of the first problems that involved the essential ideas of the Calculus of Variations was *Newton's problem* of the solid of revolution of minimum resistance. The problem is mentioned in the *Principia* (1686). If A is the origin of coordinates $(0, 0)$ and B is the point $(\overline{X}, \overline{Y})$ in the first quadrant (i.e. $\overline{X} > 0$, $\overline{Y} > 0$) we wish to find a curve joining A to B such that the solid of revolution obtained by rotating the curve about Ox shall suffer the least possible resistance when it moves (to the left) through the air at a steady speed. On the basis of a simple physical hypothesis Newton gave the formula

$$(1.9.1) \qquad 2\pi\rho V^2 \int y \sin^2 \psi \, dy$$

for the resistance, where ρ is the density of the air, V is the speed of the projectile, and $\tan\psi$ $(= y')$ is the slope of the curve. (The formula does not agree well with the empirical results, so the problem is of theoretical rather than of practical interest.) Omitting the positive multiplier $2\pi\rho V^2$, the integral we wish to minimize (if we consider the ordinary problem, in which the curves are of the form $y = \varphi(x)$) is

$$(1.9.2) \qquad I = \int_0^{\overline{X}} \frac{yy'^3}{1 + y'^2}\, dx.$$

Actually it turns out that the infimum is not attained in the ordinary problem, and it is better to deal with the parametric problem for which the corresponding formula is

$$(1.9.3) \qquad I = \int_T^{\overline{T}} \frac{y\dot{y}^3}{\dot{x}^2 + \dot{y}^2}\, dt.$$

Another early example is the problem of the *brachistochrone.* Given two points A and B in space, we wish to determine the shape of a smooth wire joining A to B, and such that a bead sliding on the wire under gravity, and starting from A with given speed, shall reach B in the shortest possible time. We may assume that the curve lies in the vertical plane through A and B. We take the axis Oy vertically downwards, and the axis Ox as the energy level, so the speed v of the bead at any point of the wire is $\sqrt{(2gy)}$. In particular the starting speed at A is $\sqrt{(2gY)}$, and since this is prescribed the energy level Ox

is determined. The time for the journey from A to B along the curve $y = \varphi(x)$ is

$$\frac{1}{\sqrt{(2g)}} \int_X^{\bar{X}} \sqrt{\left(\frac{1 + y'^2}{y}\right)}\, dx, \tag{1.9.4}$$

so the integral we have to minimize is

$$I = \int_X^{\bar{X}} \sqrt{\left(\frac{1 + y'^2}{y}\right)}\, dx. \tag{1.9.5}$$

The brachistochrone problem turns out to be much simpler than Newton's problem. In 1696 John Bernoulli proposed the brachistochrone problem as a challenge to the mathematicians of Europe, allowing six months for the solution (though this period was later increased by a year), and five mathematicians found the correct solution—John Bernoulli himself, his elder brother James (Jacob) Bernoulli, Newton, Leibniz, and de l'Hôpital. One of the famous stories illustrating Newton's unparalleled insight is that he sent the solution to a friend the next day after he received the problem! This seems an almost incredible achievement when we remember the rudimentary state of analysis at that time. (Some of the original solutions of the brachistochrone problem are given in reference **1** of the Bibliography on p. 347.)

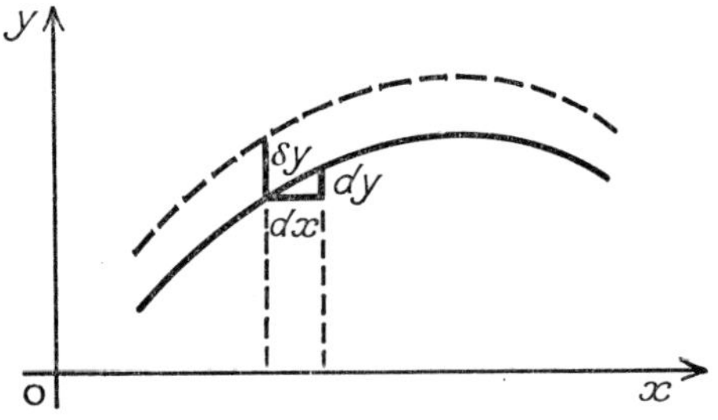

Fig. 1.9

(ii) The methods used to attack the brachistochrone problem were *ad hoc* methods, designed to cope with the particular problem, but not readily applicable to the general problem with any given integrand of the form $F(x, y, y')$. The next stage shows the emergence of a systematic theory, capable of attacking the general problem. The names prominently associated with this period are Euler and Lagrange. Lagrange, about 1760, invented the symbol δ, already mentioned in §1.7. The symbol d referred to a displacement on the original curve $y = \varphi_0(x)$ (Fig. 1.9), δ to a displacement from the original curve to a neighbouring curve $y = \varphi(x)$,

(1.9.6) $$\delta y = \varphi(x) - \varphi_0(x).$$

The operator δ played a great part in the early researches. Nowadays it is possible to develop the subject without using δ at all; possible, but not expedient, because the use of δ, particularly in the physical applications, often makes for clarity and for compactness of statement.

Euler, in 1744, discovered, in connexion with the general problem of minimizing

(1.9.7) $$I = \int_X^{\bar{X}} F\{x, \varphi(x), \varphi'(x)\}\, dx,$$

the famous differential equation that bears his name,

(1.9.8) $$\frac{d}{dx} F_{y'}\, \{x, \varphi(x), \varphi'(x)\} = F_y\{x, \varphi(x), \varphi'(x)\}.$$

If we take $\kappa \equiv C_2$, Euler's equation must be satisfied by any minimizing curve

(1.9.9) $$y = \varphi(x).$$

We sometimes write the equation in the more compact, but less precise, form

(1.9.10) $$\frac{d}{dx} F_{y'}\, (x, y, y') = F_y(x, y, y').$$

Euler's equation is the same differential equation as Lagrange's equation of motion for a dynamical system with one degree of freedom, x representing the time, and y the Lagrangian coordinate.

If $\varphi(x)$ is a function of class C_2 satisfying Euler's equation, the curve $y = \varphi(x)$ is called an *extremal* for the problem. Since the general solution of a differential equation of the second order contains two arbitrary constants, we may expect that in general a finite number of extremals will pass through the prescribed points A and B. In the brachistochrone problem, for example, there is a unique extremal through A and B (provided of course that neither A nor B is above the energy level).

Euler's equation is derived from the vanishing of the so-called first variation of the integral (1.9.7); this is closely analogous to the condition $f'(x_0) = 0$ for the minima of a function $f(x)$. In the early history of the subject it was often assumed that if there is a unique extremal through A and B the problem is solved; but this assumption involves a strong appeal to physical intuition, and the logic is incomplete.

(iii) In the next period, the classical period in the history of the subject, the prominent names are Legendre, Jacobi, and Weierstrass. In this period the distinction between conditions *necessary* for a minimizing curve, and conditions *sufficient* to ensure a minimum, emerges clearly. To begin with, the analogy with the theory of minima of a function $f(x)$ of one variable was pursued, and conditions for a relative minimum were sought analogous to the sufficient condition $f''(x_0) > 0$. But this line of attack turns out (for reasons which will appear shortly) to be a false start. To prove the *fundamental sufficiency theorem* we need a new idea, the idea of a *field of extremals* introduced by Weierstrass. Jacobi discovered the relevance of the envelope of the pencil of extremals through A (when such an envelope exists).

(iv) Among the prominent names in the most recent period are Hilbert, Bolza, Bliss, Tonelli, Marston Morse. Hilbert proved the existence theorem, setting up the conditions for the *existence* of a minimizing curve K_0 such that $I(K_0) = m$. Bolza established the famous school at Chicago, for many years the centre of research in the Calculus of Variations, where he was succeeded by Bliss. Tonelli and his school investigated the effects of widening the class κ of admissible functions, from the class D_1 to the class of absolutely continuous functions, the integrals being interpreted as Lebesgue integrals. Marston Morse approached the subject from the theory of function-spaces. Each admissible curve joining A to B is regarded as a point in a function-space, and the space is given a structure by the introduction of a suitable distance function. The integral I is now a function of position in the function-space, and we investigate the points of the space at which I has a minimum value, absolute or relative. The problem is bound up with the topology of the function-space.

1.10 Extensions of the theory

So far we have only considered the fundamental problem, which is concerned with curves in a plane joining fixed end-points A and B. But there are problems of many other types in the Calculus of Variations, and it will be helpful to consider these briefly here in order to obtain a conspectus of the subject as a whole.

(1) So far, in our discussion of the fundamental problem, we have thought only of contemporaneous variations, i.e. we have used Lagrange's operator δ to represent the variation from (x, y) on the original curve to $(x, y + \delta y)$ on a neighbouring curve. The varied curve lies, like the original curve, in the strip $X \leqslant x \leqslant \overline{X}$. Sometimes however, especially in classical dynamics, we wish to handle variations of a more general type, from (x, y) to $(x + \delta x, y + \delta y)$. This is quite practicable, and later (in view of the applications in classical dynamics) we will consider it briefly (§2.12). But this generalization of the idea of a variation is more naturally associated with the parametric problem, already mentioned in §1.4. In the parametric problem a contemporaneous variation (with t unvaried) implies variations both of x and of y. The curves considered in the parametric problem are the curves

$$x = \varphi(t), \qquad y = \psi(t), \qquad (T \leqslant t \leqslant \overline{T}), \tag{1.10.1}$$

joining A to B. This class of curves is wider than that considered in the ordinary problem. In the ordinary problem the curves considered all lie in the strip $X \leqslant x \leqslant \overline{X}$, and they all cut any line $x = \xi$, where $X < \xi < \overline{X}$, in only one point. In the parametric problem the curves do not necessarily lie in the strip $X \leqslant x \leqslant \overline{X}$, and they may cut the line $x = \xi$ in more than one point. In the parametric problem there are two dependent variables (as in (1.10.1)) and one independent variable t, and

$$I = \int_T^{\overline{T}} f\{\varphi(t), \psi(t), \dot{\varphi}(t), \dot{\psi}(t)\}\, dt, \tag{1.10.2}$$

where we write $\dot{\varphi}(t)$, $\dot{\psi}(t)$ for the first derivatives as in classical dynamics. We consider a contemporaneous variation in which $\{\varphi_0(t), \psi_0(t)\}$ changes to $\{\varphi(t), \psi(t)\}$, so that both x and y change without change of the independent variable t. We write, as in (1.7.2),

$$\delta x = \varphi(t) - \varphi_0(t), \qquad \delta y = \psi(t) - \psi_0(t), \tag{1.10.3}$$

and in the fundamental problem, with fixed end-points, we suppose δx and δy to vanish at the ends $t = T$ and $t = \overline{T}$.

We shall find that the parametric problem has many points of difference from the ordinary problem. It involves the inherent difficulty that the same curve can be represented parametrically in many different ways. We can sometimes overcome this disadvantage, since all the curves are rectifiable, by using the so-called *normal* representation. In the normal representation the parameter t of the point P of the curve is $t = s/l$, where s is the length of the arc AP and l is the length of the arc AB. In the normal representation $T = 0$ and $\overline{T} = 1$.

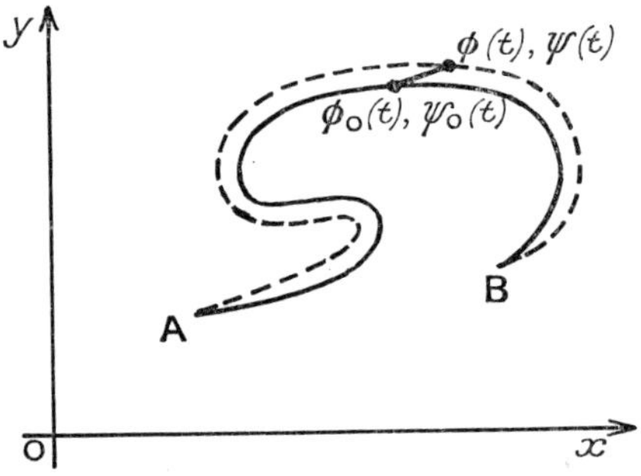

Fig. 1.10

(2) In the parametric problem we have one independent and two dependent variables. The same is true in the ordinary problem for curves in space. In three-dimensional space there are two dependent variables

(1.10.4) $$y = \varphi(x), \qquad z = \psi(x),$$

and one independent variable x. The fundamental problem is to find a curve of the form (1.10.4), with $\varphi(x)$ and $\psi(x)$ belonging to a prescribed class κ, and joining the given point A (X, Y, Z) to the given point B $(\overline{X}, \overline{Y}, \overline{Z})$, such that the integral

(1.10.5) $$I = \int_X^{\overline{X}} f(x, y, z, y', z')\, dx$$

has a minimum value. The curves considered lie in the slab $X \leqslant x \leqslant \overline{X}$, and cut any plane $x = \xi$ in this slab only once.

More generally, we consider problems with one independent variable x, and n dependent variables $y_1, y_2, \ldots, y_n$. We seek a curve

(1.10.6) $$y_1 = \varphi_1(x), y_2 = \varphi_2(x), \ldots, y_n = \varphi_n(x),$$

joining prescribed fixed end-points A and B and minimizing the integral

(1.10.7) $$I = \int_X^{\overline{X}} f(x, y_1, y_2, \ldots, y_n, y_1', y_2', \ldots, y_n')\, dx.$$

We sometimes write the integrand compactly as $f(x, y, y')$, the symbol y standing for the row $y_1, y_2, \ldots, y_n$, the symbol y' standing for the row $y_1', y_2', \ldots, y_n'$, and so on. With this notation the integral to be minimized is

$$\int_X^{\bar{X}} f\{x, \varphi(x), \varphi'(x)\}\, dx \tag{1.10.8}$$

or

$$\int_X^{\bar{X}} f(x, y, y')\, dx. \tag{1.10.9}$$

If all the functions $\varphi_r(x)$ are of class C_2 the first-order conditions for a minimizing curve are given by the n differential equations of Euler

$$\frac{d}{dx} f_{y_r'} \{x, \varphi(x), \varphi'(x)\} = f_{y_r} \{x, \varphi(x), \varphi'(x)\}, \quad (r = 1, 2, \ldots, n). \tag{1.10.10}$$

(3) Next, we consider problems with variable end-points. For example A and B may not be fixed points, but one or both may be required to lie on given curves (in the plane case) or on given curves or given surfaces (in the three-dimensional case). As a concrete illustration, we may find the brachistochrone in space from A to B, when A and the speed of starting are prescribed, and B lies on a given curve or on a given surface. Such problems are said to have *separated* end-conditions. But we may also wish to consider problems with *mixed* end-conditions, with equations of condition involving the coordinates of both end-points. As a simple concrete example, the horizontal displacement of B from A, $\bar{X} - X$, might be prescribed.

(4) We consider problems in which the integrand involves higher derivatives than the first. For example we may wish to find a curve $y = \varphi(x)$ joining the end-points A and B and minimizing the integral

$$I = \int_X^{\bar{X}} F(x, y, y', y'')\, dx. \tag{1.10.11}$$

In the fundamental problem of this class the end-points are fixed and so are the slopes at the end-points,

$$\varphi(X) = Y, \quad \varphi'(X) = P, \quad \varphi(\bar{X}) = \bar{Y}, \quad \varphi'(\bar{X}) = \bar{P}. \tag{1.10.12}$$

But a variety of end-conditions may occur; for example, y and y' may be prescribed at $x = X$, but B may be required to lie on a given curve, with y' unrestricted at B. If $\kappa \equiv C_4$ the first-order condition corresponding to Euler's equation is

$$F_y - \frac{d}{dx} F_{y'} + \frac{d^2}{dx^2} F_{y''} = 0. \tag{1.10.13}$$

(5) The isoperimetrical problem; to find the curve $y = \varphi(x)$ joining A to B, which is subject to the condition

$$J \equiv \int_X^{\overline{X}} G(x, y, y')\, dx = l, \tag{1.10.14}$$

and which minimizes the integral

$$I = \int_X^{\overline{X}} F(x, y, y')\, dx. \tag{1.10.15}$$

The eponymous special case is to find the curve of given length l joining A to B and minimizing I. The first-order necessary condition, known as *Euler's rule*, is found by considering the problem of minimizing $\int_X^{\overline{X}} F^*\, dx$, where

$$F^* = F - \lambda G, \tag{1.10.16}$$

and λ is a constant to be determined. The end-conditions and the isoperimetrical condition (1.10.14) may determine a unique solution (and of course a unique value of λ).

The most famous problem of this class is the classical isoperimetrical problem already mentioned in §1.9, to find the closed curve of given length which shall contain the greatest possible area. The answer is a circle, as every schoolboy knows.

(6) The problem of Lagrange. There is one independent variable x, and n dependent variables $y_1, y_2, \ldots, y_n$. The problem is to find in a class of arcs

$$y_1 = \varphi_1(x), y_2 = \varphi_2(x), \ldots, y_n = \varphi_n(x), \tag{1.10.17}$$

satisfying m differential equations of the first order

$$g^\beta(x, y_1, y_2, \ldots, y_n, y_1', y_2', \ldots, y_n') = 0, \qquad (\beta = 1, 2, \ldots, m;\ m < n) \tag{1.10.18}$$

and p end-conditions

$$\psi^\mu(X, Y_1, Y_2, \ldots, Y_n, \overline{X}, \overline{Y}_1, \overline{Y}_2, \ldots, \overline{Y}_n) = 0, \qquad (\mu = 1, 2, \ldots, p;\ p \leqslant 2n + 2) \tag{1.10.19}$$

one which minimizes

$$I = \int_X^{\overline{X}} f(x, y_1, y_2, \ldots, y_n, y_1', y_2', \ldots, y_n')\, dx. \tag{1.10.20}$$

The first-order necessary conditions for a minimizing curve are given by a famous theorem called the *multiplier rule*. The multiplier rule asserts that the minimizing curve must satisfy Euler's equations for

$$F = f + \sum_{r=1}^{m} l^r g^r, \tag{1.10.21}$$

where the *multipliers* l^r are functions of x to be determined.

A famous problem of this class is the principle of Least Action (Lagrange's form) in classical dynamics. The independent variable x is the time, the dependent variables $y_1, y_2, \ldots, y_n$ are the Lagrangian coordinates of the dynamical system. The integral is

$$I = \int_X^{\bar{X}} 2T\, dx, \tag{1.10.22}$$

where $2T$ is the quadratic form

$$2T = \sum_{r=1}^{n} \sum_{s=1}^{n} a_{rs} y_r' y_s', \tag{1.10.23}$$

and the coefficients a_{rs} are given functions of $y_1, y_2, \ldots, y_n$. The arcs considered satisfy the single differential equation ($m = 1$)

$$T + V = C, \tag{1.10.24}$$

where V, the potential energy function, is a given function of $y_1, y_2, \ldots, y_n$. The terminal values of $y_1, y_2, \ldots, y_n$ are fixed, but not the time of transit $\bar{X} - X$. We can take the time of departure X to be zero without loss of generality, so the end-conditions are

$$\varphi_r(0) = Y_r, \qquad \varphi_r(\bar{X}) = \bar{Y}_r, \tag{1.10.25}$$

and we have a simple variable end-point problem, since $\bar{X}$ is not prescribed. The arcs which give stationary values to I are the orbits of the dynamical system. The conditions stated usually define a finite number of orbits, but not usually a unique orbit.

Now we come to an observation of paramount importance. Lagrange's problem contains as special cases all the types previously considered. The diversity of problems can be reduced to one single type, and Lagrange's problem can legitimately be regarded as the central theme of the whole subject so far as problems with one independent variable are concerned. Logically, we could proceed directly to Lagrange's problem, and deduce all the other problems as particular applications—though this approach would be somewhat forbidding, and indeed hardly practicable.

It is easy to verify the statement that the other types are special cases of Lagrange's problem. For types (1), (2), (3) the statement is evident. Type (4), with the integral (1.10.11), can be regarded as a problem of Lagrange's type with two dependent variables, and we have to minimize

$$\int_X^{\overline{X}} F(x, y, z, z')\,dx \tag{1.10.26}$$

or

$$\int_X^{\overline{X}} F(x, y, y', z')\,dx \tag{1.10.27}$$

in the class of arcs satisfying the differential equation

$$g^1 \equiv y' - z = 0. \tag{1.10.28}$$

If both y and y' are prescribed at X and $\overline{X}$ we have a Lagrange problem with fixed end-points. To bring the isoperimetrical problem, type (5), into the form of a Lagrange problem, we introduce a new dependent variable z and consider the problem of minimizing

$$I = \int_X^{\overline{X}} F(x, y, y')\,dx \tag{1.10.29}$$

in the class of arcs

$$y = \varphi(x), \qquad z = \psi(x), \tag{1.10.30}$$

satisfying the differential equation

$$g^1 \equiv z' - G(x, y, y') = 0. \tag{1.10.31}$$

The end-conditions, if A and B are fixed in the original problem, are

$$\varphi(X) = Y, \quad \psi(X) = 0, \quad \varphi(\overline{X}) = \overline{Y}, \quad \psi(\overline{X}) = l, \tag{1.10.32}$$

so we have a Lagrange problem with fixed end-points. Actually we shall first discuss the isoperimetrical problem independently, as well as considering it as a special case of Lagrange's problem.

(7) All the problems considered so far have been problems involving one independent variable x and simple (Riemann or Lebesgue) integrals, not multiple integrals. We now turn to problems with n independent variables and (in the first instance) one dependent variable. The derivatives that occur are now partial derivatives, and the integrals are multiple integrals.

In many important problems of mathematical physics the number n of independent variables is 2 or 3. Suppose, to fix the ideas, that $n = 3$. The fundamental problem is to find a function $\varphi = \varphi(x, y, z)$ defined in the domain Δ inside a given closed surface β, and taking given values on β, which minimizes the integral

$$I = \iiint_{\Delta} F(x, y, z, \varphi, \varphi_x, \varphi_y, \varphi_z)\, dx\, dy\, dz. \tag{1.10.33}$$

A famous example occurs in potential theory, where the integral is

$$I = \iiint (\varphi_x^2 + \varphi_y^2 + \varphi_z^2)\, dx\, dy\, dz. \tag{1.10.34}$$

The investigation of the existence of a minimizing function φ, and the determination of the minimizing function if it exists, are connected with the theory of Dirichlet's principle, which we shall consider in Chapter X.

CHAPTER II

Fundamental Theory

2.1 Two lemmas

We now turn to the fundamental theorems of the Calculus of Variations for problems with one independent and one dependent variable. In order to establish these theorems we use the two lemmas which follow.

LEMMA 1. *If $M(x)$ is continuous in $[X, \bar{X}]$, and if*

$$\int_X^{\bar{X}} M(x)\eta(x)\,dx = 0 \tag{2.1.1}$$

for all functions $\eta(x)$ which belong to the class C_2 and which vanish at X and at $\bar{X}$, then $M(x) = 0$.

To prove this, suppose on the contrary that $M(x)$ does not vanish at a point ξ in $[X, \bar{X}]$, say for definiteness $M(\xi) > 0$. Then by continuity there is a range of values $a < x < b$ (where $X \leqslant a < b \leqslant \bar{X}$) in which $M(x) > 0$. If we consider the particular $\eta(x)$ which has the value $\{(b - x)(x - a)\}^3$ in $[a, b]$, and the value zero in the rest of the interval $[X, \bar{X}]$, then for this $\eta(x)$

$$\int_X^{\bar{X}} M(x)\eta(x)\,dx = \int_a^b M(x)\{(b - x)(x - a)\}^3\,dx > 0, \tag{2.1.2}$$

giving a contradiction. Thus the hypothesis $M(\xi) > 0$ is untenable, and the lemma is proved.

COROLLARY. The result is still true if (2.1.1) is satisfied only for a more restricted range of η than that described above. In particular the result still follows if (2.1.1) is satisfied only for functions η of class C_2 which are such that not only $\eta(x)$, but also $\eta'(x)$ and $\eta''(x)$, vanish at X and at $\bar{X}$.

LEMMA 2. *If $M(x)$ is bounded in $[X, \bar{X}]$, and continuous except at a finite number of points, and if*

$$\int_X^{\bar{X}} M(x)\eta'(x)\,dx = 0 \tag{2.1.3}$$

for all functions $\eta(x)$ which belong to the class D_1, and which vanish at X and at $\bar{X}$, then there is a constant C such that

$$M(x) = C \tag{2.1.4}$$

at every point at which $M(x)$ is continuous.

To prove this, let C denote the mean value of $M(x)$ in $[X, \overline{X}]$,

(2.1.5) $$C = \frac{1}{\overline{X} - X} \int_X^{\overline{X}} M(x)\, dx,$$

and consider the particular $\eta(x)$ defined by the equation

(2.1.6) $$\eta(x) = \int_X^x \{M(t) - C\}\, dt.$$

This function is of class D_1, $\eta(X) = \eta(\overline{X}) = 0$, and

(2.1.7) $$\eta'(x) = M(x) - C$$

except at the points of discontinuity of $M(x)$. Now in virtue of (2.1.3)

(2.1.8) $$\int_X^{\overline{X}} \{M(x) - C\}\eta'(x) = 0$$

for all admissible functions $\eta(x)$, and taking the particular $\eta(x)$ defined by (2.1.6) we have

(2.1.9) $$\int_X^{\overline{X}} \{M(x) - C\}^2\, dx = 0.$$

Hence $M(x) = C$ at every point at which $M(x)$ is continuous.

2.2 Necessary conditions for a weak relative minimum, the elementary theory

Let $\kappa \equiv C_2$, and suppose that K_0, $y = \varphi(x)$, is a minimizing curve in κ for the integral (1.1.2). Then K_0 is *a fortiori* a minimizing curve in the one-parameter family whose typical member K_α is

(2.2.1) $$y = \varphi(x) + \alpha\eta(x),$$

where $\eta \in C_2$, and $\eta(X) = \eta(\overline{X}) = 0$. The curves K_α are admissible for sufficiently small values of α, because the elements of K_0 are interior points of R.

We write

(2.2.2) $$\psi(\alpha) = I(K_\alpha),$$

and $\psi(\alpha)$ is a function of the single variable α, of class C_2, in a neighbourhood of $\alpha = 0$. Explicitly

(2.2.3) $$\psi(\alpha) = \int_X^{\overline{X}} F\{x, \varphi(x) + \alpha\eta(x), \varphi'(x) + \alpha\eta'(x)\}\, dx.$$

Now $\psi(\alpha)$ has a minimum at $\alpha = 0$, so

$$\psi'(0) = 0, \quad \psi''(0) \geqslant 0. \tag{2.2.4}$$

We now appeal to the theorem on the differentiation of a Riemann integral with respect to a parameter appearing in the integrand; this gives

$$\psi'(0) = \int_X^{\bar{X}} [\eta(x)F_y\{x, \varphi(x), \varphi'(x)\} + \eta'(x)F_{y'}\{x, \varphi(x), \varphi'(x)\}]\, dx \tag{2.2.5}$$

If, for the sake of brevity, we write η, φ, φ' in place of $\eta(x)$, $\varphi(x)$, $\varphi'(x)$, (2.2.5) takes the form

$$\psi'(0) = \int_X^{\bar{X}} \{\eta F_y(x, \varphi, \varphi') + \eta' F_{y'}(x, \varphi, \varphi')\}\, dx. \tag{2.2.6}$$

On integration by parts (2.2.6) leads to

(2.2.7)

$$\psi'(0) = \eta F_{y'}(x, \varphi, \varphi')\Big|_X^{\bar{X}} + \int_X^{\bar{X}} \eta\{F_y(x, \varphi, \varphi') - \frac{d}{dx} F_{y'}(x, \varphi, \varphi')\}\, dx.$$

Now $\eta(X) = \eta(\bar{X}) = 0$, and the condition $\psi'(0) = 0$ leads to

$$\int_X^{\bar{X}} \eta\{F_y(x, \varphi, \varphi') - \frac{d}{dx} F_{y'}(x, \varphi, \varphi')\}\, dx = 0. \tag{2.2.8}$$

We now come to the second step in the argument. The equation (2.2.8) holds, not only for a particular η, but for all η belonging to C_2 with $\eta(X) = \eta(\bar{X}) = 0$, and hence, by Lemma 1,

$$F_y\{x, \varphi(x), \varphi'(x)\} = \frac{d}{dx} F_{y'}\{x, \varphi(x), \varphi'(x)\}. \tag{2.2.9}$$

This is a result of fundamental importance. The equation (2.2.9), a differential equation of the second order satisfied by $\varphi(x)$, is *Euler's equation* (sometimes called the Euler-Lagrange equation) already mentioned in §1.9. We are dealing here with weak variations, since

$$\delta y = \alpha\eta(x), \quad \delta y' = \alpha\eta'(x), \tag{2.2.10}$$

and what we have found is a necessary condition for a weak relative minimum in the class C_2. It will sometimes be convenient to put y instead of $\varphi(x)$ and to write Euler's equation in the form

$$\frac{d}{dx} F_{y'}(x, y, y') = F_y(x, y, y'). \tag{2.2.11}$$

As we have already mentioned (§1.9) the curves defined by solutions of class C_2 of Euler's equation are called *extremals*.

If we develop the first member of (2.2.11) we have

$$F_{y'x} + F_{y'y}y' + F_{y'y'}y'' = F_y, \tag{2.2.12}$$

where it is understood that the arguments in the derivatives of F are x, y, y'. It is important to observe that in a part of the region R of (x, y, y') in which $F_{y'y'}$ does not vanish, Euler's equation has the form

$$y'' = A(x, y, y'), \tag{2.2.13}$$

where $A \in C_2$. The geometrical significance of (2.2.13) is that Euler's equation defines the *curvature* of an extremal when the element (x, y, y') of the extremal is prescribed.

Consider now a problem in which the element of the curve K_0 at the end-point A, for example, lies on the frontier of R. We suppose that $[X, \varphi(X), \varphi'(X)]$ lies on the frontier of R, but that the other elements of K_0 are interior points of R. If we assume as before that K_0 is a minimizing arc, then Euler's equation is satisfied for $X < x < \bar{X}$. To prove this we have only to observe that otherwise we could obtain a larger value for I by applying a suitable variation to a suitable sub-arc $A'B$, leaving the arc AA' unvaried. Since the varied curve obtained must be of class C_2 the variation must be such that $\eta = \eta' = \eta'' = 0$ at A', and we use the Corollary to Lemma 1 (§2.1). The extension to the case where the elements at both end-points lie on the frontier of R is immediate.

2.3 Necessary conditions for a weak relative minimum

Let $\kappa \equiv D_1$, and let us suppose that the curve K_0,

$$y = \varphi(x), \tag{2.3.1}$$

is a minimizing curve in the class κ. Then K_0 is *a fortiori* a minimizing curve in the one-parameter family whose typical member K_α is

$$y = \varphi(x) + \alpha\eta(x), \tag{2.3.2}$$

where $\eta \in D_1$, and $\eta(X) = \eta(\bar{X}) = 0$. The curves K_α are admissible for sufficiently small values of α.

We write

$$\psi(\alpha) = I(K_\alpha) = \int_X^{\bar{X}} F\{x, \varphi(x) + \alpha\eta(x), \varphi'(x) + \alpha\eta'(x)\}\, dx, \tag{2.3.3}$$

and we recall that the integrand is continuous except at the corners of φ and η. Now $\psi(\alpha)$ is a function of the single variable α, of class C_2

for a range of α about $\alpha = 0$, and, since $\psi(\alpha)$ has a minimum value at $\alpha = 0$, we have

$$\psi'(0) = 0, \qquad \psi''(0) \geqslant 0. \tag{2.3.4}$$

We may suppose the range of integration $[X, \bar{X}]$ in (2.3.3) divided into a finite number of segments at the discontinuities of φ' and η', and applying the theorem on differentiation under the integral sign to the integral along each of these segments we have

(2.3.5)

$$\psi'(0) = \int_X^{\bar{X}} [\eta(x)F_y\{x, \varphi(x), \varphi'(x)\} + \eta'(x)F_{y'}\{x, \varphi(x), \varphi'(x)\}]\, dx,$$

$$\begin{aligned}\psi''(0) = \int_X^{\bar{X}} [\eta(x)^2 F_{yy}&\{x, \varphi(x), \varphi'(x)\} \\ &+ 2\eta(x)\eta'(x)F_{yy'}\{x, \varphi(x), \varphi'(x)\} \\ &+ \eta'(x)^2 F_{y'y'}\{x, \varphi(x), \varphi'(x)\}]\, dx.\end{aligned} \tag{2.3.6}$$

We can write these results concisely in the forms

$$\psi'(0) = \int_X^{\bar{X}} (\eta F_y + \eta' F_{y'})\, dx, \tag{2.3.7}$$

$$\psi''(0) = \int_X^{\bar{X}} (\eta^2 F_{yy} + 2\eta\eta' F_{yy'} + \eta'^2 F_{y'y'})\, dx, \tag{2.3.8}$$

where it is to be understood that the arguments in the derivatives of F are the elements $\{x, \varphi(x), \varphi'(x)\}$ of K_0. Thus the coefficients of η and η' in the second member of (2.3.7), and the coefficients of η^2 and $\eta\eta'$ and η'^2 in the second member of (2.3.8), are known functions of x, continuous except at the corners of K_0.

We are dealing here with weak variations. The numbers we have calculated are coefficients in the Taylor expansion

$$\psi(\alpha) = \psi(0) + \alpha\psi'(0) + \frac{\alpha^2}{2!}\psi''(0) + \frac{\alpha^3}{3!}\psi'''(\theta\alpha), \tag{2.3.9}$$

where $0 < \theta < 1$. We speak of the terms

$$\alpha\psi'(0), \qquad \frac{\alpha^2}{2!}\psi''(0), \tag{2.3.10}$$

or sometimes merely of the coefficients

$$\psi'(0), \qquad \psi''(0), \tag{2.3.11}$$

as the first and second variations of I.

So far our calculations are similar to those in the elementary theory, but here we reach the parting of the ways. We cannot use the same technique as before because we do not know that

$$\frac{d}{dx} F_{y'}\{x, \varphi(x), \varphi'(x)\}$$

exists, so instead we proceed as follows.

We write

(2.3.12) $$\chi(x) = \int_X^x F_y\{t, \varphi(t), \varphi'(t)\}\, dt,$$

so that

(2.3.13) $$\chi(X) = 0$$

and

(2.3.14) $$\chi'(x) = F_y\{x, \varphi(x), \varphi'(x)\}$$

except at the corners of K_0 (where the integrand in (2.3.12) is no longer continuous). Then

(2.3.15) $$\frac{d}{dx}\{\eta(x)\chi(x)\} = \eta(x)F_y\{x, \varphi(x), \varphi'(x)\} + \eta'(x)\chi(x),$$

except at corners of φ and η, and hence, from (2.3.5),

(2.3.16)

$$\psi'(0) = \int_X^{\overline{X}} \left[\frac{d}{dx}\{\eta(x)\chi(x)\} - \eta'(x)\chi(x) + \eta'(x)F_{y'}\{x, \varphi(x), \varphi'(x)\}\right] dx$$

$$= \eta(x)\chi(x)\Big|_X^{\overline{X}} + \int_X^{\overline{X}} \eta'(x)[F_{y'}\{x, \varphi(x), \varphi'(x)\} - \chi(x)]\, dx.$$

But $\psi'(0) = 0$, and the integrated term disappears since $\eta(X) = \eta(\overline{X}) = 0$, so we find

(2.3.17) $$\int_X^{\overline{X}} \eta'(x)[F_{y'}\{x, \varphi(x), \varphi'(x)\} - \chi(x)]\, dx = 0.$$

Now (2.3.17) holds, not merely for a particular choice of $\eta(x)$, but for all $\eta(x)$ of class D_1 with $\eta(X) = \eta(\overline{X}) = 0$. Hence, by Lemma 2,

(2.3.18) $$F_{y'}\{x, \varphi(x), \varphi'(x)\} = \chi(x) + C,$$

where C is a constant. The actual value of C is, in virtue of (2.3.13), $F_{y'}\{X, \varphi(X), \varphi'(X)\}$, and we can write (2.3.18) in the form

(2.3.19) $$F_{y'}\{x, \varphi(x), \varphi'(x)\} - F_{y'}\{X, \varphi(X), \varphi'(X)\} = \chi(x).$$

The equation (2.3.18) is *du Bois-Reymond's equation.* It is a fundamental result, with a similar status to that of Euler's equation in the elementary theory. Du Bois-Reymond's equation is a first necessary condition for a minimizing curve: an admissible curve $y = \varphi(x)$ that gives to I a weak relative minimum value in the class D_1 must satisfy the condition

$$F_{y'}\{x, \varphi(x), \varphi'(x)\} = \int_X^x F_y\{t, \varphi(t), \varphi'(t)\}\, dt + C \tag{2.3.20}$$

at every point at which $\varphi'(x)$ exists.

We have derived du Bois-Reymond's equation from Lemma 2, and this is perhaps the most natural line of attack. But it should be noticed that Lemma 2 is in fact a more powerful result than we need, and (2.3.20) can be derived from a consideration of many special forms for $\eta(x)$ without appeal to the result in Lemma 2 for a general form of $\eta(x)$.

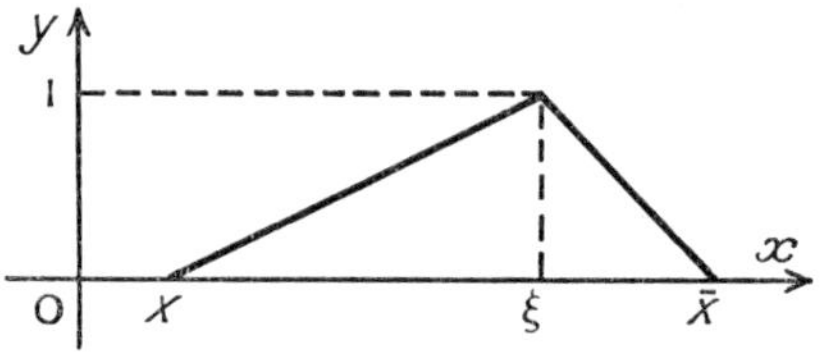

Fig. 2.3

Consider for example the particular form of $\eta(x)$ whose graph is shown in Fig. 2.3: here ξ is a value between X and $\bar{X}$, and $\eta'(x) = 1/(\xi - X)$ in (X, ξ) and $\eta'(x) = -1/(\bar{X} - \xi)$ in $(\xi, \bar{X})$. For this particular choice of $\eta(x)$, (2.3.17) becomes

$$\frac{\int_X^\xi \rho(x)\, dx}{\xi - X} = \frac{\int_\xi^{\bar{X}} \rho(x)\, dx}{\bar{X} - \xi}, \tag{2.3.21}$$

where $\rho(x)$ is written for $F_{y'}\{x, \varphi(x), \varphi'(x)\} - \chi(x)$, and $\rho(x)$ is a known function of x. Each fraction in (2.3.21) is equal to

$$\frac{\int_X^{\bar{X}} \rho(x)\, dx}{\bar{X} - X}, \tag{2.3.22}$$

which has a value, say C, independent of ξ. Thus

$$\int_X^\xi \{\rho(x) - C\}\, dx = 0, \tag{2.3.23}$$

and since this holds for all values of ξ in $(X, \bar{X})$, we have

$$\rho(x) - C = 0 \tag{2.3.24}$$

for all x in $(X, \bar{X})$ at which $\rho(x)$ is continuous, and this is du Bois-Reymond's equation.

If y does not occur explicitly in F, du Bois-Reymond's equation (2.3.20) leads to

$$F_{y'}\{x, \varphi(x), \varphi'(x)\} = C, \tag{2.3.25}$$

which is an important result that is frequently useful. Some other important deductions from (2.3.20) are discussed in the succeeding sections.

If the element $[X, \varphi(X), \varphi'(X)]$ at the end-point A of K_0 lies on the frontier of R, but the other elements $[x, \varphi(x), \varphi'(x)]$ are interior points of R, du Bois-Reymond's equation is still a necessary condition for a minimizing curve. To prove this we consider a sub-arc $A'B$ as in the concluding remarks of §2.2. The extension to the case where the elements of K_0 at both end-points lie on the frontier of R is immediate.

2.4 Euler's equation

On an arc between consecutive corners of K the integrand in the second member of (2.3.20) is continuous, so Euler's equation

$$\frac{d}{dx} F_{y'}\{x, \varphi(x), \varphi'(x)\} = F_y\{x, \varphi(x), \varphi'(x)\} \tag{2.4.1}$$

is satisfied on such an arc.

It is important to observe that (2.4.1) is satisfied all along the arc, right up to a corner, provided that $F_{y'y'}$ does not vanish at the corner, and that the derivatives $\varphi'(x)$ and $\varphi''(x)$ are interpreted at an end-point as one-sided derivatives. But we postpone the proof of this statement for the moment (cf. §2.7).

2.5 The first corner condition

The second member of (2.3.20) is continuous even at a corner (where the integrand is *not* continuous) and hence the first member is continuous at a corner,

$$F_{y'}(x, y, p) = F_{y'}(x, y, \varpi), \tag{2.5.1}$$

where p, ϖ are the values of the slope $\varphi'(x)$ to left and to right of the corner. This is the first Weierstrass-Erdmann corner condition.

It is convenient to have special names for some of the functions that appear frequently in the theory. We shall use the symbol V for $F_{y'}$,

$$V(x, y, y') \equiv F_{y'}(x, y, y'), \tag{2.5.2}$$

and the first corner condition can be written in the form

$$V(x, y, p) = V(x, y, \varpi). \tag{2.5.3}$$

Some simple properties of a corner on a minimizing curve follow from the first corner condition. If p and ϖ are the slopes to left and right of a corner (x, y) we see, by Rolle's theorem, that there is a number q between p and ϖ at which

(2.5.4) $$F_{y'y'}(x, y, q) = 0.$$

We shall use the symbol N for $F_{y'y'}$,

(2.5.5) $$N(x, y, y') \equiv F_{y'y'}(x, y, y'),$$

and (2.5.4) can be written in the form

(2.5.6) $$N(x, y, q) = 0.$$

Further

(2.5.7) $$V(x, y, \varpi) - V(x, y, p) = \int_p^{\varpi} N(x, y, z)\, dz,$$

so the mean value of $N(x, y, z)$ for z in $[p, \varpi]$ is zero.

The first corner condition sometimes enables us to see that, in a particular problem, a minimizing curve cannot have a corner. Consider for example the type of problem, frequently encountered, in which $F(x, y, z)$ has the form $f(x, y)\sqrt{(1 + z^2)}$. In this case

(2.5.8) $$V(x, y, y') = f(x, y)\frac{y'}{\sqrt{(1 + y'^2)}} = f(x, y) \sin \psi,$$

where $\tan \psi$ is the slope of the curve, and $-\frac{1}{2}\pi < \psi < \frac{1}{2}\pi$. Now V is continuous at a corner (where there is a discontinuity in $\sin \psi$) so if there is a corner it must lie on the curve

(2.5.9) $$f(x, y) = 0.$$

2.6 The second corner condition

There is a second condition that must be satisfied at a corner on a minimizing curve, namely

(2.6.1) $$F(x, y, p) - pF_{y'}(x, y, p) = F(x, y, \varpi) - \varpi F_{y'}(x, y, \varpi).$$

We shall use the symbol U for the function appearing in the two members of this equation,

(2.6.2) $$U(x, y, z) \equiv F(x, y, z) - zF_z(x, y, z),$$

and the second Weierstrass-Erdmann corner condition can be written

(2.6.3) $$U(x, y, p) = U(x, y, \varpi).$$

The function $U(x, y, y')$ is continuous at a corner on a minimizing curve.

To establish the second corner condition we consider a variation of a different type. Let us suppose, as before, that $K_0, y = \varphi(x)$, is a minimizing curve in the class D_1. In particular it is a minimizing curve in a one-parameter family, and we construct a particular one-parameter family as follows.

We think of K_0 as expressed parametrically

(2.6.4) $$x = t, \qquad y = \varphi(t),$$

and we consider the one-parameter family for which the typical member K_α is defined by

(2.6.5) $$x = t + \alpha\lambda(t), \qquad y = \varphi(t),$$

where $\lambda(t) \in D_1$, and $\lambda(t)$ vanishes at $t = X$ and at $t = \bar{X}$. The variation now involves a horizontal instead of a vertical displacement. Now for sufficiently small values of α, $\dot{x} > 0$ in $[X, \bar{X}]$, and it follows that all the curves can be expressed in the required form $y = \mu(x)$. We write $\psi(\alpha)$ for $I(K_\alpha)$, and a necessary condition for K_0 to be a minimizing curve is

(2.6.6) $$\psi'(0) = 0.$$

Now

(2.6.7) $$\psi(\alpha) = \int_X^{\bar{X}} F\left(t + \alpha\lambda, \varphi, \frac{\dot{\varphi}}{1 + \alpha\dot{\lambda}}\right)(1 + \alpha\dot{\lambda})\, dt,$$

and

(2.6.8) $$\psi'(0) = \int_X^{\bar{X}} \{\dot{\lambda}(F - \dot{\varphi}F_{y'}) + \lambda F_x\}\, dt,$$

where the arguments in F and its derivatives are t, $\varphi(t)$, $\dot{\varphi}(t)$. If now

(2.6.9) $$\chi(t) = \int_X^t F_x\{\theta, \varphi(\theta), \dot{\varphi}(\theta)\}\, d\theta,$$

we have

(2.6.10) $$\chi(X) = 0,$$

and

(2.6.11) $$\dot{\chi}(t) = F_x\{t, \varphi(t), \dot{\varphi}(t)\}$$

except at corners of K_0. Hence, by an argument exactly similar to that used in §2.3, we deduce the equation analogous to du Bois-Reymond's equation

(2.6.12) $$F - \dot{\varphi}F_{y'} = \int_X^t F_x\{\theta, \varphi(\theta), \dot{\varphi}(\theta)\}\, d\theta + C,$$

where the arguments in F and $F_{y'}$ are t, $\varphi(t)$, $\dot{\varphi}(t)$. We can rewrite (2.6.12) in the form

$$F - \varphi' F_{y'} = \int_X^x F_x\{\theta, \varphi(\theta), \varphi'(\theta)\}\, d\theta + C, \tag{2.6.13}$$

where the arguments in F and $F_{y'}$ are now x, $\varphi(x)$, $\varphi'(x)$. The second member of (2.6.13) is continuous even at a corner of K_0, so the first member is also continuous. Thus $U(x, y, y')$ is continuous at a corner, and this is the condition we set out to prove.

On an arc between corners

$$\frac{d}{dx}(F - y'F_{y'}) = F_x. \tag{2.6.14}$$

But this can readily be deduced from Euler's equation, and is not an essentially new result.

Let (x, y) be a corner on a minimizing curve, and let p, ϖ be the values of y' to left and to right of the corner. Then (using the notation defined in (2.6.2))

$$\begin{aligned} U(x, y, \varpi) - U(x, y, p) &= F(x, y, \varpi) - \varpi F_{y'}(x, y, \varpi) \\ &\quad - \{F(x, y, p) - pF_{y'}(x, y, p)\}, \end{aligned} \tag{2.6.15}$$

and therefore, using the first corner condition,

$$\begin{aligned} U(x, y, \varpi) - U(x, y, p) &= F(x, y, \varpi) - F(x, y, p) \\ &\quad - (\varpi - p)F_{y'}(x, y, p). \end{aligned} \tag{2.6.16}$$

The second corner condition tells us that the second member of (2.6.16) vanishes at a corner on a minimizing curve.

The function

$$\begin{aligned} E(x, y, y', \varpi) &\equiv F(x, y, \varpi) - F(x, y, y') \\ &\quad - (\varpi - y')F_{y'}(x, y, y'), \end{aligned} \tag{2.6.17}$$

a function of the four independent variables (x, y, y', ϖ), is the *excess function* of Weierstrass, which will play an important part in the sequel. It is easily remembered from the Taylor expansion of $F(x, y, \varpi)$ about the value $\varpi = y'$. For the moment our only concern with the excess function is the property contained in the formula

$$E(x, y, p, \varpi) = 0, \tag{2.6.18}$$

where (x, y) is a corner on a minimizing curve, and p and ϖ are the slopes to left and right of the corner.

Some other simple results may be mentioned. From (2.6.16)

(2.6.19) $$U(x, y, \varpi) - U(x, y, p) = (\varpi - p)\{F_{y'}(x, y, q) - F_{y'}(x, y, p)\},$$

where q lies between p and ϖ, and hence, in virtue of the second corner condition;

(2.6.20) $$F_{y'}(x, y, p) = F_{y'}(x, y, q) = F_{y'}(x, y, \varpi).$$

Therefore there are two numbers q_1 and q_2, q_1 between p and q, and q_2 between q and ϖ, at which N vanishes (not merely one number as was proved in (2.5.6)). Also

(2.6.21) $$U(x, y, \varpi) - U(x, y, p) = -\int_p^\varpi zN(x, y, z)\,dz,$$

so the mean value of $zN(x, y, z)$—as well as the mean value of $N(x, y, z)$—is zero for z in $[p, \varpi]$.

EXAMPLE 1. If

(2.6.22) $$F = f(x, y)\sqrt{(1 + y'^2)},$$

(2.6.23) $$U = f(x, y)\cos\psi.$$

But we have seen already (§2.5) that if there is a corner it must lie on the curve $f(x, y) = 0$, so the second corner condition gives no new information. (We could deduce from the second corner condition, using (2.6.23), that at a corner either $f(x, y) = 0$ or $\alpha + \beta = 0$, where α and β are the values of ψ to left and to right of the corner. But we know in fact that only the first of these alternatives is possible.)

EXAMPLE 2. If

(2.6.24) $$F = (y'^2 - 1)^2,$$

then

(2.6.25) $$U = -(3y'^4 - 2y'^2 - 1), \qquad V = 4y'(y'^2 - 1),$$

and, if there is a minimizing curve with a corner, the two corner conditions give

(2.6.26) $$(p + \varpi)\{3(p^2 + \varpi^2) - 2\} = 0, \qquad p^2 + p\varpi + \varpi^2 = 1.$$

Let us consider separately the two possibilities

(2.6.27) $$p + \varpi = 0, \qquad p^2 + \varpi^2 = \tfrac{2}{3}.$$

The first gives $p^2 = 1$, and the solutions for (p, ϖ) are $(1, -1)$ and $(-1, 1)$ as we expect. The second gives $p\varpi = \frac{1}{3}$, whence

(2.6.28) $$(p - \varpi)^2 = 0,$$

and this is impossible since $p \neq \varpi$. The only possibilities are $(1, -1)$ and $(-1, 1)$.

EXAMPLE 3. If

$$F = y'^2 + y'^3, \tag{2.6.29}$$

then

$$U = -y'^2 - 2y'^3, \qquad V = 2y' + 3y'^2, \tag{2.6.30}$$

and, if there is a corner on a minimizing curve, the two corner condition give

$$(p + \varpi) + 2(p^2 + p\varpi + \varpi^2) = 0, \qquad 2 + 3(p + \varpi) = 0. \tag{2.6.31}$$

It follows that

$$p^2 + p\varpi + \varpi^2 = \tfrac{1}{3}, \qquad p^2 + 2p\varpi + \varpi^2 = \tfrac{4}{9}, \tag{2.6.32}$$

whence

$$4(p^2 + p\varpi + \varpi^2) = 3(p^2 + 2p\varpi + \varpi^2), \tag{2.6.33}$$

i.e. $(p - \varpi)^2 = 0$. But this is impossible, since $p \neq \varpi$, and therefore there cannot be a corner on a minimizing curve.

2.7 Regular arcs, existence and continuity of $\varphi''(x)$

Let K_0 be an (open) arc between consecutive corners on a minimizing curve. On K_0, $\varphi'(x)$ exists and is continuous: but we do not know, to begin with, whether $\varphi'(x)$ is differentiable or not. The fundamental result in this context is that, if $N\{x, \varphi(x), \varphi'(x)\}$ does not vanish on K_0, then $\varphi''(x)$ exists at every point of K_0 and is continuous.

Let us suppose that

$$N\{x, \varphi(x), \varphi'(x)\} > 0 \tag{2.7.1}$$

for all elements of K_0. We call such an arc a *regular arc*. In some important problems $N(x, y, z) > 0$ throughout R, and such a problem is called a *regular problem*. (We assume as usual that R is z-convex.) In a regular problem every admissible arc is a regular arc.

Supposc that K_0 is a regular arc; then, on K_0, $\varphi'(x)$ is continuous, and (2.7.1) holds, and $\varphi(x)$ satisfies Euler's equation

$$\frac{d}{dx} F_{y'}(x, \varphi, \varphi') = F_y(x, \varphi, \varphi'). \tag{2.7.2}$$

On such an arc $\varphi''(x)$ exists and is continuous. We give two proofs of this result; the first proof is straightforward, the second slightly more sophisticated.

(1) Let (x, φ, φ') be an element of K_0, and $(x + \delta x,\ \varphi + \delta\varphi,\ \varphi' + \delta\varphi')$ a neighbouring element of K_0. Then $\delta\varphi$, $\delta\varphi'$ tend to zero

with δx. Since $F_{y'}$ is a *differentiable function* of its three arguments at (x, φ, φ') we have

$$\delta F_{y'} = l\,\delta x + m\,\delta\varphi + n\,\delta\varphi', \tag{2.7.3}$$

where

$$l \to F_{y'x}(x, \varphi, \varphi'), \quad m \to F_{y'y}(x, \varphi, \varphi'), \quad n \to N(x, \varphi, \varphi'), \tag{2.7.4}$$

as $\delta x \to 0$. In virtue of (2.7.1), $n > 0$ when δx is sufficiently small. It follows from (2.7.3) that, if $\delta x \neq 0$,

$$\frac{\delta\varphi'}{\delta x} = \left(\frac{\delta F_{y'}}{\delta x} - l - m\frac{\delta\varphi}{\delta x}\right)\Big/ n. \tag{2.7.5}$$

If now δx tends to zero, the second member of (2.7.5) (using (2.7.2) and (2.7.4)) tends to

$$(F_y - F_{y'x} - F_{y'y}\varphi')/N, \tag{2.7.6}$$

where the arguments in the derivatives of F are (x, φ, φ'). Hence $\varphi''(x)$ exists and has the value (2.7.6). Since (2.7.6) is a continuous function of (x, φ, φ'), $\varphi''(x)$ is a continuous function of x.

Actually we can go further. Since φ'' exists and is continuous, and since F has continuous third derivatives, (2.7.6) can be differentiated, so $\varphi'''(x)$ exists and is continuous. And similarly, since $F \in C_4$, $\varphi^{\text{iv}}(x)$ also exists and is continuous.

(2) The equation of du Bois-Reymond (2.3.18) is

$$F_{y'}\{x, \varphi(x), \varphi'(x)\} - \chi(x) - C = 0. \tag{2.7.7}$$

Let us write

$$\lambda(x, u) \equiv F_{y'}\{x, \varphi(x), u\} - \chi(x) - C. \tag{2.7.8}$$

The equation

$$\lambda(x, u) = 0 \tag{2.7.9}$$

defines u implicitly as a function of x. Now, by the *implicit function theorem*, if

$$\lambda(x_0, u_0) = 0 \tag{2.7.10}$$

there is, in a neighbourhood of x_0, a solution $u = u(x)$ taking the value u_0 at x_0, provided that $\lambda_u(x_0, u_0) \neq 0$. Moreover if $\lambda \in C_n$ then the function $u(x)$ defined by (2.7.9) is of class C_n.

If $\{x_0, \varphi(x_0), \varphi'(x_0)\}$ is an element of K_0, and $u_0 = \varphi'(x_0)$,

$$\lambda(x_0, u_0) = 0, \qquad \lambda_u(x_0, u_0) = N\{x_0, \varphi(x_0), \varphi'(x_0)\} > 0, \tag{2.7.11}$$

and the requisite conditions are fulfilled. Hence the solution $u(x)$ of (2.7.9) exists, and in fact $u(x) = \varphi'(x)$. Moreover, it is easy to see that $\lambda \in C_1$ in a neighbourhood of (x_0, u_0); this follows since $\varphi'(x)$ is continuous and $F \in C_2$ in R, and in particular $F \in C_2$ in a neighbourhood of $\{x_0, \varphi(x_0), \varphi'(x_0)\}$. Thus the solution $u(x)$ of (2.7.9) is of class C_1, i.e. $\varphi''(x)$ exists and is continuous.

As before, we can go further. Since $F \in C_3$, and since $\varphi''(x)$ is continuous, $\lambda(x, u) \in C_2$. It follows that $u(x)$ has a continuous second derivative, so $\varphi'''(x)$ exists and is continuous. And finally, taking the argument a step further, since $F \in C_4$ and $\varphi'''(x)$ is continuous, $\lambda \in C_3$, so $u'''(x)(= \varphi^{\text{iv}}(x))$ exists and is continuous. This completes the second proof.

All of this refers to a point which is not a corner; now let us consider a corner at x_0 on a minimizing curve, and the arc (say) to the right of x_0. We shall assume that $N\{x_0, \varphi(x_0), \varphi'(x_0 + 0)\} \neq 0$. Then $N \neq 0$ on a sufficiently short arc following the corner, and on this arc $\varphi(x)$ has a continuous second derivative $\varphi''(x)$ having the value (2.7.6). Thus $\varphi''(x)$ tends to a unique limit σ as $x \to x_0 + 0$, since $\varphi(x)$ and $\varphi'(x)$ tend to unique limits. Further, this limit is the (one-sided) derivative of $\varphi'(x)$ at x_0. To prove this we have only to notice that

$$\frac{\varphi'(x) - \varphi'(x_0 + 0)}{x - x_0} = \varphi''(\xi), \tag{2.7.12}$$

where $x_0 < \xi < x$, and therefore the first member of (2.7.12) tends to σ as $x \to x_0 + 0$ (since $\xi \to x_0 + 0$ as $x \to x_0 + 0$). This completes the proof of the statement made at the end of §2.4.

2.8 The solutions of Euler's equation

For values of (x, y, y') near the elements of a regular extremal arc K_0, Euler's equation can be expressed in the form (2.2.13),

$$y'' = A(x, y, y'), \tag{2.8.1}$$

and $A \in C_2$. This equation has a unique solution through each initial element ξ, η, η' in a sufficiently small neighbourhood of the elements of K_0. The functions defining these extremals form the two-parameter family (ξ being chosen and fixed once for all)

$$y = \varphi(x, \eta, \eta'), \tag{2.8.2}$$

where $\varphi \in C_2$, and the function φ has the properties

$$\eta = \varphi(\xi, \eta, \eta'), \qquad \eta' = \varphi'(\xi, \eta, \eta'). \tag{2.8.3}$$

More generally, the solutions of Euler's equation have the form

$$y = \varphi(x, a, b), \tag{2.8.4}$$

where the parameters a, b are any convenient parameters, not necessarily the values η, η' at ξ as in the form (2.8.2). The extremal K_0 itself is given by (2.8.4) for the particular values (a_0, b_0) of (a, b), and (2.8.4) is an extremal for (a, b) in a certain neighbourhood of (a_0, b_0); the extremal K_0 is then said to be *embedded* in the family (2.8.4). The function $\varphi(x, a, b)$ in (2.8.4), and its x-derivative $\varphi'(x, a, b)$, have continuous second-order derivatives with respect to (x, a, b) in a neighbourhood of the sets (x, a_0, b_0) belonging to K_0.

The determinant

$$\Delta \equiv \Delta(x, a, b) \equiv \begin{vmatrix} \varphi_a & \varphi_b \\ \varphi_a' & \varphi_b' \end{vmatrix} \tag{2.8.5}$$

does not vanish on a regular extremal arc. We may notice first that if we choose the parameters (a, b) to be the values (η, η') at ξ, then

$$\Delta(\xi, a,b) = 1. \tag{2.8.6}$$

More generally, in whatever way we choose the parameters (a, b),

$$N\,\Delta = \text{constant} \tag{2.8.7}$$

on an extremal arc. To prove this we first establish the following lemma.

LEMMA. On an extremal arc

$$\frac{1}{N}\frac{dN}{dx} = -A_{y'}. \tag{2.8.8}$$

To prove this we recall that A is defined by the equation (2.2.12), i.e.

$$AN = F_y - F_{y'x} - F_{y'y}y', \tag{2.8.9}$$

where the arguments in the derivatives of F are (x, y, y'). Differentiating partially with respect to y' we have

$$A_{y'}N + AN_{y'} = F_{yy'} - F_{y'xy'} - F_{y'yy'}y' - F_{y'y}. \tag{2.8.10}$$

Now

$$\frac{dN}{dx} = F_{y'y'x} + F_{y'y'y}y' + F_{y'y'y'}y''. \tag{2.8.11}$$

On adding the two results (2.8.10) and (2.8.11) we have

$$A_{y'}N + AN_{y'} + \frac{dN}{dx} = y''N_{y'}, \tag{2.8.12}$$

and the result (2.8.8) follows, since $y'' = A$ on the arc. This completes the proof of the Lemma.

To deduce (2.8.7) we notice that

$$\varphi'' = A(x, \varphi, \varphi') \tag{2.8.13}$$

identically in (a, b), so long as (a, b) lies in the appropriate neighbourhood of (a_0, b_0). Thus

$$\varphi_a'' = \varphi_a A_y(x, \varphi, \varphi') + \varphi_a' A_{y'}(x, \varphi, \varphi'), \tag{2.8.14}$$

$$\varphi_b'' = \varphi_b A_y(x, \varphi, \varphi') + \varphi_b' A_{y'}(x, \varphi, \varphi'), \tag{2.8.15}$$

whence

$$\frac{d\Delta}{dx} = \begin{vmatrix} \varphi_a & \varphi_b \\ \varphi_a'' & \varphi_b'' \end{vmatrix} = A_{y'}\Delta. \tag{2.8.16}$$

From (2.8.8) and (2.8.16) we see that

$$\frac{d}{dx}(N\Delta) = 0, \tag{2.8.17}$$

and (2.8.7) follows.

We have noticed that in general a solution of Euler's equation is determined if the values of y and y' for a given x are prescribed. Thus if P is the point (X, Y), in general we expect to find a pencil of extremals through P, one for each value of the slope y' at P, or at least for each value of y' in a certain range. But this fails if P is a point at which N vanishes for all values of y'. For example, suppose that F has the form $f(x, y)\,\psi(y')$. Then $N = 0$ at all points on the curve $f(x, y) = 0$. Euler's equation is

$$f\psi'' y'' = f_y\psi - f_x\psi' - f_y y'\psi', \tag{2.8.18}$$

and if $f(X, Y) = 0$ this equation determines, in general, a discrete set of values of y' at (X, Y). Moreover in general to each member of this set there corresponds an infinity of extremals, not merely one extremal. For Euler's equation does not now determine the curvature at (X, Y)—the formula (2.7.6) for y'' takes the indeterminate form 0/0—and when the particular value of y' at (X, Y) has been chosen from the permissible set, we can in general give to y'' a prescribed value.

2.9 Some special cases

There are some special cases in which it is easy to find a first integral of Euler's equation.

(i) If we write, as in §2.6,

$$U = F(x, y, y') - y'F_{y'}(x, y, y'), \tag{2.9.1}$$

we have

$$\begin{aligned} \frac{dU}{dx} &= F_x + y'F_y + y''F_{y'} - y''F_{y'} - y'\frac{d}{dx}F_{y'} \\ &= F_x + y'\left(F_y - \frac{d}{dx}F_{y'}\right), \end{aligned} \tag{2.9.2}$$

and therefore, on an extremal arc,

$$\frac{dU}{dx} = F_x, \tag{2.9.3}$$

a result already encountered in (2.6.14). In particular, if F does not contain x, F_x is identically zero, and we have the first integral

$$U = C \tag{2.9.4}$$

on a minimizing arc.

In fact the statement just made is unnecessarily restricted. For a problem in which F_x is identically zero, U is constant, not merely on an arc between corners on a minimizing curve, but for the whole extent of a minimizing curve of class D_1. We can deduce this generalization from the second corner condition, or, more naturally, from the analogue (2.6.13) of du Bois-Reymond's equation.

We must take care at this point to avoid an awkward fallacy. If F does not contain x, all extremals satisfy (2.9.4), but not all solutions of (2.9.4) are extremals. The equation (2.9.4) is always satisfied by the curves $y =$ constant (which in general are not extremals) as well as by the extremals. Consider for example the problem of finding the geodesics on a sphere. Using spherical polar coordinates θ, φ, with φ (instead of x) as independent variable, and θ (instead of y) as dependent variable, the integral we wish to minimize is

$$\int \sqrt{(\theta'^2 + \sin^2 \theta)}\, d\varphi. \tag{2.9.5}$$

The integrand does not contain φ, and the first integral $U = C$ (where U now means $F - \theta' F_{\theta'}$) is

$$\frac{\sin^2 \theta}{\sqrt{(\theta'^2 + \sin^2 \theta)}} = C. \tag{2.9.6}$$

This is satisfied by $\theta =$ constant, but the small circles on the sphere are not geodesics!

As a concrete example of the integral $U = C$, consider a problem for which

$$F = f(y)\sqrt{(1 + y'^2)}. \tag{2.9.7}$$

Then

$$U = f(y) \frac{1}{\sqrt{(1 + y'^2)}} = f(y) \cos \psi, \tag{2.9.8}$$

where $\tan \psi$ is the slope of the extremal, and the first integral (2.9.4) of Euler's equation can be written in the form

$$f(y) \cos \psi = C. \tag{2.9.9}$$

In this case $f(y) \cos \psi$ is constant along a minimizing arc.

The result suggests a brief digression about optics. The path of a ray of light in a medium of variable refractive index $\mu(x, y, z)$ minimizes (or at least makes stationary) the integral $\int \mu \, ds$. This is Fermat's principle. In the case where μ is a function of y only, and the path lies in the plane $z = 0$, we can find the path by an intuitive physical argument as follows.

Suppose first that the medium consists of strata parallel to $y = 0$, the refractive index in each stratum being constant. Then the ray in each stratum is straight, and at each refraction $\mu \cos \psi$ is unchanged; this is Snell's law, accepted here as an empirical result.

If we now consider the limiting case in which the breadth of the strips tends to zero, and μ varies continuously with y, it is natural to suppose that the direction of the ray will follow the same law

(2.9.10) $$\mu \cos \psi = \text{constant},$$

and if $\mu = f(y)$ the path of the light satisfies the condition (2.9.9). We thus recover, on physical grounds, the first integral of Euler's equation already found. The argument is of great historic interest, because it is the method by which John Bernoulli solved the brachistochrone problem.

(ii) If F does not contain y we have at once the first integral

(2.9.11) $$V = C,$$

where we write V for $F_{y'}$ as in §2.5. But the statement that (for a problem in which F_y is identically zero) V is constant on an arc between corners of a minimizing curve is unnecessarily restricted. In fact the statement is true for a minimizing curve of class D_1, as we have noticed earlier, in §2.3; this is an immediate deduction from the equation of du Bois-Reymond, as in (2.3.25). (We notice that the step from the restricted result, for curves of class C_1, to the general result for curves of class D_1, is in agreement with the first corner condition.)

Let us consider the particular case in which

(2.9.12) $$F = f(x)\sqrt{(1 + y'^2)},$$

(2.9.13) $$V = f(x)\frac{y'}{\sqrt{(1 + y'^2)}} = f(x) \sin \psi,$$

and $f(x) \sin \psi$ is constant along an extremal. Of course this result also can be found by the same plausible reasoning as that used above to establish (2.9.9).

(iii) Suppose now that both the above conditions are satisfied. Neither x nor y appears in F, which is a function of y' only. The extremals are the straight lines in the plane.

The first integrals found in (i) and (ii) are important in classical dynamics. If F is the Lagrangian function for a dynamical system with one degree of freedom, x representing the time and y the Lagrangian coordinate describing the configuration of the system at time x, the Euler equation for F is the Lagrangian equation of motion. If F does not contain the time we have the first integral $U = C$, which is the *integral of (or equation of) energy*. If F does not contain y, which is then spoken of as an ignorable coordinate, we have the integral $V = C$, which is the *integral of momentum* corresponding to the ignorable coordinate.

2.10 Second-order conditions and the search for sufficient conditions

Our study of du Bois-Reymond's equation in §2.3 arose from the condition $\psi'(0) = 0$, where

(2.10.1) $$\psi(\alpha) = I(K_\alpha),$$

and K_α is the curve

(2.10.2) $$y = \varphi(x) + \alpha\eta(x).$$

We found that, if $\psi'(0) = 0$ for all admissible η (i.e. $\eta \in D_1$, and $\eta(X) = \eta(\bar{X}) = 0$), then $\varphi(x)$ satisfies du Bois-Reymond's equation.

The analogy of the theory of maxima and minima of functions of one variable would lead us to seek for sufficient conditions for a relative minimum in terms of $\psi''(0)$. *If we suppose the function η to be prescribed*, and the conditions

(2.10.3) $$\psi'(0) = 0, \qquad \psi''(0) > 0,$$

are satisfied, then I has a relative minimum at $\alpha = 0$ in the class (2.10.2).

It may seem natural to expect that if $\psi''(0) > 0$, not only for a particular choice of η, but for all admissible η, then the curve K_0, $y = \varphi(x)$, gives a relative minimum. But this is fallacious. The curve K_0 may give a relative minimum to I in every one-parameter family of the form $y = \varphi(x) + \alpha\eta(x)$, and yet not give a strong relative minimum in the prescribed class κ. The result is perhaps not surprising if we recall that the variation from K_0 to K_α is a weak variation if α is small. Moreover it is by no means obvious without explicit proof that a curve K_0 giving a weak relative minimum in every one-parameter family of the particular form (2.10.2) will give even a weak relative minimum in the whole class κ. The search for sufficient conditions requires a new line of attack.

To prove the statement just made, that K_0 may provide a relative minimum in every one-parameter family of the form (2.10.2), and yet not provide a strong relative minimum in the class κ, let us consider a simple concrete example. Let

$$I = \int_0^1 (y'^2 + y'^3)\, dx, \tag{2.10.4}$$

where A is (0, 0) and B is (1, 0). The extremal K_0 is the segment from $x = 0$ to $x = 1$ of the straight line $y = 0$, and

$$\psi(\alpha) = \alpha^2 \int_0^1 \eta'^2\, dx + \alpha^3 \int_0^1 \eta'^3\, dx. \tag{2.10.5}$$

Thus

$$\psi'(0) = 0, \qquad \psi''(0) = 2\int_0^1 \eta'^2\, dx, \tag{2.10.6}$$

and

$$\psi''(0) > 0 \tag{2.10.7}$$

for all choices of η. Thus K_0 surely gives a relative minimum in any one-parameter family of the form (2.10.2).

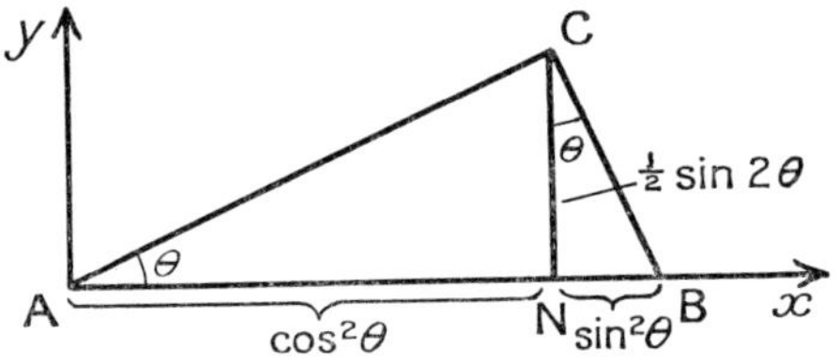

Fig. 2.10*a*

But K_0 does not give a strong relative minimum in the class D_1, nor even in the class C_1. If we take for η the function represented in Fig. 2.10*a* by ACB, consisting of two straight lines AC, CB at right angles, AC making an angle θ with AB, we have

$$\begin{aligned} I &= (\tan^2\theta + \tan^3\theta)\cos^2\theta + (\cot^2\theta - \cot^3\theta)\sin^2\theta \\ &= 1 - 2\cot 2\theta, \end{aligned} \tag{2.10.8}$$

which tends to $-\infty$ as $\theta \to 0$; at the same time the maximum ordinate

$\frac{1}{2}\sin 2\theta \to 0$. Now $I(K_0) = 0$, and I takes arbitrarily large negative values on curves arbitrarily near to K_0, so K_0 emphatically does not supply a strong relative minimum in the class D_1. We are here concerned with a one-parameter family (since C lies on the semi-circle above the diameter AB) but not a family of the form (2.10.2).

A similar result is true if we take as the prescribed class κ the class C_1. This is in fact evident from the example just given, in virtue of the rounding argument (§1.6); by rounding off the corner we can find a curve of class C_1 arbitrarily near to K_0 which gives to I an arbitrarily large negative value. It is of interest, and not difficult, to exhibit explicitly a curve of class C_1 with this property. Consider the curve

$$y = \lambda\left(x - \frac{\tan(\beta x)}{\tan\beta}\right), \tag{2.10.9}$$

where $\lambda > 0$, $0 < \beta < \frac{1}{2}\pi$. For this curve (Fig. 2.10*b*)

$$y' = \lambda(1 - p\sec^2(\beta x)), \tag{2.10.10}$$

where

$$p = \beta/t, \qquad t = \tan\beta, \tag{2.10.11}$$

and the corresponding value of I is

$$I = \lambda^2\int_0^1 \{1 - p\sec^2(\beta x)\}^2\,dx + \lambda^3\int_0^1\{1 - p\sec^2(\beta x)\}^3\,dx. \tag{2.10.12}$$

The integration is elementary, and leads to the result

$$\begin{aligned} I = {} & \lambda^2\left(\frac{1}{3}\beta t - 1 + \frac{\beta}{t}\right) \\ & + \lambda^3\left(-\frac{1}{5}\beta^2 t^2 + \beta t - 2 - \frac{2}{3}\beta^2 + \frac{3\beta}{t} - \frac{\beta^2}{t^2}\right). \end{aligned} \tag{2.10.13}$$

If β is near to $\frac{1}{2}\pi$, $t\,(= \tan\beta)$ is large, and the dominating term in the first bracket is $\beta t/3$, and the dominating term in the second bracket is $-\beta^2t^2/5$.

So far λ is at our disposal; we now choose the value $\lambda = 1/\sqrt{t}$. Then

$$I = -\frac{1}{5}\beta^2 t^{\frac{1}{2}} + \frac{1}{3}\beta + 0\left(\frac{1}{\sqrt{t}}\right), \tag{2.10.14}$$

which tends to $-\infty$ as $\beta \to \frac{1}{2}\pi$. Moreover the maximum ordinate is less than $\lambda\,(= 1/\sqrt{t})$, and tends to zero as $\beta \to \frac{1}{2}\pi$. Thus we have a curve of class C_1, arbitrarily near to K_0, and giving to I an arbitrarily large negative value.

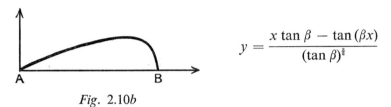

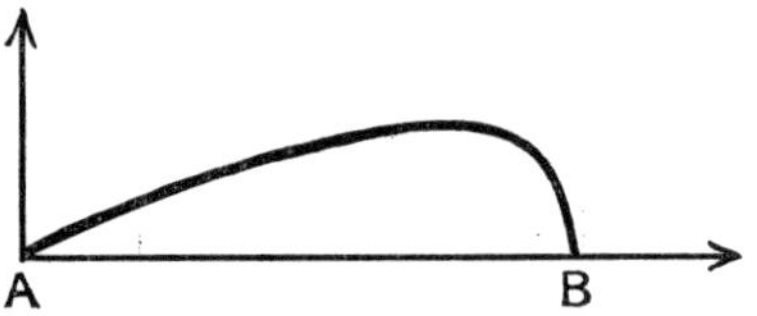

$$y = \frac{x \tan \beta - \tan(\beta x)}{(\tan \beta)^{\frac{3}{2}}}$$

Fig. 2.10*b*

Before leaving the example with the integral (2.10.4) it is worth while to notice that the segment AB does provide a *weak* relative minimum, for if ε is a small positive number and if $|y'| < \varepsilon$ on K,

(2.10.15) $$0 \leqslant I(K) < 2\varepsilon^2.$$

(We shall find later (§5.16) a general theorem of which this is a particular example.)

Consider, more generally, the case in which F is any function of y' only. If K_0, the straight-line extremal AB, has slope k, and $\psi(\alpha) = I(K_\alpha)$, then

(2.10.16) $$\psi'(0) = F'(k)\int_X^{\overline{X}} \eta'(x)\,dx = 0, \quad \psi''(0) = F''(k)\int_X^{\overline{X}} \{\eta'(x)\}^2\,dx,$$

and $\psi''(0) > 0$, for all choices of η, if $F''(k) > 0$. But, as we have seen, this does not suffice to ensure that K_0 gives a strong relative minimum.

2.11 Legendre's necessary condition

As we have seen, the conditions (2.10.3) are not sufficient to ensure a strong relative minimum. But the necessary condition

(2.11.1) $$\psi''(0) \geqslant 0$$

for a relative minimum in the one-parameter family (2.3.2) does lead to an important condition that must be satisfied if K_0 is to give even a weak relative minimum. This is Legendre's condition,

(2.11.2) $$N\{x, \varphi(x), \varphi'(x)\} \geqslant 0$$

for every element $\{x, \varphi(x), \varphi'(x)\}$ of an arc of a minimizing curve.

To establish this result, let us suppose on the contrary that $N(= F_{y'y'})$ is negative at $x = \xi$ on K_0,

(2.11.3) $$N\{\xi, \varphi(\xi), \varphi'(\xi)\} = -C,$$

where $C > 0$. Then, by continuity, there is a range $(\xi - h, \xi + h)$ in which $N < -\frac{1}{2}C$. Let us consider the particular η, of class D_1, whose graph is shown in the figure, where $0 < \varepsilon < h$. In the range $(\xi - \varepsilon, \xi + \varepsilon)$ we have $|\eta| \leqslant 1$ and $|\eta'| = 1/\varepsilon$. Let A, B be constants such that $|F_{yy}| < A$, $|F_{yy'}| < B$ in $(\xi - h, \xi + h)$. Now, as in (2.3.8),

$$\psi''(0) = \int_{\xi-\varepsilon}^{\xi+\varepsilon} (\eta^2 F_{yy} + 2\eta\eta' F_{yy'} + \eta'^2 F_{y'y'})\, dx, \tag{2.11.4}$$

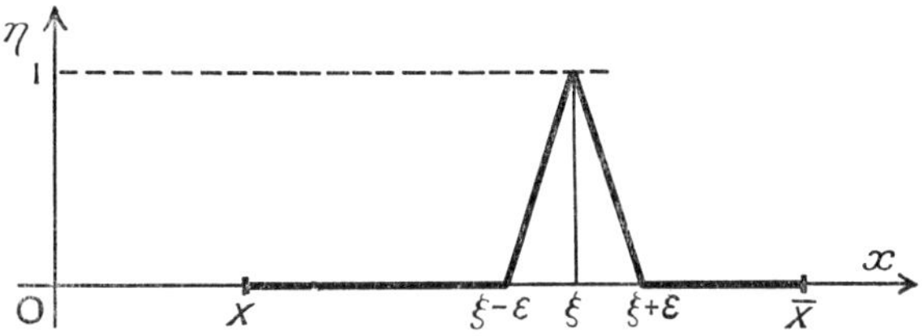

Fig. 2.11

and the last term in the bracket is dominating when ε is sufficiently small. For, considering the terms separately,

$$\int_{\xi-\varepsilon}^{\xi+\varepsilon} \eta^2 F_{yy}\, dx \leqslant \left| \int_{\xi-\varepsilon}^{\xi+\varepsilon} \eta^2 F_{yy}\, dx \right| \leqslant \int_{\xi-\varepsilon}^{\xi+\varepsilon} |\eta|^2 |F_{yy}|\, dx < \int_{\xi-\varepsilon}^{\xi+\varepsilon} |F_{yy}|\, dx < 2A\varepsilon, \tag{2.11.5}$$

$$\int_{\xi-\varepsilon}^{\xi+\varepsilon} 2\eta\eta' F_{yy'}\, dx \leqslant \left| \int_{\xi-\varepsilon}^{\xi+\varepsilon} 2\eta\eta' F_{yy'}\, dx \right| \leqslant 2\int_{\xi-\varepsilon}^{\xi+\varepsilon} |\eta||\eta'||F_{yy'}|\, dx < \frac{2}{\varepsilon} \int_{\xi-\varepsilon}^{\xi+\varepsilon} |F_{yy'}|\, dx < \frac{2}{\varepsilon}(2B\varepsilon) = 4B, \tag{2.11.6}$$

$$\int_{\xi-\varepsilon}^{\xi+\varepsilon} \eta'^2 F_{y'y'}\, dx = \frac{1}{\varepsilon^2} \int_{\xi-\varepsilon}^{\xi+\varepsilon} F_{y'y'}\, dx < \frac{1}{\varepsilon^2}(-C\varepsilon) = -\frac{C}{\varepsilon}. \tag{2.11.7}$$

Thus

$$\psi''(0) < 2A\varepsilon + 4B - (C/\varepsilon), \tag{2.11.8}$$

which is negative when ε is sufficiently small. This contradicts the hypothesis that K_0 is a minimizing curve. Therefore the assumption (2.11.3) is untenable, and this proves the stated condition (2.11.2).

COROLLARY. A necessary condition for a weak relative maximum is $N \leqslant 0$ for all elements of the curve.

2.12 Non-contemporaneous variations

In some applications in classical dynamics it is convenient to use non-contemporaneous variations; these are variations, not from (x, y) to $(x, y + \delta y)$ as used by Lagrange, but from (x, y) to $(x + \delta x, y + \delta y)$. This represents an approach to the parametric problem, in which the curve is defined by the equations

$$x = \varphi(t), \qquad y = \psi(t), \tag{2.12.1}$$

and in which a variation to a point with the same value of t on a neighbouring curve implies a variation in x as well as in y. For the present, however, we are concerned with the ordinary, not the parametric, problem. The non-contemporaneous variations lie a little way from the main line of development, but they deserve a brief mention on account of their value in the physical applications.

We consider then a variation from the point (x, y) on the minimizing curve to a neighbouring point $(x + \delta x, y + \delta y)$. Here δx and δy are functions of x of class C_2, and the variations are weak variations. Thus δx, δy, and their derivatives are all small of order ε.

The two fundamental results, correct to order ε, are as follows.

$$\delta \frac{dy}{dx} = \frac{d}{dx}\,\delta y - \frac{dy}{dx}\frac{d}{dx}\,\delta x, \tag{2.12.2}$$

$$\delta \int_X^{\bar{X}} F(x, y, y')\, dx = \int_X^{\bar{X}} (\delta F + F\frac{d}{dx}\,\delta x)\, dx. \tag{2.12.3}$$

To prove the first result we have

$$\begin{aligned} \delta \frac{dy}{dx} &= \frac{d(y + \delta y)}{d(x + \delta x)} - \frac{dy}{dx} \\ &= \frac{\dfrac{dy}{dx} + \dfrac{d}{dx}\,\delta y}{1 + \dfrac{d}{dx}\,\delta x} - \frac{dy}{dx} \\ &= \frac{\dfrac{d}{dx}\,\delta y - \dfrac{dy}{dx}\dfrac{d}{dx}\,\delta x}{1 + \dfrac{d}{dx}\,\delta x}. \end{aligned} \tag{2.12.4}$$

This is exact whatever the magnitude of δx and δy and their derivatives. For the weak variations contemplated we can replace the denominator by unity, since we need the result correct to order ε, and this establishes the first result.

We can exhibit the result in another way, which is perhaps even simpler; it is merely an application of the rule for differentiating a quotient. Let us for the moment introduce a parameter t on the curve, and a parameter α to distinguish the members of a family of neighbouring curves, of which the typical member K_α is

(2.12.5) $$x = \varphi(t, \alpha), \qquad y = \psi(t, \alpha).$$

The original curve is given by $\alpha = \alpha_0$, and the parameters are so chosen that the operation δ takes us from the point with parameter t on K_{α_0} to the point with the same parameter t on $K_{\alpha_0+\delta\alpha}$,

(2.12.6)
$$\delta x = \frac{\partial x}{\partial \alpha}\,\delta\alpha = \varphi_\alpha(t, \alpha_0)\,\delta\alpha, \qquad \delta y = \frac{\partial y}{\partial \alpha}\,\delta\alpha = \psi_\alpha(t, \alpha_0)\,\delta\alpha.$$

Let T, $\overline{T}$ be the extreme values of t on K_{α_0},

(2.12.7) $$X = \varphi(T, \alpha_0), \qquad \overline{X} = \varphi(\overline{T}, \alpha_0),$$

and let us assume that t increases steadily from T to $\overline{T}$ as x increases along K_{α_0} from X to $\overline{X}$. We assume that the functions φ and ψ are of class C_2, and that $\varphi_t(t, \alpha) > 0$, in a domain containing the segment

(2.12.8) $$T \leqslant t \leqslant \overline{T}, \qquad \alpha = \alpha_0.$$

We must now interpret the formulae occurring in (2.12.2). We have

(2.12.9) $$\frac{dy}{dx} = \frac{\dfrac{\partial y}{\partial t}}{\dfrac{\partial x}{\partial t}} = \frac{\psi_t(t, \alpha)}{\varphi_t(t, \alpha)},$$

(2.12.10) $$\frac{d}{dx}\,\delta x = \frac{\dfrac{\partial}{\partial t}\,\delta x}{\dfrac{\partial x}{\partial t}} = \frac{\dfrac{\partial^2 x}{\partial t\,\partial \alpha}}{\dfrac{\partial x}{\partial t}}\,\delta\alpha = \frac{\varphi_{\alpha t}(t, \alpha_0)}{\varphi_t(t, \alpha_0)}\,\delta\alpha,$$

(2.12.11) $$\frac{d}{dx}\,\delta y = \frac{\dfrac{\partial}{\partial t}\,\delta y}{\dfrac{\partial x}{\partial t}} = \frac{\dfrac{\partial^2 y}{\partial t\,\partial \alpha}}{\dfrac{\partial x}{\partial t}}\,\delta\alpha = \frac{\psi_{\alpha t}(t, \alpha_0)}{\varphi_t(t, \alpha_0)}\,\delta\alpha,$$

where the formulae on the extreme right can be dispensed with, but are added for the sake of clarity. Thus

$$\text{(2.12.12)} \qquad \delta\frac{dy}{dx} = \frac{\partial}{\partial\alpha}\left(\frac{\dfrac{\partial y}{\partial t}}{\dfrac{\partial x}{\partial t}}\right)\delta\alpha = \left(\frac{\dfrac{\partial^2 y}{\partial\alpha\,\partial t}}{\dfrac{\partial x}{\partial t}} - \frac{\dfrac{\partial y}{\partial t}\dfrac{\partial^2 x}{\partial\alpha\,\partial t}}{\left(\dfrac{\partial x}{\partial t}\right)^2}\right)\delta\alpha$$

and hence, since φ and ψ are of class C_2,

$$\text{(2.12.13)} \qquad \delta\frac{dy}{dx} = \left(\frac{\dfrac{\partial^2 y}{\partial t\,\partial\alpha}}{\dfrac{dx}{\partial t}} - \frac{\dfrac{\partial y}{\partial t}}{\dfrac{\partial x}{\partial t}}\frac{\dfrac{\partial^2 x}{\partial t\,\partial\alpha}}{\dfrac{\partial x}{\partial t}}\right)\delta\alpha = \frac{d}{dx}\delta y - \frac{dy}{dx}\frac{d}{dx}\delta x,$$

which is the required result (2.12.2).

We now turn to the second theorem (2.12.3). We use the substitution $x = \varphi(t, \alpha)$ in the integral, giving

$$\text{(2.12.14)} \qquad I(K_\alpha) = \int_T^{\bar{T}} F\frac{\partial x}{\partial t}\,dt,$$

where, in the integrand, F stands for

$$\text{(2.12.15)} \qquad F\left(x, y, \frac{\dfrac{\partial y}{\partial t}}{\dfrac{\partial x}{\partial t}}\right) = F\left\{\varphi(t, \alpha), \psi(t, \alpha), \frac{\psi_t(t, \alpha)}{\varphi_t(t, \alpha)}\right\}.$$

We now have an integrand with fixed limits of integration, and

$$\text{(2.12.16)} \quad \delta I = \delta\alpha\int_T^{\bar{T}}\frac{\partial}{\partial\alpha}\left(F\frac{\partial x}{\partial t}\right)dt = \int_T^{\bar{T}}\left(\delta F\frac{\partial x}{\partial t} + F\frac{\partial^2 x}{\partial\alpha\,\partial t}\delta\alpha\right)dt,$$

where δF stands for $\dfrac{\partial F}{\partial\alpha}\delta\alpha = (F_x\,\delta x + F_y\,\delta y + F_{y'}\,\delta y')$. Thus, in virtue of (2.12.10),

$$\text{(2.12.17)} \qquad \delta I = \int_T^{\bar{T}}\left(\delta F + F\frac{d}{dx}\delta x\right)\frac{\partial x}{\partial t}\,dt,$$

and, expressing this result as an integral with respect to x instead of t, we arrive at the desired equation (2.12.3).

2.13 An outline of the theory of the second variation

In §2.2 and §2.3 we considered an admissible curve K_0, $y = \varphi(x)$, whose minimizing property we wish to test. We considered the one-parameter family whose typical member K_α is

$$y = \varphi(x) + \alpha\eta(x) \tag{2.13.1}$$

where $\eta(X) = \eta(\bar{X}) = 0$. If $\psi(\alpha) = I(K_\alpha)$, and if $\psi'(0) = 0$, a necessary condition for a minimizing curve is

$$\psi''(0) \geqslant 0. \tag{2.13.2}$$

The condition

$$\psi''(0) > 0 \tag{2.13.3}$$

is sufficient to ensure that $\psi(\alpha)$ has at least a relative minimum at $\alpha = 0$, so that in this case K_0 provides at least a relative minimum in the one-parameter family (2.13.1). But, as we have seen in §2.10, the condition (2.13.3), even when it is satisfied for all admissible η, does not ensure that K_0 is minimizing in the class κ. It is not sufficient even to ensure that K_0 is minimizing in every one-parameter family of κ (§2.10).

The early workers in the Calculus of Variations supposed that the conditions $\psi'(0) = 0$, $\psi''(0) > 0$, when satisfied for all admissible η, were sufficient to prove that K_0 gives at least a relative minimum, and the theory of the second variation is largely concerned with conditions which ensure $\psi''(0) > 0$. When it was realized that $\psi''(0) > 0$ does not in fact prove that K_0 is minimizing, the theory of the second variation lost much of its importance. Nevertheless the topic has played so prominent a part in the history of the subject that it deserves a brief mention.

There is a second fallacy, closely related to the first, which emerges at this point. We found, in §2.11, Legendre's necessary condition for a minimum

$$N\{x, \varphi(x), \varphi'(x)\} \geqslant 0 \tag{2.13.4}$$

for all elements (x, φ, φ') of K_0. (Here, as usual, N stands for $F_{y'y'}$.) It was supposed that the stronger condition

$$N\{x, \varphi(x), \varphi'(x)\} > 0 \tag{2.13.5}$$

for all elements of K_0, would imply $\psi''(0) > 0$, and that this would in turn imply that K_0 is minimizing. But in fact, as we shall see in a moment, $N > 0$ does not imply $\psi''(0) > 0$.

We found in (2.3.8) the formula

$$\psi''(0) = \int_X^{\bar{X}} (L\eta^2 + 2M\eta\eta' + N\eta'^2)\, dx, \tag{2.13.6}$$

where L, M, N are certain known functions of x: explicitly

$$L = F_{yy}(x, \varphi, \varphi'), \quad M = F_{yy'}(x, \varphi, \varphi'), \quad N = F_{y'y'}(x, \varphi, \varphi'). \tag{2.13.7}$$

5

We shall confine our attention to the case where φ itself is without corners and has a continuous second derivative, so that L, M, N, and their first derivatives L', M', N', are continuous functions of x. We shall assume also that K_0 is a regular arc, i.e. $N > 0$ for all elements of K_0.

We see from (2.13.6) that, if w is any function of class C_1,

$$\psi''(0) = \int_X^{\bar{X}} \{(L + w')\eta^2 + 2(M + w)\eta\eta' + N\eta'^2\}\, dx, \tag{2.13.8}$$

since the terms that have been added to the second member of (2.13.6) are equal to $w\eta^2 \Big|_X^{\bar{X}}$, which is zero. Let us now attempt to find a function w such that the integrand in (2.13.8) is a perfect square. Then (2.13.8) becomes

$$\psi''(0) = \int_X^{\bar{X}} N\left(\eta' + \frac{M + w}{N}\eta\right)^2 dx, \tag{2.13.9}$$

and this seems, at first sight, to lead to the conclusion mentioned, that $N > 0$ on K_0 implies $\psi''(0) > 0$. But the conclusion is invalid, because in fact, it may happen that no function w with the desired property exists.

Let us consider the first-order differential equation satisfied by w, namely

$$N(w' + L) = (w + M)^2. \tag{2.13.10}$$

It is an equation of Riccati's type. If we introduce a new dependent variable u defined by

$$w + M = -N(u'/u), \tag{2.13.11}$$

then u satisfies the equation

$$Nu'' + N'u' + (M' - L)u = 0. \tag{2.13.12}$$

This is a linear differential equation of the second order, and, because of the assumptions we have made about K_0, the coefficients are continuous functions of x in $[X, \bar{X}]$, and $N > 0$ in $[X, \bar{X}]$; hence any solution of class C_1 in $[X, \bar{X}]$ is in fact of class C_2. The equation (2.13.12) is called Jacobi's linear equation, or *the accessory equation*. It can also be written in the form

$$\frac{d}{dx}(Nu') + (M' - L)u = 0. \tag{2.13.13}$$

We easily establish the two theorems which follow.

THEOREM 1. *If there is a solution u, of class C_2, of the accessory equation which does not vanish in the (closed) interval $[X, \bar{X}]$, then $\psi''(0) > 0$.*

If such a solution exists we see from (2.13.9) that

$$\psi''(0) = \int_X^{\bar{X}} N\left(\frac{u\eta' - u'\eta}{u}\right)^2 dx, \tag{2.13.14}$$

and since $N > 0$ this implies $\psi''(0) \geqslant 0$. But $\psi''(0) = 0$ is impossible, because it would require $u\eta' - u'\eta$ to vanish everywhere in $[X, \bar{X}]$, which implies $u = C\eta$; and this is precluded, because u does not vanish at X or at $\bar{X}$.

It may happen, however, that no solution of the accessory equation of this type exists, and in that event we cannot infer the existence of a function w ($= -M - N(u'/u)$) continuous in $(X, \bar{X})$. The statement $N > 0$ does not always imply $\psi''(0) > 0$.

THEOREM 2. *If a solution of the accessory equation of class C_2 vanishing at X has no other zero in $[X, \bar{X}]$, then $\psi''(0) > 0$.*

The general solution of class C_2 of the accessory equation has the form

$$A\lambda(x) + B\mu(x), \tag{2.13.15}$$

where λ and μ are two linearly independent solutions, and A and B are arbitrary constants. The solution vanishing at ξ is definite save for a constant multiplier; it is in fact a multiple of

$$u(x, \xi) = \mu(\xi)\lambda(x) - \lambda(\xi)\mu(x). \tag{2.13.16}$$

Let the next zero greater than ξ be $\zeta(\xi)$. Then $\zeta(\xi)$ is a continuous function of ξ. Therefore if $\zeta(X) > \bar{X}$, then also $\zeta(X - \varepsilon) > \bar{X}$ when $\varepsilon\ (> 0)$ is sufficiently small, and therefore the solution $u(x, X - \varepsilon)$ has no zero in $[X, \bar{X}]$. Thus the conditions for Theorem 1 are fulfilled, and $\psi''(0) > 0$.

The zeros of $u(x, \xi)$ other than ξ are said to be *conjugate* to ξ. Theorem 2 can be stated in the form that $\psi''(0) > 0$ if the interval $X < x \leqslant \bar{X}$ contains no point conjugate to X.

The accessory equation also arises in another way. We found above

$$\psi''(0) = \int_X^{\bar{X}} (L\eta^2 + 2M\eta\eta' + N\eta'^2)\, dx. \tag{2.13.6}$$

The coefficients L, M, N are of class C_1, since φ is assumed to be of class C_2; and $\eta \in D_1$ with $\eta(x) = \eta(\bar{X}) = 0$. If the infimum m_0 for the integral on the right in (2.13.6) is positive, then $\psi''(0) > 0$ for all admissible η. We are thus led to a new problem in the Calculus of Variations, the minimizing problem for the integral on the right in (2.13.6). Now Euler's equation for this new problem is

$$N\eta'' + N'\eta' + (M' - L)\eta = 0, \tag{2.13.17}$$

and this is the accessory equation (2.13.12) with η as dependent variable instead of u.

The solutions of class C_2 of the accessory equation are given, as we have seen, by (2.13.15). If we write

$$2\omega = L\eta^2 + 2M\eta\eta' + N\eta'^2, \tag{2.13.18}$$

then (2.13.6) can be written

$$
\begin{aligned}
\text{(2.13.19)} \qquad \psi''(0) &= \int_X^{\bar{X}} \left(\eta \frac{\partial \omega}{\partial \eta} + \eta' \frac{\partial \omega}{\partial \eta'} \right) dx \\
&= \eta \frac{\partial \omega}{\partial \eta'} \Big|_X^{\bar{X}} - \int_X^{\bar{X}} \eta \left(\frac{d}{dx} \frac{\partial \omega}{\partial \eta'} - \frac{\partial \omega}{\partial \eta} \right) dx \\
&= - \int_X^{\bar{X}} \eta \left(\frac{d}{dx} \frac{\partial \omega}{\partial \eta'} - \frac{\partial \omega}{\partial \eta} \right) dx \\
&= - \int_X^{\bar{X}} \eta \, \{ N\eta'' + N'\eta' + (M' - L)\eta \} \, dx.
\end{aligned}
$$

It follows that $\psi''(0) = 0$ if we choose η (which is of class D_1) to be built-up of solutions of the accessory equation in some parts of the range $[X, \bar{X}]$ and of $\eta = 0$ in the rest of this interval. Suppose in particular that $\zeta(X) < \bar{X}$; in other words, suppose there is a point conjugate to X in $(X, \bar{X})$. Then we can choose for η the function $\eta = u(x, X)$ from X to $\zeta(X)$, and $\eta = 0$ from $\zeta(X)$ to $\bar{X}$ (Fig. 2.13). Therefore, for this η,

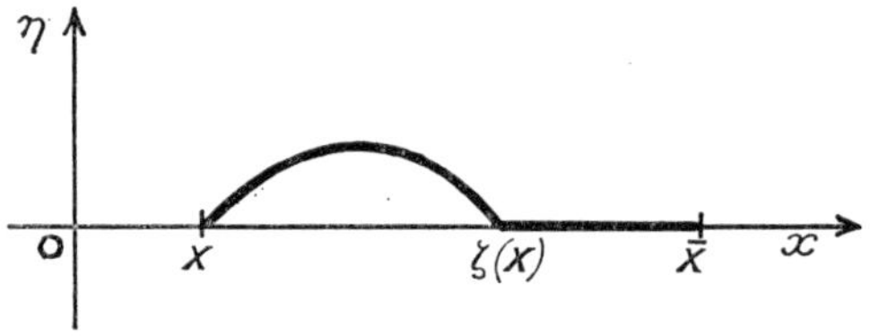

Fig. 2.13

$\psi''(0) = 0$, and in this case K_0 is not a minimizing curve. (Of course, as in the ordinary theory of maxima and minima, it might happen for this η that $\psi'''(0) = 0$ also, and then we should have to consider the sign of $\psi^{iv}(0)$. But we shall not consider this exceptional case in detail.)

The fact that K_0 cannot be minimizing if $\zeta(X) < \bar{X}$ is closely related to a theorem of Jacobi that we shall prove later (§5.4). To trace the connexion we notice first that the solutions of the accessory equation can be derived from the general solution $\varphi(x, a, b)$ of Euler's equation for the original problem. As in §2.8, $\varphi(x, a, b)$ and $\varphi'(x, a, b)$ have continuous second-order derivatives with respect to (x, a, b) in a neighbourhood of the sets (x, a_0, b_0) belonging to K_0. We shall prove that $\varphi_a(x, a_0, b_0)$ and $\varphi_b(x, a_0, b_0)$ are two linearly independent solutions of the accessory equation, so that for the general solution of class C_2 of the accessory equation the formula (2.13.15) may be written

$$\text{(2.13.20)} \qquad A\varphi_a + B\varphi_b.$$

To begin with φ_a and φ_b are surely linearly independent, since

$$\Delta = \begin{vmatrix} \varphi_a & \varphi_b \\ \varphi_a' & \varphi_b' \end{vmatrix}$$

does not vanish on a regular extremal arc (§2.8).

Next, to prove that φ_a satisfies the accessory equation, we start from Euler's equation for φ,

$$\frac{d}{dx} F_{y'} = F_y, \tag{2.13.21}$$

where the arguments in the derivatives of F are the elements $\{x, \varphi(x, a, b), \varphi'(x, a, b)\}$ of an extremal. This is satisfied identically in (a, b) in a sufficiently small neighbourhood of (a_0, b_0), so differentiating partially with respect to a, and putting (a_0, b_0) for (a, b) after differentiation, we have

$$\frac{d}{dx}(M\varphi_a + N\varphi_a') = L\varphi_a + M\varphi_a', \tag{2.13.22}$$

whence

$$\frac{d}{dx}(N\varphi_a') + (M' - L)\varphi_a = 0. \tag{2.13.23}$$

Thus φ_a satisfies the accessory equation (2.13.13), and similarly so also does φ_b.

The solution of the accessory equation vanishing at X is a multiple of

$$u(x, X) = \begin{vmatrix} \varphi_a(x, a_0, b_0) & \varphi_b(x, a_0, b_0) \\ \varphi_a(X, a_0, b_0) & \varphi_b(X, a_0, b_0) \end{vmatrix}, \tag{2.13.24}$$

and we defined the zeros of $u(x, X)$ other than X as values conjugate to X. We speak of the points on K_0 determined by values of x conjugate to X as points on K_0 conjugate to (X, Y). Now these points on K_0 conjugate to (X, Y) can be interpreted geometrically. The pencil of extremals (for the original problem) through (X, Y) is given by

$$y = \varphi(x, a, b), \tag{2.13.25}$$

where a and b are not independent, but are related by the condition

$$Y = \varphi(X, a, b). \tag{2.13.26}$$

Now if this pencil has an envelope, the x-coordinates of the points of contact of the extremal K_0 with the envelope are given by the zeros (other than X) of $u(x, X)$. Thus the points on K_0 conjugate to (X, Y), originally defined as the points determined by the other zeros of $u(x, X)$, can also be defined as the points of contact of K_0 with the envelope of the pencil of extremals through (X, Y). We have seen that K_0 cannot be minimizing if there is a point conjugate to A on the arc AB. All of this will reappear in the context of the geometrical theory of envelopes (§5.4); it is interesting to observe that the fundamental result can be found, as we have seen, without any appeal to the geometrical theory of envelopes.

A relation between the determinant (2.13.24) and the determinant Δ, defined in (2.8.5), which we shall need later (§5.15), may be noticed at this point; since

$$u'(x, x) = -\Delta(x, a_0, b_0), \tag{2.13.27}$$

we see that $u'(x, x)$ does not vanish on a regular extremal arc.

CHAPTER III

Illustrative Examples

3.1 Application of the theory to concrete problems

We now consider the application of the theory developed in the preceding Chapters to concrete problems.

Let us examine the tools that are available to us at this stage. We start from Euler's equation

$$\frac{d}{dx} F_{y'}\{x, \varphi(x), \varphi'(x)\} = F_y\{x, \varphi(x), \varphi'(x)\}, \tag{3.1.1}$$

and a minimizing curve, if there is one, consists of a finite number of arcs $y = \varphi(x)$ satisfying this equation. There may be a corner where one of these arcs joins another, and at each corner U and V are continuous, where

$$U = F - y'F_{y'}, \quad V = F_{y'}. \tag{3.1.2}$$

At each element $\{x, \varphi(x), \varphi'(x)\}$ of an arc of a minimizing curve,

$$N\{x, \varphi(x), \varphi'(x)\} \geqslant 0, \tag{3.1.3}$$

where

$$N = F_{y'y'}, \tag{3.1.4}$$

and in fact (3.1.3) must be satisfied even if the arc provides merely a weak relative minimum. On a minimizing arc which is regular (i.e. an arc for each of whose elements $N > 0$) the second derivative $\varphi''(x)$ exists and is continuous. If F does not contain x, Euler's equation has the first integral $U = C$; and if F does not contain y, Euler's equation has the first integral $V = C$.

To begin with the procedure is tentative, because the conditions established so far are merely necessary conditions; but it is vitally important to observe that it may nevertheless lead to a complete solution of the problem. The conditions may serve to define a curve K, and when this curve has been found we may be able to produce an *ad hoc* proof that it is indeed a minimizing curve, either in the sense of an absolute minimum or of a strong or a weak relative minimum. Or, on the contrary, we may be able to show that it cannot be a minimizing curve in either sense.

Some examples containing elementary proofs of the minimizing property of a particular curve have already appeared (§1.4 and §1.5). As a further example, consider the integral

$$I = \int_X^{\bar{X}} (py'^2 + qy^2)\,dx, \tag{3.1.5}$$

where p and q are given functions of x of class C_1, each of which is positive in $(X, \bar{X})$, the end-points are $A(X, Y)$ and $B(\bar{X}, \bar{Y})$ as usual, and the curves admitted to competition are of class C_2. If we can find a curve K_0, $y = \varphi(x)$, of this class, joining A to B and satisfying Euler's equation

$$\frac{d}{dx}(py') = qy, \tag{3.1.6}$$

it is a minimizing curve. The least possible value for I is

$$I(K_0) = p\varphi\varphi' \Big|_X^{\bar{X}}. \tag{3.1.7}$$

To prove this, consider a curve K, $y = \varphi(x) + \zeta(x)$, where $\zeta(x) \in C_2$, and $\zeta(X) = \zeta(\bar{X}) = 0$. Then

$$\begin{aligned} I(K) - I(K_0) &= \int_X^{\bar{X}} \{p(2\varphi'\zeta' + \zeta'^2) + q(2\varphi\zeta + \zeta^2)\}\,dx \\ &= 2p\varphi'\zeta \Big|_X^{\bar{X}} + \int_X^{\bar{X}} (p\zeta'^2 + q\zeta^2)\,dx \\ &= \int_X^{\bar{X}} (p\zeta'^2 + q\zeta^2)\,dx > 0. \end{aligned} \tag{3.1.8}$$

As a trivial illustration, the least value of $\int(x^2y'^2 + 2y^2)\,dx$ for curves joining $A(0, 0)$ to $B(1, 1)$ is 1; the minimizing curve is the straight line AB.

3.2 Line integral

We consider the line integral

$$I = \int_\Gamma P\,dx + Q\,dy, \tag{3.2.1}$$

where P and Q are given functions of (x, y) of class C_1. Integrals of this type appear frequently in mathematical physics. For example, (3.2.1) represents the work done by a field of force (P, Q) when a particle moves in the field along a curve Γ from A to B. In these problems the integrand

$$F = P + Qy' \tag{3.2.2}$$

is linear in y', and $N(= F_{y'y'})$ is identically zero. Euler's equation

$$\frac{d}{dx} Q = P_y + Q_y y' \tag{3.2.3}$$

reduces to

$$J \equiv Q_x - P_y = 0, \tag{3.2.4}$$

which is not a differential equation, and various cases arise as follows.

(i) The condition (3.2.4) is satisfied identically. The Pfaffian form $P\,dx + Q\,dy$ is a perfect differential $-d\mathscr{V}$, where $\mathscr{V}$ $(= \mathscr{V}(x, y))$ is a function of (x, y) of class C_2. In this case the field (P, Q) is said to be *conservative* and $\mathscr{V}$ is the *potential function* of the field. We sometimes use the notation $\mathscr{V}(P)$, instead of $\mathscr{V}(x, y)$, if P is the point (x, y). The integral I has the value

$$I = \mathscr{V}(A) - \mathscr{V}(B), \tag{3.2.5}$$

and this value is the same for all paths of class D_1 lying in the field of force and joining A to B. No question of a minimizing curve arises.

In this case the integrand F has the form

$$F = \frac{d}{dx} f(x, y) = f_x + f_y y', \tag{3.2.6}$$

and whenever F has this form the expression

$$\frac{d}{dx} F_{y'} - F_y$$

is identically zero. In forming Euler's equation for the integrand $F(x, y, y')$, any terms in F of the form $\dfrac{d}{dx} f(x, y)$ can be ignored.

(ii) The condition (3.2.4) cannot be satisfied. For example, in the simple case

$$P = -y, \qquad Q = x, \tag{3.2.7}$$

the value of J is 2, and no solution of (3.2.4) exists. If A is the origin

$$I = \int x\,dy - y\,dx = -2\,\Delta, \tag{3.2.8}$$

where Δ is the area shaded in Fig. 3.2*a*. We can choose a path K to give an arbitrarily large negative value, and $I(K)$ is not bounded below.

(iii) The condition (3.2.4) represents a curve or curves, and there is no solution unless A and B lie on an arc K_0 satisfying $J = 0$. If they do, in general the arc is a minimizing arc if $J < 0$ above K_0 and $J > 0$ below K_0. For suppose this condition is satisfied, and let us compare the values of I for K_0 and for another curve K. If for example the curves lie as in Fig. 3.2b the difference $I(K_0) - I(K)$ is the sum of two integrals round closed circuits, an integral I_1 round the circuit CBD traversed in the positive sense, and an integral I_2 round the circuit ACE traversed in the negative sense. Now the integral (3.2.1) taken round a closed circuit in the positive sense is equal to the integral $\iint J\,dx\,dy$ over the area enclosed by the circuit. Thus both the integrals I_1 and I_2 have negative values, and

$$I(K_0) < I(K).$$

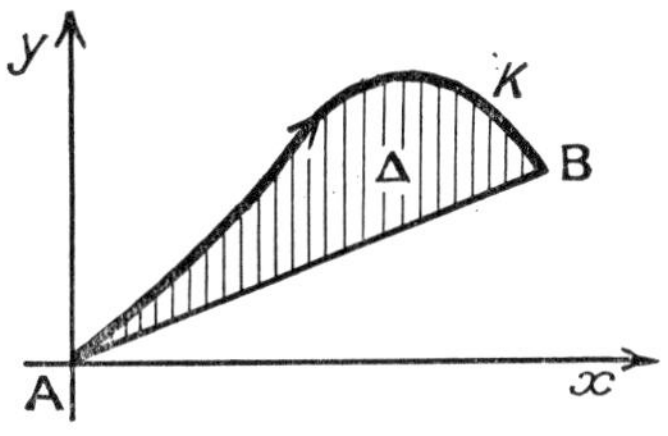

Fig. 3.2a

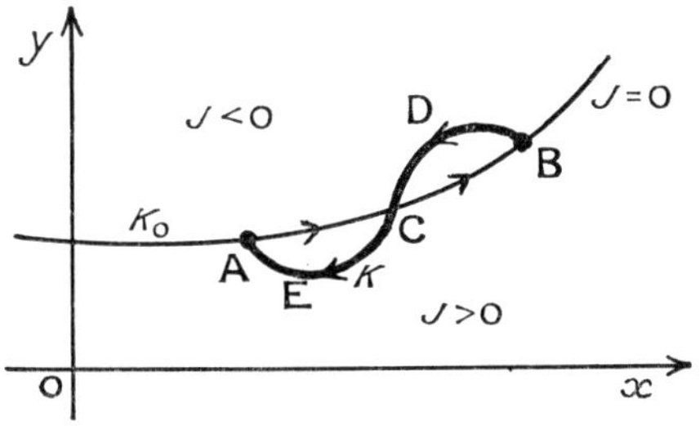

Fig. 3.2b

Consider as a concrete illustration the line-integral

(3.2.9) $$\int (x^2 + y^2)\,dx + y\,dy,$$

so that

(3.2.10) $$P = x^2 + y^2, \qquad Q = y, \qquad J = -2y.$$

There is no minimizing curve through A and B unless both these points lie on the x-axis. If they do, the line-segment AB gives a proper absolute minimum. This is clear from the criterion just mentioned, since $J < 0$ in the upper half-plane and $J > 0$ in the lower half-plane. It is easy to find the result independently. For if K, $y = \varphi(x)$, is any other curve joining $A(X, 0)$ to $B(\bar{X}, 0)$ we have

(3.2.11) $$I(K) - I(K_0) = \int_X^{\bar{X}} \varphi^2\,dx > 0.$$

We can find functions $\lambda(x, y)$ and $\mu(x, y)$ such that

(3.2.12) $$P = \lambda \frac{\partial \mu}{\partial x}, \qquad Q = \lambda \frac{\partial \mu}{\partial y},$$

and the integral (3.2.1) can be written $\int \lambda\, d\mu$. Then J is the Jacobian $\dfrac{\partial(\lambda, \mu)}{\partial(x, y)}$. For the particular example (3.2.9)

(3.2.13) $$\lambda = \tfrac{1}{2}e^{-2x}, \; \mu = (y^2 + x^2 - x + \tfrac{1}{2})e^{2x}.$$

If $Q = 0$ we have the special case $\int_\Gamma P(x, y)\, dx$ in which the integrand does not contain y'. Euler's equation is $P_y = 0$, and (if we exclude the extraordinary case in which both A and B lie on the curve $P_y = 0$) there is no extremal through A and B. The minimizing curve, if there is one, is a boundary minimum, not a stationary value. In practice the infimum value may not be attained in the class D_1. As a trivial example, if A and B lie in the upper half-plane ($Y > 0$, $\overline{Y} > 0$), the

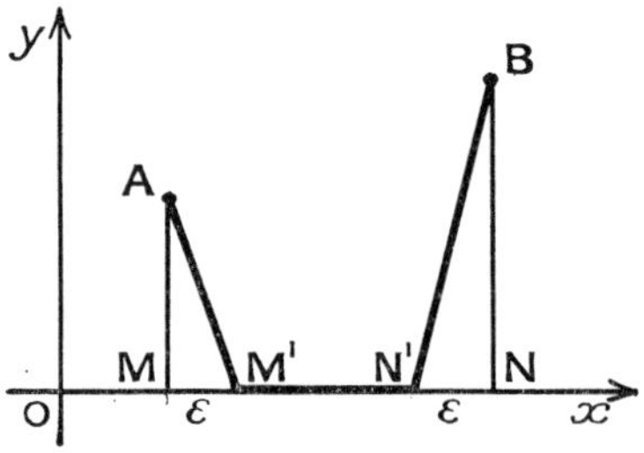

Fig. 3.2c

infimum value for $\int x^2y^2\, dx$ is zero, but this value is not attained in the class D_1. For the path $AM'N'B$ shown in Fig. 3.2*c* (where AM and BN are perpendicular to Ox, and $MM' = N'N = \varepsilon$) the integral has the value

(3.2.14) $$\tfrac{1}{3}(X^2Y^2 + \overline{X}^2\overline{Y}^2)\varepsilon + O(\varepsilon^2),$$

which can be made as near to zero as we please.

3.3 The integrand a function of y'

We consider a problem in which the integrand is $F(y')$; we have met particular examples of this type already, $\sqrt{(1 + y'^2)}$, $(y'^2 - 1)^2$, $(y'^2 + y'^3)$. The extremals are straight lines, and the minimizing curve, if there is one, consists of a straight line or a number of straight segments. We have noticed that the straight line-segment L joining A to B gives a relative minimum in any one-parameter family of the form

(3.3.1) $$y = \varphi(x) + \alpha\eta(x)$$

if $F''(k) > 0$, where k is the slope of AB (cf. (2.10.16)). But this does not imply that L gives a strong relative minimum.

On the other hand, if the problem is *regular* (§2.7), so that

$$F''(\theta) > 0 \tag{3.3.2}$$

for all admissible values of θ, the linear segment AB is a minimizing curve. For if K, $y = \varphi(x)$, is any other curve of class D_1 joining A to B, we have

$$\begin{aligned} I(K) - I(L) &= \int_X^{\bar{X}} \{F(\varphi') - F(k)\}\, dx \\ &= \int_X^{\bar{X}} \{(\varphi' - k)F'(k) + \tfrac{1}{2}(\varphi' - k)^2 F''(\theta)\}\, dx, \end{aligned} \tag{3.3.3}$$

where θ $(= \theta(x))$ lies between k and $\varphi'(x)$, and we assume as usual that R is z-convex. Thus

$$I(K) - I(L) = \int_X^{\bar{X}} \tfrac{1}{2}(\varphi' - k)^2 F''(\theta)\, dx > 0 \tag{3.3.4}$$

for all K other than L. The line-segment L gives a proper absolute minimum in the class D_1. Here we have a simple example of a *sufficiency theorem*, i.e. a theorem giving *sufficient* conditions for a minimizing curve.

We now consider some concrete examples of integrals in which the integrand is a function of y'.

EXAMPLE 1.

$$F = y'^2.$$

We seek a curve joining (X, Y) to $(\bar{X}, \bar{Y})$ and minimizing

$$I = \int_X^{\bar{X}} y'^2\, dx. \tag{3.3.5}$$

If $Y = \bar{Y}$ the solution is obvious; the line $y = Y$ makes $I = 0$, and this is clearly a minimum. If $Y \neq \bar{Y}$ the line-segment L joining A to B is minimizing in the class D_1. This follows from the simple sufficiency theorem above, since the problem is regular, $N = 2 > 0$ for all values of y'.

Let us suppose, to fix the ideas, that A is the origin and B is the point (1, 1). It is easy to see that L is minimizing without appealing to the general result for the regular problem. For, if K is the curve

$$y = x + \zeta(x), \tag{3.3.6}$$

where $\zeta(x) \in D_1$, and $\zeta(0) = \zeta(1) = 0$, we have

$$I(K) - I(L) = \int_0^1 (2\zeta' + \zeta'^2)\, dx = \int_0^1 \zeta'^2\, dx > 0, \tag{3.3.7}$$

and $I(K) > I(L)$ unless $\zeta = 0$ for all x in [0, 1].

The problem merits further discussion. Let us give up for a moment the restriction that $\varphi(x) \in D_1$, and assume only that $\varphi'(x)$ exists p.p. Now we can construct a continuous curve, $y = \varphi(x)$, joining (0, 0) to (1, 1), and such that $\varphi'(x) = 0$ p.p. For such a curve the integral (3.3.5), interpreted now as a Lebesgue integral, is zero, whereas $I(L) = 1$. The straight line L is not now a minimizing curve.

But the comparison curve we have used has the disagreeable property that $\varphi(x)$ is not the integral of $\varphi'(x)$, since for this curve $\int_0^1 \varphi'(x)\, dx = 0$. It is more satisfactory to confine our attention to the class of *absolutely continuous functions*; for these functions $\varphi'(x)$ exists p.p., and $\varphi(x)$ is the integral of $\varphi'(x)$. Now in this class the straight line L does minimize I. For, by Schwarz's inequality,

$$\sqrt{\left(\int_0^1 \varphi'^2\, dx\right)} \geqslant \int_0^1 \varphi'\, dx, \tag{3.3.8}$$

and, since φ is absolutely continuous,

$$\int_0^1 \varphi'\, dx = \varphi(1) - \varphi(0) = 1. \tag{3.3.9}$$

Hence

$$I(K) \geqslant I(L) \tag{3.3.10}$$

for all curves K, $y = \varphi(x)$, for which $\varphi(x)$ is absolutely continuous, and for which $\varphi(0) = 0$ and $\varphi(1) = 1$. The straight line L gives an absolute minimum, not merely in the class D_1, but also in the wider class of absolutely continuous functions.*

EXAMPLE 2. We consider the integral

$$I = \int_0^1 (y'^2 - 1)^2\, dx, \tag{3.3.11}$$

where A is (0, 0) and B is $(1, k)$, where $k = \tan \beta$, $0 \leqslant \beta < \frac{1}{2}\pi$; the line AB makes an angle β with Ox. For this problem

$$N = F''(y') = 12(y'^2 - \tfrac{1}{3}). \tag{3.3.12}$$

(*a*) If $0 \leqslant \beta < \pi/4$ the straight line L joining A to B is not a minimizing curve in the class D_1, nor in the class C_1; we have noticed this already in the case $\beta = 0$ (§1.5). If $0 \leqslant \beta < \pi/4$ there are again infinitely many minimizing curves giving I the value zero; the simplest is the broken line ACB illustrated in Fig. 3.3*a*. If $0 \leqslant \beta < \pi/6$, Legendre's necessary condition is violated on L; for this range of β, L does not give even a weak relative minimum, and we need look no

* A generalization of the same argument appears in the second of the miscellaneous Examples on p. 338.

further to assure ourselves that L is not a minimizing curve. But if $\pi/6 \leqslant \beta < \pi/4$, Legendre's necessary condition *is* satisfied on L, although as we have seen, L is not a minimizing curve. There is no discrepancy here, since Legendre's condition is only a necessary condition for a weak relative minimum. (We shall see later (§5.16) that L *does* in fact provide a weak relative minimum if $\pi/6 < \beta < \pi/4$, but not if $\beta = \pi/6$.)

(*b*) If $\beta = \pi/4$ the integral has the value zero for the line L, and a value greater than zero for any other curve, so L is a minimizing curve.

(*c*) If $k > 1$, $\pi/4 < \beta < \pi/2$, L is a minimizing curve. For, if K is the curve $y = kx + \zeta$,

$$I(K) - I(L) = \int_0^1 (2k\zeta' + \zeta'^2)^2\,dx + 2(k^2 - 1)\int_0^1 \zeta'^2\,dx + 4k(k^2 - 1)\int_0^1 \zeta'\,dx, \tag{3.3.13}$$

and this is positive, since the last integral on the right vanishes.

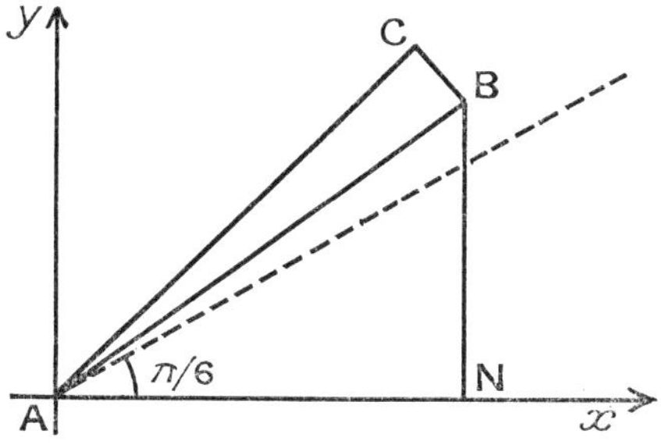

Fig. 3.3*a*

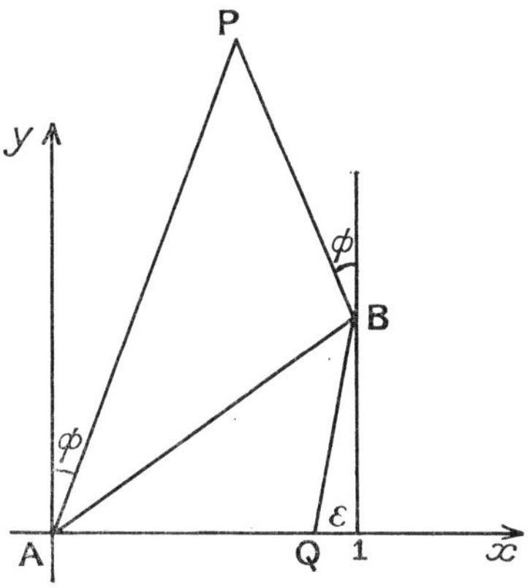

Fig. 3.3*b*

EXAMPLE 3. Let

$$I = \int_0^1 \frac{1}{1 + y'^2}\,dx, \tag{3.3.14}$$

the end-points being as in Example 2. It is clear that $0 < I < 1$, and indeed $m = 0$ and $M = 1$. Neither of these bounds is attained in the class D_1, but we can, of course, find curves giving values as near to 0 and to 1 as we please. Thus for the curve APB (Fig. 3.3*b*), consisting of two linear segments, each making an angle φ with the vertical, $I = \sin^2 \varphi$, which can be made as near to zero as we wish by taking φ sufficiently small. For the path AQB

$$I = 1 - \frac{k^2\varepsilon}{k^2 + \varepsilon^2} > 1 - \varepsilon, \tag{3.3.15}$$

which can be made as near to 1 as we wish by taking ε sufficiently small.

EXAMPLE 4. Let us consider the problem of finding a minimizing curve for the integral

$$I = \int_0^1 \{y'^2 - \lambda\sqrt{(1 + y'^2)}\}\, dx, \tag{3.3.16}$$

where λ is a positive constant, and the end points are $A(0, 0)$ and $B(1, 0)$. Since the integrand is a function of y' the extremals are straight lines. The curve we seek is either the line-segment L, which is the segment AB of the x-axis, or it is built up of line-segments. We ask therefore if a minimizing curve can have a corner. Now

$$U = -y'^2 - \frac{\lambda}{\sqrt{(1 + y'^2)}} = -\tan^2 \psi - \lambda \cos \psi, \tag{3.3.17}$$

$$V = 2y' - \lambda\frac{y'}{\sqrt{(1 + y'^2)}} = 2 \tan \psi - \lambda \sin \psi.$$

If therefore the minimizing curve has a corner, and if the values of ψ to left and to right of the corner are α and β, the corner conditions require

$$\tan^2 \alpha - \tan^2 \beta = \lambda(\cos \beta - \cos \alpha), \tag{3.3.18}$$

$$2(\tan \alpha - \tan \beta) = \lambda(\sin \alpha - \sin \beta), \tag{3.3.19}$$

where α and β lie in $(-\frac{1}{2}\pi, \frac{1}{2}\pi)$, and $\alpha - \beta \neq 0$.

If $\alpha + \beta \neq 0$ the two members of (3.3.18) are non-zero, and from (3.3.18–19), by division, we find

$$\tfrac{1}{2}(\tan \alpha + \tan \beta) = \frac{\cos \beta - \cos \alpha}{\sin \alpha - \sin \beta} = \tan \tfrac{1}{2}(\alpha + \beta). \tag{3.3.20}$$

If we put $\tan \frac{1}{2}(\alpha + \beta) = t_1$ and $\tan \frac{1}{2}(\alpha - \beta) = t_2$, the equation (3.3.20) becomes

$$\frac{t_1 + t_2}{1 - t_1t_2} + \frac{t_1 - t_2}{1 + t_1t_2} = 2t_1, \tag{3.3.21}$$

leading to

$$t_1t_2^2(1 + t_1^2) = 0, \tag{3.3.22}$$

which is false, since neither t_1 nor t_2 is zero. Therefore $\alpha + \beta = 0$, and then (3.3.19) shows that $\sec \alpha = \frac{1}{2}\lambda$. Thus if $\lambda > 2$ we can have a corner on a minimizing curve, the values of x to left and to right of the corner being α and $-\alpha$, where $\sec \alpha = \frac{1}{2}\lambda$. If $\lambda \leqslant 2$ no corner is possible, and only the line-segment L comes into consideration.

If $\lambda > 2$ the conditions are satisfied by the broken line K shown in Fig. 3.3*c*; the solution is not unique, since the reflexion of ACB in AB will serve equally well, or indeed any curve consisting of linear segments inclined at angles α and $-\alpha$ to Ox (cf. Fig. 1.5). The value of the integral for the broken line K, if $\lambda > 2$, is $I(K) = -1 - \frac{1}{4}\lambda^2$; the value of the integral for the line-segment L is, in all cases, $I(L) = -\lambda$. These values are exhibited, as functions of λ, in Fig. 3.3*d*. We notice that $I(L) - I(K) = (\frac{1}{2}\lambda - 1)^2$, so if $\lambda > 2$ (when both curves come into consideration) $I(K) < I(L)$.

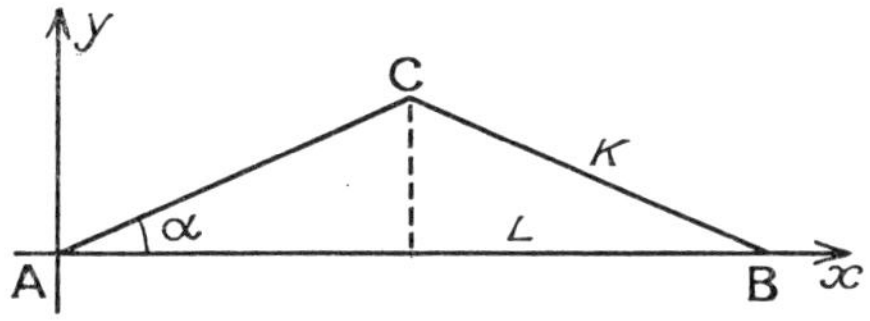

Fig. 3.3*c*

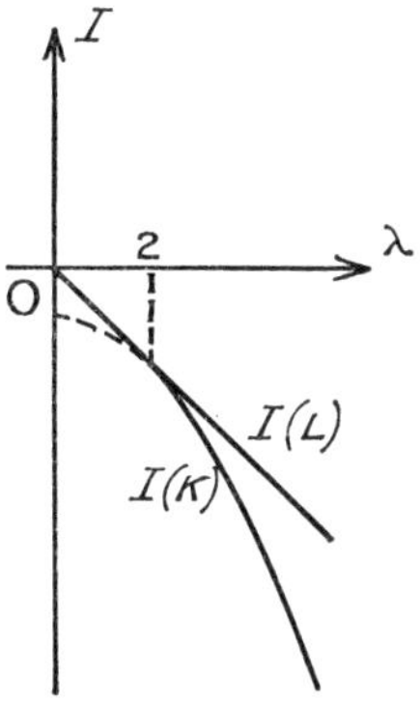

Fig. 3.3*d*

Now consider Legendre's condition. We have

$$N = 2 - \frac{\lambda}{(1 + y'^2)^{3/2}} = 2 - \lambda \cos^3 \psi. \tag{3.3.23}$$

Thus $N > 0$ on L if $\lambda < 2$, and Legendre's necessary condition is satisfied. If $\lambda > 2$, $N < 0$ on L (so that L cannot provide even a weak relative minimum in this case), but on K, $N = \dfrac{2}{\lambda^2}(\lambda^2 - 4) > 0$, so Legendre's necessary condition is satisfied on K. The evidence suggests that L is the minimizing curve if $\lambda \leqslant 2$, and that K is the minimizing curve if $\lambda > 2$.

It is easy to prove formally that this expectation is fulfilled. Let Γ be any curve of class D_1 joining A to B; we denote the inclination of the curve Γ to the x-axis by $\psi(=\psi(x))$. If $\lambda \leqslant 2$,

$$(3.3.24)\quad I(\Gamma) - I(L) = \int_0^1 (\tan^2\psi - \lambda\sec\psi + \lambda)\,dx$$
$$= \int_0^1 (\sec\psi - 1)(\sec\psi + 1 - \lambda)\,dx.$$

Thus, if Γ is any curve other than L, $I(\Gamma) > I(L)$, and L is genuinely a minimizing curve. If $\lambda > 2$, K is a minimizing curve; for the integrand in $I(K)$can be written in the form

$$(3.3.25)\qquad (\sec\psi - \tfrac{1}{2}\lambda)^2 - (1 + \tfrac{1}{4}\lambda^2),$$

which has a minimum value when $\sec\psi = \frac{1}{2}\lambda$, $\psi = \pm\alpha$.

3.4 Hamilton's principle

Hamilton's principle asserts that the motion of a dynamical system from one configuration to another renders stationary the integral

$$(3.4.1)\qquad I = \int_\tau^{\bar\tau} (T - \mathscr{V})\,dt$$

in comparison with other paths of class C_2 joining the same termini (in the q-space) and having the same times τ and $\bar\tau$ of departure and arrival. The Lagrangian coordinates defining the configuration of the system, are $q_1, q_2, \ldots, q_n$, the time is denoted by t, $T(=T(q,\dot q,t))$ is the kinetic energy function, and $\mathscr{V}(=\mathscr{V}(q))$ is the potential energy function of the dynamical system.

For a system with one degree of freedom, writing x for the time and y for the Lagrangian coordinate defining the configuration (to come into line with the notation previously used) the integral has the form

$$(3.4.2)\qquad \int_X^{\bar X} (\tfrac{1}{2}ay'^2 - \mathscr{V})\,dx$$

where we confine our attention to the usual case in which a is a function of y only (not of x), and $\mathscr{V}$ is a function of y. We have here the ordinary problem *par excellence.* There is no loss of generality in dealing here with the ordinary rather than with the parametric problem, since the curves all lie in the strip $X \leqslant x \leqslant \bar X$, and no curve cuts a line x = constant in more than one point; the system cannot have two different configurations at the same time!

Let us consider more particularly the simple problem of a particle of mass m moving on a straight line in a uniform field of force mc. If x is the time, and y the displacement on the line from a fixed origin, we have

$$T = \tfrac{1}{2}my'^2, \qquad \mathscr{V} = -mcy, \tag{3.4.3}$$

and the integral arising from Hamilton's principle is

$$\int_X^{\overline{X}} (\tfrac{1}{2}y'^2 + cy)\,dx. \tag{3.4.4}$$

Here X, $\overline{X}$ represent the instants of departure and arrival, Y, $\overline{Y}$ the initial and final positions of the particle.

Euler's equation is

$$y'' = c, \tag{3.4.5}$$

which is simply Newton's law of motion for motion in a uniform field, and the extremals are the curves

$$y = a + bx + \tfrac{1}{2}cx^2. \tag{3.4.6}$$

The equation (3.4.6) represents a family of parabolas, all with their axes vertical and vertices downwards, and all having the same length of *latus rectum*. Now if A and B are prescribed, a unique extremal passes through A and B. We can prove this easily in various ways. (i) We can use a geometrical argument of a type that is frequently useful in the Calculus of Variations. If we take one particular parabola of the family, and consider the chords parallel to AB, we notice that just one of these chords $A'B'$ has the same length as AB. We have only to slide the parabola, thought of as a rigid curve with axis vertical, in the plane until $A'B'$ coincides with AB, and we have the unique extremal through A and B. (ii) If we write the conditions that (X, Y) and $(\overline{X}, \overline{Y})$ lie on (3.4.6) we have two linear equations for a and b, which are uniquely determined. In fact it is evident that the unique extremal K_0 through A and B is represented by the equation

$$y = \varphi(x) = \frac{Y(\overline{X} - x) + \overline{Y}(x - X)}{\overline{X} - X} + \tfrac{1}{2}c(x - X)(x - \overline{X}). \tag{3.4.7}$$

This is a minimizing curve. For if we compare the value of I, given by (3.4.4), along K_0, with its value along another curve K of class D_1,

$$y = \varphi(x) + \zeta(x), \tag{3.4.8}$$

we have

$$I(K) - I(K_0) = \int_X^{\bar{X}} (\varphi'\zeta' + \tfrac{1}{2}\zeta'^2 + c\zeta)\,dx \tag{3.4.9}$$
$$= \varphi'\zeta\Big|_X^{\bar{X}} + \int_X^{\bar{X}} (c - \varphi'')\zeta\,dx + \int_X^{\bar{X}} \tfrac{1}{2}\zeta'^2\,dx$$
$$= \int_X^{\bar{X}} \tfrac{1}{2}\zeta'^2\,dx > 0.$$

3.5 Weierstrass's problem

The end-points are $A(-1, -1)$ and $B(1, 1)$, and the integrand is $x^2y'^2$,

$$I = \int_{-1}^{1} x^2 y'^2\,dx. \tag{3.5.1}$$

The integrand is non-negative, so $I \geqslant 0$, and the infimum of I for curves of class D_1 is zero, $m = 0$. In this case the infimum is not attained; there is no curve of class D_1 joining A to B for which $I = 0$. But of course we can find curves giving to I a value as

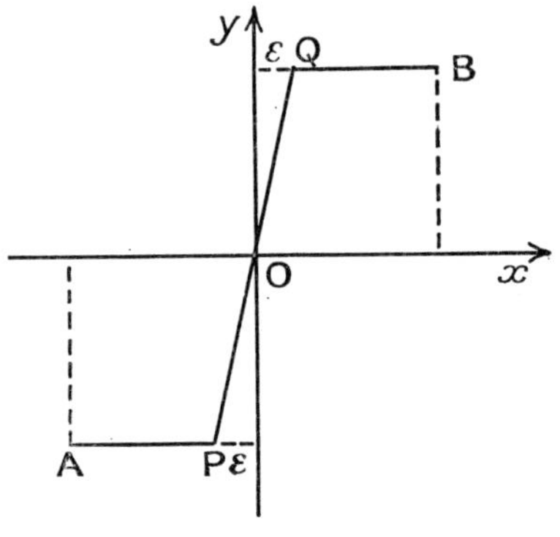

Fig. 3.5*a*

small as we please. Thus for the curve *APQB* shown in Fig. 3.5*a*, consisting of three linear segments, we have

$$I = \frac{2}{\varepsilon^2}\int_0^{\varepsilon} x^2\,dx = \frac{2}{3}\,\varepsilon. \tag{3.5.2}$$

We can also find curves of class C_1 giving an arbitrarily small value to I. This is evident from the rounding argument. But it is also of interest to exhibit an explicit example of such a curve (as we did in a similar situation in §2.10). Consider the curve

(3.5.3)
$$y = \frac{\arc\tan \dfrac{x}{\varepsilon}}{\arc\tan \dfrac{1}{\varepsilon}} = \frac{1}{\beta} \arc\tan \frac{x}{\varepsilon},$$

where

(3.5.4)
$$0 < \varepsilon < 1, \quad \tan \beta = \frac{1}{\varepsilon}, \quad \tfrac{1}{4}\pi < \beta < \tfrac{1}{2}\pi.$$

For this curve

(3.5.5)
$$y' = \frac{\varepsilon}{\beta(x^2 + \varepsilon^2)},$$

and

(3.5.6)
$$I = 2\int_0^1 x^2 y'^2\,dx < 2\int_0^1 (x^2 + \varepsilon^2) y'^2\,dx = \frac{2\varepsilon^2}{\beta^2}\int_0^1 \frac{dx}{x^2 + \varepsilon^2} = \frac{2\varepsilon}{\beta} < \frac{8}{\pi}\varepsilon,$$

and we can make I (which is $\geqslant 0$) arbitrarily small by choice of ε.

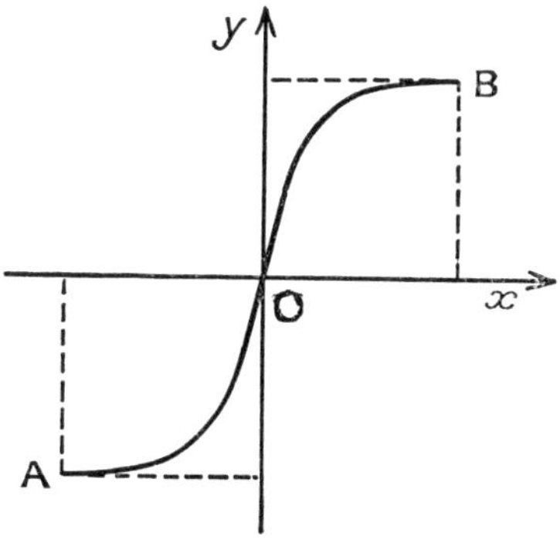

Fig. 3.5*b*

If we take $\kappa \equiv D_1$, the infimum $m = 0$ is not attained in the class D_1. We might expect that the infimum *is* attained in the class of absolutely continuous functions, but in fact this expectation is not fulfilled. For $I = 0$ would imply $y' = 0$ p.p., and this is impossible, since y is the integral of y'. We have met other examples (in §1.5 and §3.3) in which I is bounded below, but the infimum is not attained in the class κ; though in some cases, if $\kappa \equiv C_1$, the infimum *is* attained in the class D_1. Here we have an example in which the infimum is not attained in κ, even when we take for κ the widest possible choice, the class of absolutely continuous functions.

Now turn to Euler's equation. Since F does not contain y we have the first integral

$$x^2y' = \text{constant}, \tag{3.5.7}$$

and the extremals are arcs of hyperbolas

$$y = a + \frac{b}{x}. \tag{3.5.8}$$

There is no extremal through A and B. It is true that one branch of the hyperbola

$$y = \frac{1}{x} \tag{3.5.9}$$

goes through A, and the other branch of the same hyperbola goes through B. But the two branches are disjoint, and (3.5.9) is not of the prescribed form $y = \varphi(x)$ because of the discontinuity at $x = 0$.

If we take the inferior end-point A to be $(\frac{1}{2}, 0)$ instead of $(-1, -1)$, and leave the superior end-point B at $(1, 1)$ as before, everything is changed. There is a unique extremal K_0 through A and B, namely

$$y = 2 - \frac{1}{x}, \tag{3.5.10}$$

and it is genuinely minimizing in the class D_1. For K_0, $I = 1$, and if K is the curve

$$y = 2 - \frac{1}{x} + \zeta(x), \tag{3.5.11}$$

we have

$$\begin{aligned} I(K) - I(K_0) &= \int_{\frac{1}{2}}^{1} x^2\left(\frac{2\zeta'}{x^2} + \zeta'^2\right) dx \\ &= \int_{\frac{1}{2}}^{1} (2\zeta' + x^2\zeta'^2)\, dx = \int_{\frac{1}{2}}^{1} x^2\zeta'^2 dx > 0. \end{aligned} \tag{3.5.12}$$

3.6 The integral $\int y^n\, ds$, genesis of the problem

We now consider some problems in which the integral has the form $\int y^n\, ds$. Here s denotes the arc-length, and

$$F = y^n\sqrt{(1 + y'^2)}. \tag{3.6.1}$$

Let us see how these problems arise in geometry and in physics.

Let A and B be given points in the upper half-plane, $Y > 0$ and $\overline{Y} > 0$. Let us consider the problem of finding a curve joining A to B, and lying in the region $y \geqslant 0$, such that the surface of revolution formed when the curve is rotated about Ox has minimum area. This curve is a minimizing curve for the integral

$$\int y\,ds, \tag{3.6.2}$$

and this is of the type mentioned, with $n = 1$.

The same integral arises in statics. Suppose two small smooth rings A and B are fixed at heights Y and $\overline{Y}$ above a horizontal table. A long uniform flexible string is threaded through the rings and hangs in equilibrium, the spare parts of the string being coiled on the table at the points M and N vertically below A and B. Now the potential energy of a particle of mass m at a height y above the table is $mg(y + h)$, where h is a constant. Thus the potential energy of the whole string is

$$\mathscr{V} = \int g\rho\,(y + h)\,ds + g\rho\lambda h + g\rho\,Y(\tfrac{1}{2}Y + h) + g\rho\,\overline{Y}(\tfrac{1}{2}\overline{Y} + h), \tag{3.6.3}$$

where ρ is the line-density and λ is the length of the part of the string coiled at M and N. Thus

$$\mathscr{V} = g\rho\int y\,ds + g\rho h(l + \lambda + Y + \overline{Y}) + \tfrac{1}{2}g\rho(Y^2 + \overline{Y}^2), \tag{3.6.4}$$

where l is the length of the string between A and B, so finally (since $l + \lambda$ has a given constant value)

$$\mathscr{V} = g\rho\int_A^B y\,ds + \text{constant}. \tag{3.6.5}$$

In the position of equilibrium $\mathscr{V}$ is a minimum, so to find the form of the string between A and B we must find a minimizing curve for $\int y\,ds$. A strong relative minimum will suffice to determine a position of stable equilibrium.

Next, let us consider a particle of unit mass moving in a plane field of force derived from the potential function $\mathscr{V}(x, y)$. Jacobi's form of the principle of Least Action asserts that the orbits of the particle for which the energy constant is h are the extremals for the integral

$$\int \sqrt{\{2(h - \mathscr{V})\}}\,ds. \tag{3.6.6}$$

Suppose in particular that the field is uniform with Oy taken in the direction of the field, and Ox as the energy level for the problem. Then

$$\mathscr{V} = -gy, \qquad h = 0, \tag{3.6.7}$$

and the orbits are the extremals for the integral

$$\int \sqrt{y}\, ds. \tag{3.6.8}$$

This is a problem of the type we are considering, with $n = \frac{1}{2}$.

The problem just mentioned was a problem of *free* motion in a field of force. The brachistochrone problem is a problem of *constrained* motion in a field of force. We wish to find the curve joining A to B such that a particle (of mass m) sliding freely along it under the action of the field shall complete the journey from A to B in the shortest possible time. The speed at which the particle leaves A is prescribed, so the energy constant h has a prescribed value. Now the velocity v of the particle at any point of the curve is determined by the energy equation

$$\tfrac{1}{2}mv^2 + \mathscr{V} = h, \tag{3.6.9}$$

and the time of the journey from A to B is

$$\int \frac{1}{v}\, ds = \sqrt{\left(\frac{m}{2}\right)} \int \frac{1}{\sqrt{(h - \mathscr{V})}}\, ds. \tag{3.6.10}$$

In particular, in the classical brachistochrone problem, the field is uniform, and $\mathscr{V} = -mgy$, where we measure y in the direction of the field (i.e. vertically downwards if the field is that of gravity). If we choose the axes so that Ox is the energy level, the brachistochrone is the curve which minimizes

$$\int \frac{1}{\sqrt{y}}\, ds. \tag{3.6.11}$$

This is the case $n = -\frac{1}{2}$.

Finally we consider a problem of wave-propagation in a medium in which the wave-velocity v is a linear function of the distance from a given line, say (with an appropriate choice of axes) $v = cy$. This arises in the seismic survey of the earth's outer layers. An explosion is made near the surface, and the times of arrival of the waves at points on the surface at various distances from the source are recorded.

The time of transmission from A to B (where A and B are points in the upper half-plane) is

$$\int_{x}^{\bar{x}} \frac{1}{cy}\, ds, \tag{3.6.12}$$

and the path of a ray is such as to minimize this integral. This is the case $n = -1$. In the particular problem mentioned, $Y = \bar{Y} = k$, A and B being in the earth's surface, supposed plane; the wave-velocity at a depth z below the surface is assumed to be $c(k + z)$, where c and k are given positive constants.

Let us then consider the problem of finding a curve to minimize $\int y^n\, ds$. The cases we shall consider more particularly are $n = -1, -\frac{1}{2}, 0, \frac{1}{2}, 1$. ($n = 0$ is the geodesic problem already discussed, and only mentioned again here for the sake of completeness.) In each case we suppose A and B to lie above the x-axis. For $n = -1, -\frac{1}{2}$, the curves considered lie in the region $y > 0$, since the integrand is discontinuous on $y = 0$; for $n = \frac{1}{2}, 1$, the curves all lie in the region $y \geqslant 0$. In virtue of the first corner condition, §2.5, we see that there can be no corners on a minimizing curve for $n = -1, -\frac{1}{2}$, and for $n = \frac{1}{2}, 1$, if corners exist they must lie on $y = 0$.

For the problem of minimizing $\int y^n\, ds$, a first integral of Euler's equation is, as in (2.9.9),

$$y^n = b^n \sec \psi, \tag{3.6.13}$$

Taking logs, and forming the differential of each side,

$$\frac{n}{y}\, dy = \tan \psi\, d\psi. \tag{3.6.14}$$

But

$$dy = \tan \psi\, dx, \tag{3.6.15}$$

so

$$n\, dx = y\, d\psi, \tag{3.6.16}$$

and from this we can express x in terms of ψ. Thus we have the parametric representation of the extremals, x and y being expressed in terms of ψ.

Another approach to the problem of finding the extremals starts from the first integral of Euler's equation

$$\frac{y^n}{\sqrt{(1 + y'^2)}} = \text{constant}, \tag{3.6.17}$$

or say

$$b^{2n}(1 + y'^2) = y^{2n}. \tag{3.6.18}$$

Using the formula $y'' = \dfrac{d}{dy}(\tfrac{1}{2}y'^2)$ we find

$$b^{2n}y'' = ny^{2n-1}. \tag{3.6.19}$$

Thus if we define the function $\psi(x)$ as that solution of the equation

$$\psi'' = n\psi^{2n-1} \tag{3.6.20}$$

for which $\psi(0) = 1$ and $\psi'(0) = 0$, the extremals are the curves

$$\frac{y}{b} = \psi\left(\frac{x-a}{b}\right). \tag{3.6.21}$$

The equation involves the two parameters a and b, and represents a two-fold infinity of curves.

3.7 The integral $\int y^n\,ds$ for $n = -1$ and for $n = -\frac{1}{2}$

For $n = -1$ we have, as in (3.6.13),

$$y = b\cos\psi, \qquad (b > 0) \tag{3.7.1}$$

and from (3.6.16)

$$-dx = b\cos\psi\,d\psi, \tag{3.7.2}$$

$$x - a = -b\sin\psi, \tag{3.7.3}$$

and the extremal is the part of the circle

$$(x-a)^2 + y^2 = b^2 \tag{3.7.4}$$

lying above $y = 0$. The circle has its centre at $(a, 0)$, and the extremals are semi-circles in the upper half-plane with their centres on $y = 0$. The extremals are concave to Ox.

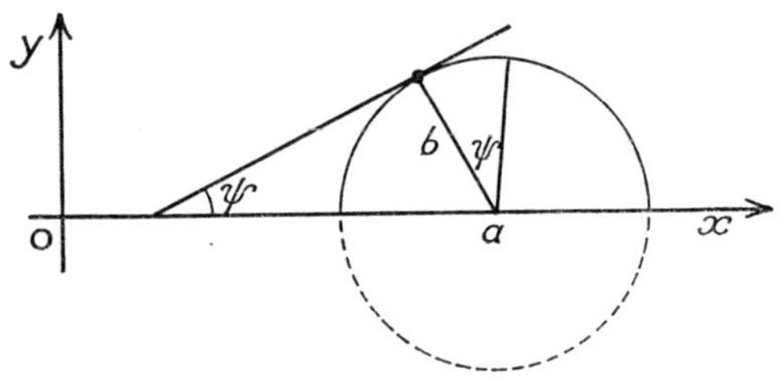

Fig. 3.7*a*

Two comments may be made which we shall find to be important in the sequel. The first is that there is a *unique* extremal through A and B, namely an arc of the circle ABA', where A' is the image of A in Ox. The second is that we can construct a *field of extremals*, in the domain $y > 0$, in which the extremal through A and B is embedded. A field of extremals is a region containing a one-parameter family of extremals, one and only one of which passes through each point of the region. It is evident that in this problem the circles concentric with the extremal through A and B have the desired property. One and only one of these passes through each point of the half-plane $y > 0$, and the unique extremal through A and B is embedded in the field, i.e. it is itself an extremal of the field.

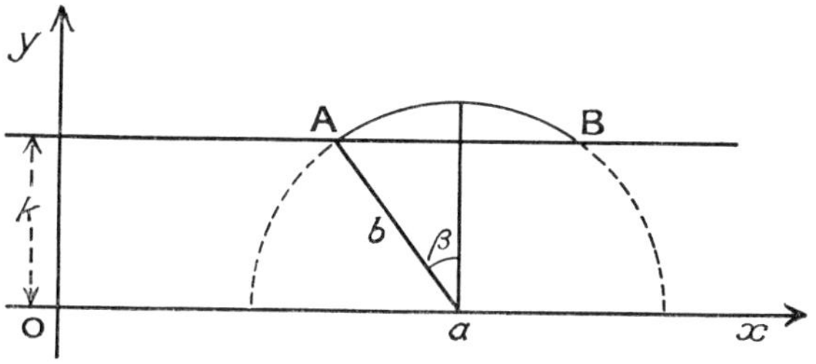

Fig. 3.7*b*

Before leaving this problem it may be of interest to complete the solution of the seismological problem mentioned above. In this case $Y = \bar{Y} = k$, and if the ray starts off from the source A at an angle β to the surface, the distance AB, say R, is given by

(3.7.5) $$R = 2k \tan \beta.$$

The time t_0 for the disturbance to travel from A to B is

(3.7.6) $$t_0 = \frac{1}{c}\int_X^{\bar{X}} \frac{ds}{y} = \frac{2}{c}\int_0^\beta \frac{d\psi}{\cos\psi} = \frac{2}{c}\log(\sec\beta + \tan\beta).$$

Thus

(3.7.7)

$$\sec\beta + \tan\beta = e^{ct_0/2},\ \sec\beta - \tan\beta = e^{-ct_0/2},\ \tan\beta = \sinh(ct_0/2).$$

Hence finally the relation between the time t_0 and the distance R is

(3.7.8) $$R = 2k \sinh(ct_0/2).$$

From observations of the value of t_0 for different values of R the parameters k and c can be determined. We have here a physical problem of the type mentioned in §1.8, where the first-order conditions alone suffice to determine the solution.

For the brachistochrone problem, $n = -\frac{1}{2}$, we have, as in (3.6.13),

$$y = b\cos^2\psi = \tfrac{1}{2}b(1 + \cos 2\psi) \tag{3.7.9}$$

and from (3.6.16)

$$-\tfrac{1}{2}\,dx = \tfrac{1}{2}b(1 + \cos 2\psi)\,d\psi. \tag{3.7.10}$$

Hence

$$x = a - \tfrac{1}{2}b(2\psi + \sin 2\psi), \tag{3.7.11}$$

and the curves are arcs of cycloids with cusps on Ox (Fig. 3.7*c*). The extremals are concave to Ox.

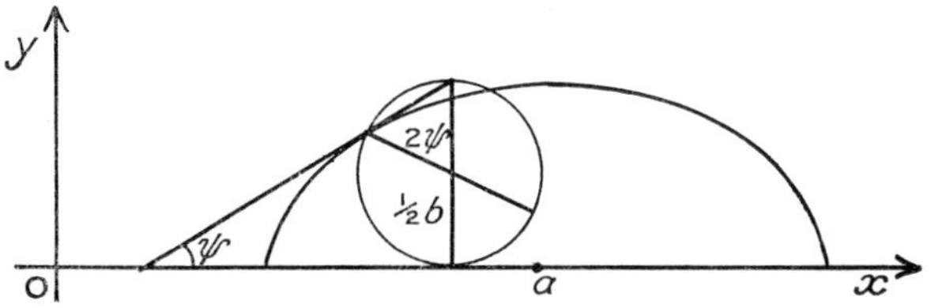

Fig. 3.7*c*

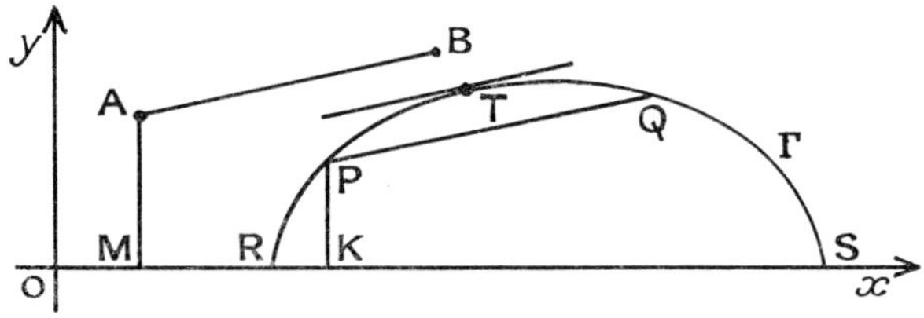

Fig. 3.7*d*

Two observations similar to those made above for $n = -1$ are valid here also; there is a unique extremal through A and B, and we can easily construct a field in which it is embedded.

For the uniqueness, an algebraic proof is not difficult, but a straightforward geometrical argument is even simpler. Let AM be the perpendicular from A on to Ox. Consider any fixed cycloid Γ of the system, with cusps R and S on Ox (Fig. 3.7*d*). Let P be a variable point on Γ, PK the perpendicular from P on Ox, PQ the chord through P parallel to AB, and let T be the point on Γ at which the tangent is parallel to AB. We suppose for definiteness that $\overline{Y} \geqslant Y$.

Consider how the ratio KP/PQ varies as P moves along Γ from the cusp R to T; the length KP continually increases, the length PQ continually decreases, so the ratio KP/PQ increases steadily from 0 to ∞, and passes just once through the value MA/AB, say when P is at P_0. There is a unique chord P_0Q_0 of Γ which is parallel to AB, and which is such that $K_0P_0/P_0Q_0 = MA/AB$. It follows, by the theory of similar figures, that a unique cycloid of the system passes through A and B. (The proof needs only trivial modification if $\overline{Y} < Y$.)

It is again easy to construct a field of extremals covering the upper half-plane. This can be done in many ways. The simplest is to start from the extremal defined by (3.7.9) and (3.7.11), and to take the family of curves found by keeping a fixed and replacing b by other values; we thus obtain a system of arches, all with the same axis of symmetry, and one of these curves is the extremal through A and B.

The actual time of travel from A to B along the cycloidal arc is easily found; it is

(3.7.12) $$\frac{1}{\sqrt{(2g)}}\int\sqrt{\left(\frac{1+y'^2}{y}\right)}\,dx = -\sqrt{\left(\frac{2b}{g}\right)}\int d\psi,$$

using (3.7.9) and (3.7.10). The time from A to B is

(3.7.13) $$\sqrt{\left(\frac{2b}{g}\right)}(\alpha-\beta),$$

where α is the value of ψ at A, and β is the value of ψ at B.

So far, both for $n = -1$ and for $n = -\frac{1}{2}$, we have supposed the end-points A and B to lie in the region $y > 0$. Let us now consider briefly the case when A, for example, lies on the x-axis. Let us take, for definiteness, the brachistochrone problem, $n = -\frac{1}{2}$. The starting-point lies on the energy level, the initial velocity of the particle is zero. If a unique minimizing curve exists, it must be the cycloidal arc with a cusp at A, since if A' is any point on this arc, the arc $A'B$ satisfies the necessary condition for a minimizing curve. But the arc AB is not itself an admissible arc, since $y' \to \infty$ at A. Moreover the integral along the arc AB is an improper integral, since the integrand tends to infinity as $x \to X + 0$. The integral is convergent, as we expect; its value is $\sqrt{\left(\frac{2b}{g}\right)}(\frac{1}{2}\pi - \beta)$. The proof that the cycloidal arc is actually a minimizing curve, both for the simpler case when A

lies below the energy level, and for the limiting case when A lies on the energy level, will be given in §5.8.

3.8 The integral $\int \sqrt{y}\, ds$

The extremals are the orbits of a particle moving in a uniform field. The direction of the field is the direction Oy, and the energy level is $y = 0$. This is the familiar projectile problem of elementary dynamics, and the orbits are parabolas, as Galileo knew more than three centuries ago, and as every schoolboy knows today. The first integral (3.6.13) is

(3.8.1) $$y = b \sec^2 \psi,$$

and (3.6.16) gives

(3.8.2) $$\tfrac{1}{2}\, dx = b \sec^2 \psi \, d\psi,$$

whence

(3.8.3) $$x - a = 2b \tan \psi.$$

The extremal is a parabola with Ox as directrix

(3.8.4) $$(x - a)^2 = 4b(y - b),$$

or, expressed differently,

(3.8.5) $$\frac{y}{b} = 1 + \frac{1}{4}\left(\frac{x - a}{b}\right)^2.$$

The result can be found equally simply from (3.6.21). The curves are convex to Ox.

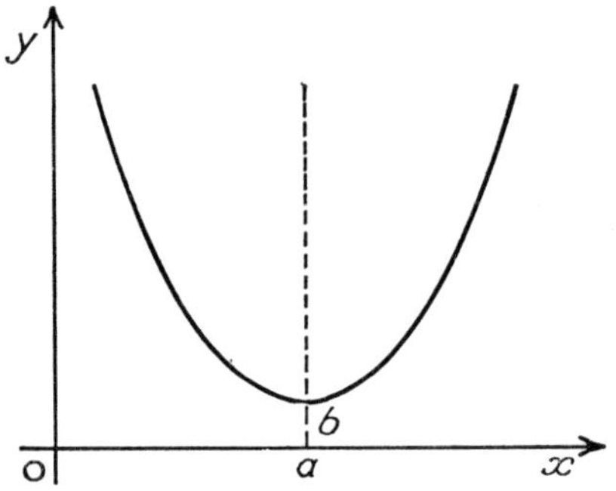

Fig. 3.8*a*

There is an important difference between this problem and the two problems discussed in §3.7. It is not true that there is a unique extremal through the two given points A and B in the upper half-plane; as we shall see, there may be two, or one, or none.

The construction of a field needs some care. If we adopt the same device as in §3.7, keeping a fixed and letting b vary, we get a family of parabolas touching the lines

(3.8.6) $$y = \pm(x - a),$$

and in the trough

(3.8.7) $$y > |x - a|$$

we obtain a field of extremals by retaining the part of each parabola between the points of contact and erasing the rest (Fig. 3.8b).

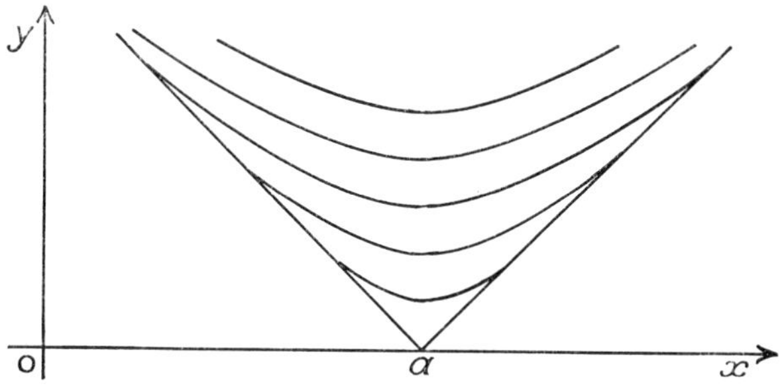

Fig. 3.8b

We now turn to another topic which will turn out to be important in the sequel, the *pencil of extremals* through the given point A. If $-\theta$ is the value of ψ at (X, Y), so that θ is the "angle of projection" in the dynamical problem, we have

(3.8.8) $$b = Y\cos^2\theta,$$

(3.8.9) $$a = X + 2b\tan\theta = X + Y\sin 2\theta,$$

and the equation of the parabola, expressed in terms of the parameter θ, is

(3.8.10) $$(x - X - Y\sin 2\theta)^2 = 4Y\cos^2\theta(y - Y\cos^2\theta).$$

It is easily seen, either from this equation or from the geometry, that this one-parameter family has an envelope D, which is the parabola having A as focus and Ox as tangent at the vertex. It may be of interest to exhibit both proofs.

(i) *Analytical.* We write the equation (3.8.10) in the form

$$4Y(y - Y) = -4Y(x - X)\tan\theta + (x - X)^2\sec^2\theta$$
$$= -4Y(x - X)\tan\theta + (x - X)^2(1 + \tan^2\theta). \quad (3.8.11)$$

The equation of the envelope is given by the condition for equal roots in the parameter $\tan\theta$, namely

$$(x - X)^2 = 4Yy, \quad (3.8.12)$$

a parabola touching the x-axis at $(X, 0)$ and with its focus at (X, Y).

(ii) *Geometrical.* If there is an extremal through A and B it is a parabola whose focus S lies on the circle which has A as centre and which touches Ox; S also lies on the circle with B as centre which touches Ox. If these circles intersect in real points there are two extremals through A and B (Fig. 3.8c). If the circles are external to one another, there is no extremal through A and B.

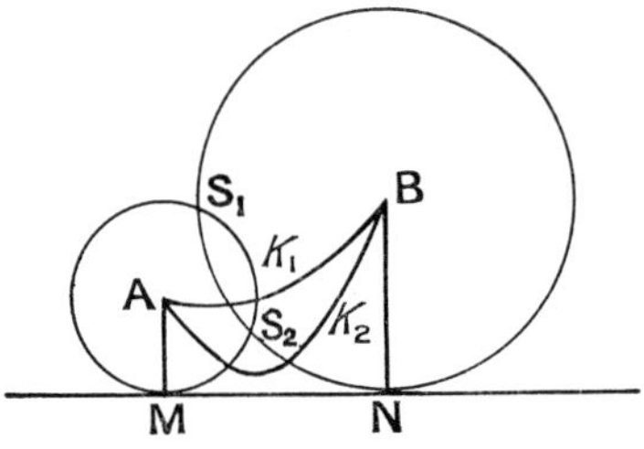

Fig. 3.8c

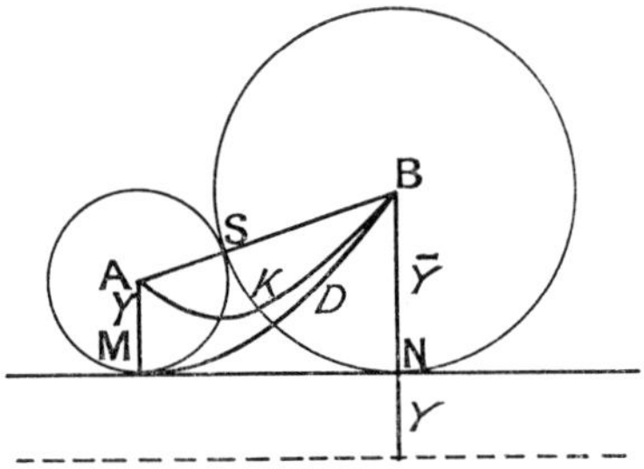

Fig. 3.8d

Consider now the critical case when the circles touch one another; there is just one extremal through A and B. It is clear from the elementary geometry (Fig. 3.8d) that this happens when B lies on the parabola D which has its focus at A and has Ox as tangent at the vertex. The unique extremal K through A and B touches D at B; for AB is a focal chord both for K and for D, and the tangent to each of these curves at B bisects the angle ABN, where BN is the perpendicular from B on Ox. Thus D is the *envelope* of the pencil of extremals through A. All of this is familiar in the elementary theory of projectiles, where D is the *enveloping parabola* for projection from A with Ox as the energy level.

A point on an extremal through A where it touches the envelope of the pencil of extremals through A is said to be *conjugate* to A.

One further property may be noticed. The tangent to an extremal K at A and the tangent to it at the conjugate point T meet on Ox. For AT is a focal chord of K, and the tangents at its ends meet on the directrix, which is the line Ox. We shall find that this property reappears in a more general case. (But the property that the tangents at A and T are at right angles is special to the parabolas.)

If we draw the pencil of extremals through A, and erase those parts of the extremals beyond the points of contact with the envelope D, we obtain the *semi-field* through A. In the part of the half-plane $x > X$ lying above or on D there is just one extremal of the semi-field through each point, and all these extremals pass through A.

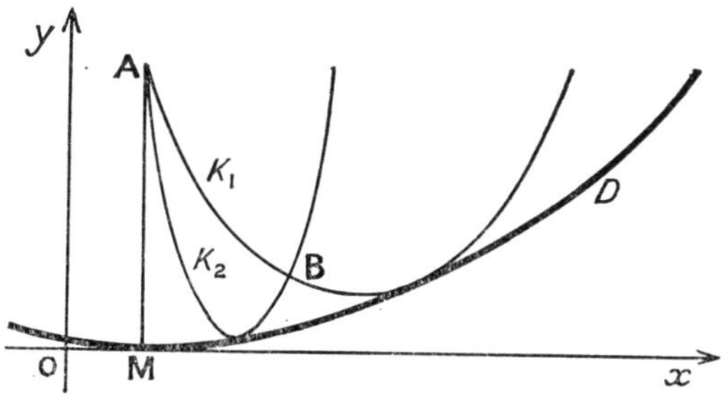

Fig. 3.8*e*

We are now in a position to answer the question, "How many extremals pass through A and B?" We construct the parabola D which has A as focus and Ox as tangent at the vertex. If B lies above D the two circles shown in Fig. 3.8*c* intersect in real points, and there are *two* extremals through A and B. If B lies on D there is just *one* extremal through A and B, and if B lies below D there are *none*. In the first case, when B lies above D, the upper extremal K_1 does not touch D between A and B, the lower extremal K_2 does (Fig. 3.8*e*). In other words, for K_1 there is no point on the arc AB conjugate to A, whereas for K_2 there is such a point. We shall find that the upper extremal K_1 always provides a relative, and sometimes (but not always) an absolute minimum for the integral $\int\sqrt{y}\,ds$. The lower extremal K_2 never provides even a relative minimum.

Let us now consider the case when B lies below D, and no extremal joins A and B. In this case the infimum m of $\int\sqrt{y}\,ds$ for curves of class D_1 is not attained in the class D_1. If we turn for a moment from the ordinary to the parametric problem we find, from the vanishing of the first variation, the curve consisting of three straight lines AM, MN, NB, where AM, BN are the perpendiculars from A, B on Ox (Fig. 3.8f). This solution was discovered by B. C. W.

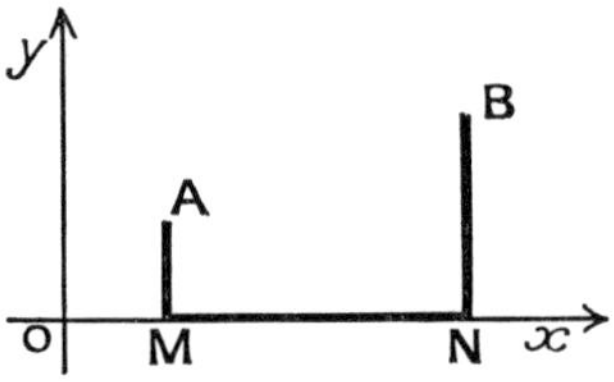

Fig. 3.8f

Goldschmidt in 1831, and is known as the Goldschmidt curve. We can find a curve of class D_1, in the ordinary problem, giving to I a value as near to m as we like, but no curve actually giving the value m. In the parametric problem, taking as our fundamental class κ curves with a finite number of corners, the infimum is actually attained by the Goldschmidt curve. Explicitly

$$m = \tfrac{2}{3}(Y^{3/2} + \bar{Y}^{3/2}), \tag{3.8.13}$$

and the curve $AM'N'B$ (Fig. 3.8g) consisting of three linear segments, makes

$$I = m \sec \theta, \tag{3.8.14}$$

which exceeds m by as little as we please.

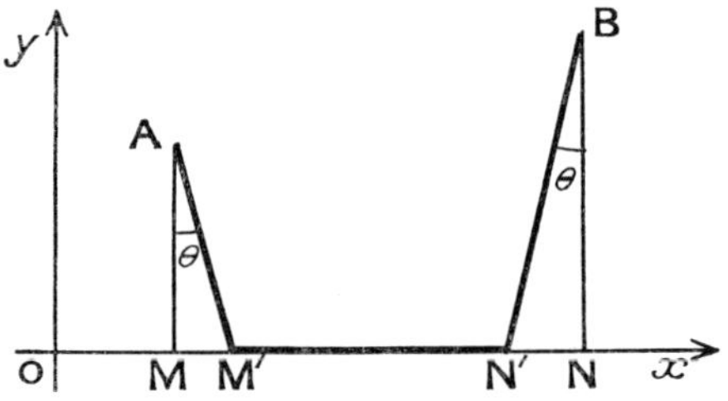

Fig. 3.8g

Actually we can foresee the appearance of the Goldschmidt curve in an intuitive way from the first integral (3.8.1)

$$y \cos^2 \psi = b. \tag{3.8.15}$$

If $b = 0$ this is satisfied by $y = 0$ and by $\cos \psi = 0$, giving the Goldschmidt curve; but the argument is merely plausible, since the Goldschmidt curve is not of the form $y = \varphi(x)$.

We shall find that the Goldschmidt curve always gives a strong relative minimum wherever B lies in relation to A. If B lies below D it gives the absolute minimum. If B lies above D both the upper parabola K_1 and the Goldschmidt curve give relative minima, and one or other of these gives the absolute minimum. Later (§5.16) we will return to the problem and determine which gives the absolute minimum.

3.9 The integral $\int y\, ds$

This is the problem of the surface of revolution of minimum area. As in (3.6.13) we have the first integral

$$y = b \sec \psi, \tag{3.9.1}$$

and from (3.6.16)

$$dx = b \sec \psi\, d\psi, \tag{3.9.2}$$

whence

$$x - a = b \log (\sec \psi + \tan \psi), \tag{3.9.3}$$

and (3.9.1) and (3.9.3) give the parametric representation of an extremal. To find the (x, y)-equation, which is rather more convenient, we have

$$\sec \psi + \tan \psi = e^{\frac{x-a}{b}}, \tag{3.9.4}$$

whence

$$\sec \psi - \tan \psi = e^{-\frac{x-a}{b}}, \tag{3.9.5}$$

and from (3.9.4) and (3.9.5) we have

$$\sec \psi = \cosh \frac{x-a}{b}, \quad \tan \psi = \sinh \frac{x-a}{b}. \tag{3.9.6}$$

The extremal is the curve

$$\frac{y}{b} = \cosh \frac{x-a}{b}, \tag{3.9.7}$$

a catenary with the axis Ox as directrix (Fig. 3.9). The result can be found equally simply from (3.6.21). The extremals are convex to Ox. We may notice, for future reference, that, if we denote the arc-length by s,

$$ds = \sec \psi\, dx = b \sec^2 \psi\, d\psi, \tag{3.9.8}$$

whence, measuring s from the lowest point of the curve,

$$s = b \tan \psi = b \sinh \frac{x - a}{b}. \tag{3.9.9}$$

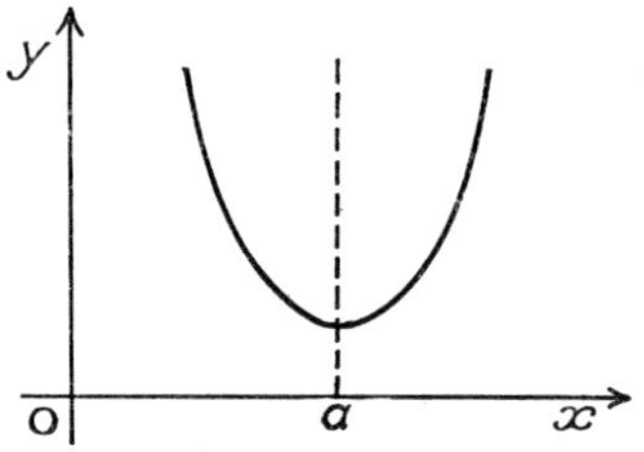

Fig. 3.9

The properties of the family of catenaries (3.9.7) are very similar to those of the family of parabolas (3.8.5).

(i) If, in (3.9.7), we fix a and vary b, we get a one-parameter family of catenaries touching two straight lines. We can construct a field in the trough bounded by these two lines if we retain the part of each catenary between the points of contact and erase the rest.

(ii) The pencil of catenaries through A (X, Y) has an envelope D touching Ox at $(X, 0)$. If B lies above D there are two extremals through A and B. The upper extremal K_1 does not touch D between A and B, the lower extremal K_2 does. If B lies below D there is no extremal through A and B. The Goldschmidt curve again gives a relative minimum if we turn from the ordinary to the parametric problem.

(iii) If an extremal K through A touches the envelope D at T, thc tangents to K at A and at T meet on Ox.

These three statements are true, not only for the families (3.8.5) and (3.9.7), but for any family of the form

$$\frac{y}{b} = f\left(\frac{x - a}{b}\right) \tag{3.9.10}$$

if we impose suitable restrictions on the function f. These are: $f \in C_2$, $f(0) > 0$, $f'(0) = 0$, $f''(x) > \mu$ for all values of x, where μ is a fixed positive number. These conditions are fulfilled, for example, by the extremals (3.6.21) if n is positive. In the specific cases discussed,

f is an even function, and we easily verify that the prescribed conditions are fulfilled:

(3.9.11) $\quad n = \frac{1}{2}; \quad f = 1 + \frac{1}{4}x^2, \quad f' = \frac{1}{2}x, \quad f'' = \frac{1}{2},$

(3.9.12) $\quad n = 1; \quad f = \cosh x, \quad f' = \sinh x, \quad f'' = \cosh x.$

The proofs of the three properties for the catenaries (3.9.7), and for the general case (3.9.10), are somewhat more laborious than for the parabolas (3.8.5). Let us be content to exhibit the proof of (i) for the general case. We can take the fixed number a to be zero without loss of generality, and then the curves are

(3.9.13) $$\frac{y}{b} = f\left(\frac{x}{b}\right).$$

These are, for different values of b, similar figures with O as centre of similarity, and therefore the tangents from O are the same for all the curves. Explicitly, if (x_0, y_0) is the point of contact in the first quadrant of the tangent from O,

(3.9.14) $$\frac{y_0}{b} = f\left(\frac{x_0}{b}\right), \quad \frac{y_0}{x_0} = f'\left(\frac{x_0}{b}\right),$$

whence

(3.9.15) $$f\left(\frac{x_0}{b}\right) = \frac{x_0}{b} f'\left(\frac{x_0}{b}\right),$$

and therefore x_0/b satisfies the equation

(3.9.16) $$g(\xi) \equiv f(\xi) - \xi f'(\xi) = 0.$$

Now

(3.9.17) $$g'(\xi) = -\xi f''(\xi) < -\mu\xi \quad \text{for} \quad \xi > 0,$$

and

(3.9.18) $$g(0) = f(0) > 0,$$

so $g(\xi)$ decreases steadily to $-\infty$ as ξ increases from 0 to ∞. Thus $g(\xi)$ passes just once through the value zero, say at $\xi = \xi_0$. The curves of the family (3.9.13) all touch the line

(3.9.19) $$\frac{y}{x} = f'(\xi_0),$$

and there is another common tangent in the second quadrant. If $f(x)$

is an even function (as it is in the two specific problems mentioned) the other common tangent is

$$\frac{y}{x} = -f'(\xi_0). \tag{3.9.20}$$

For the parabolas (3.9.11) the equation for ξ_0 is

$$1 + \tfrac{1}{4}\xi^2 = \tfrac{1}{2}\xi^2, \quad \xi_0 = 2, \tag{3.9.21}$$

and the tangents are, as we know,

$$\frac{y}{x} = \pm 1. \tag{3.9.22}$$

For the catenaries (3.9.12) the equation for ξ_0 is

$$\coth \xi_0 = \xi_0, \quad \xi_0 = 1{\cdot}2 \text{ approximately}, \tag{3.9.23}$$

and the tangents are

$$\frac{y}{x} = \pm\sinh \xi_0 = \pm 1{\cdot}51 \text{ approximately}. \tag{3.9.24}$$

Finally, let us return to the special case of the integral $\int y\, ds$, and consider what happens if B lies below the envelope D of the pencil of extremals through A. There is no catenary of the form (3.9.7) through A and B. As in the similar problem of $\int \sqrt{y}\, ds$ discussed in §3.8, the infimum value of the integral is not attained by any curve of the form $y = \varphi(x)$. It is attained by the Goldschmidt curve $AMNB$ (Fig. 3.8f), where M, N are the feet of the perpendiculars from A, B on Ox.

3.10 The integral $\int \sqrt{\{y(1 - y'^2)\}}\, dx$

We consider the integral

$$I = \int_X^{\bar{X}} \sqrt{\{y(1 - y'^2)\}}\, dx, \tag{3.10.1}$$

in which we interpret the radical to mean the positive value. For the integrand to be real we need $y'^2 \leqslant 1$ in the upper half-plane $(y > 0)$ and $y'^2 \geqslant 1$ in the lower half-plane $(y < 0)$. Euler's equation has the first integral

$$\sqrt{\left(\frac{y}{1 - y'^2}\right)} = \text{constant}, \tag{3.10.2}$$

or say

$$y = b(1 - y'^2), \qquad (b > 0), \tag{3.10.3}$$

and on integration we find the equation of the extremals in the form

(3.10.4) $$b - y = \frac{1}{4b}(x - a)^2.$$

This represents a parabola with its axis vertical and vertex upwards. The focus S is at $(a, 0)$ on Ox, and the vertex is at (a, b). The parabola cuts Ox at an angle $\pm\pi/4$, and $y'^2 < 1$ above Ox, and $y'^2 > 1$ below Ox (as is indeed evident from (3.10.3)).

Let us consider the simple case in which the end-points A and B lie in the upper half-plane, so $Y > 0$ and $\overline{Y} > 0$, and in which the curves are restricted to lie in the region $y \geqslant 0$. Since $|y'| < 1$ in the upper half-plane the points on an extremal through A must lie in the sector

(3.10.5) $$\left|\frac{y - Y}{x - X}\right| < 1,$$

and when we add the condition $\overline{Y} > 0$ we see that B must lie in the region $\mathscr{R}$, bounded by three straight lines, shown in Fig. 3.10.

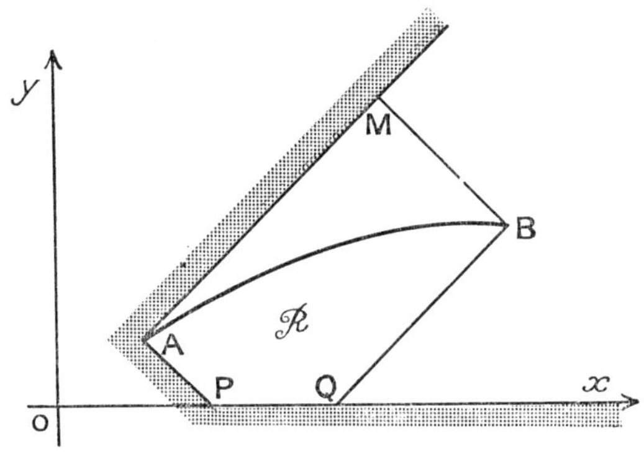

Fig. 3.10

If the curves admitted are restricted to the class C_1, there is a unique parabolic arc (3.10.4) through the given points A and B, and it lies entirely in the region $\mathscr{R}$. (We can prove uniqueness by an argument similar to that used for the cycloids in §3.7, or from the fact that the focus S is the point on Ox such that $AS - SB = \bar{Y} - Y$.) If we admit curves of class D_1, then curves consisting of two or three straight segments, such as the curves AMB and $APQB$ in Fig. 3.10, give to I the value zero, and these are clearly minimizing curves.

We shall see later (§5.14) that the parabolic arc gives a maximum value to I in the class D_1.

We have in this problem an example of a phenomenon mentioned in §2.8. For N vanishes at all elements (x, y, y') for which $y = 0$, and, for any point on the line $y = 0$, only members of a discrete set of values of y' can occur. Euler's equation is

$$2yy'' + (1 - y'^2) = 0, \tag{3.10.6}$$

and at a point on $y = 0$, y' can have only the values $+1$ and -1. Of course this corresponds to a familiar property of the parabolas with axes vertical and with foci on Ox.

Through a point A on $y = 0$, with the chosen value of y' ($+1$ or -1) at A, there are infinitely many extremals, not just one extremal. Suppose for definiteness that A is the origin and that $y' = +1$. The extremals are

$$y = x - \frac{x^2}{4b}, \qquad b > 0, \tag{3.10.7}$$

a family of parabolas all with the same tangent at A. We notice that, at A,

$$y' = 1, \qquad y'' = -\frac{1}{2b}, \tag{3.10.8}$$

and y'' may have any prescribed negative value.

We may take for the domain R of (x, y, y') in this problem the domain defined by the equations

$$y > 0, \qquad -1 < y' < 1, \tag{3.10.9}$$

and the element of (3.10.7) at the origin, namely (0, 0, 1), lies on the frontier of R. The extremal (3.10.7) still gives a stationary value to I, although the element of the curve at one end-point lies on the frontier of R (§2.2).

3.11 Polar coordinates

If we express a geometric problem in terms of polar coordinates, taking θ (instead of x) as the independent variable and r (instead of y) as the dependent variable, our problem is to find a curve $r = \varphi(\theta)$ to minimize

$$\int_\alpha^\beta F(\theta, r, r')\, d\theta, \tag{3.11.1}$$

where $r' = dr/d\theta$. In the fundamental problem, with fixed end-points,

$\varphi(\alpha)$ has the prescribed value a and $\varphi(\beta)$ has the prescribed value b, and the curves admitted to competition are curves in which $\varphi(\theta)$ *is a uniform (one-valued) function of* θ *in* (α, β). The conditions imposed on $F(\theta, r, r')$ and on the curve $r = \varphi(\theta)$ are similar to the conditions imposed on $F(x, y, y')$ and on the curve $y = \varphi(x)$ in §1.3.

As a first example we may consider the geodesic problem. In fact polar coordinates are not particularly well suited to this problem, but the solution may be of interest as an example of the appropriate technique. We choose axes of reference such that the inferior end-point A is $\theta = -\beta$, $r = c \sec \beta$, and the superior end-point B is $\theta = \beta$, $r = c \sec \beta$; the positive constant c is the distance of the origin O from the line AB, and the angle β is acute. We wish to minimize

$$\int_{-\beta}^{\beta} \sqrt{(r'^2 + r^2)}\, d\theta. \tag{3.11.2}$$

The class of curves admitted to competition are, as already mentioned, curves for which $\varphi(\theta)$ is a uniform function of θ in $(-\beta, \beta)$. Let us be content to confine attention to the case in which $\varphi \in C_2$. The integrand in (3.11.2) does not contain θ, so Euler's equation has the first integral $U =$ constant (where U now means $F - r'F_{r'}$ instead of the corresponding formula with x and y), giving

$$\frac{r^2}{\sqrt{(r'^2 + r^2)}} = \text{constant}, \tag{3.11.3}$$

$$k^2 r'^2 = r^2(r^2 - k^2), \qquad (k > 0). \tag{3.11.4}$$

It is clear that $r \geqslant k$, and to integrate (3.11.4) we introduce a parameter u in place of r, where $r = k \sec u$. Substitution in (3.11.4) leads to $u'^2 = 1$, $u = \theta - \theta_0$, and the solution is

$$r = k \sec (\theta - \theta_0). \tag{3.11.5}$$

This represents a straight line, and the line goes through A and B if $\theta_0 = 0$, $k = c$. The extremal required is the straight line AB,

$$r = c \sec \theta. \tag{3.11.6}$$

The length of the line, from the geometry of the figure or from the integral (3.11.2), is $l = 2c \tan \beta$.

It is easy to see that the straight line (3.11.6) has minimum length in the class of curves considered. Let us consider the curve

$$r = c \sec \theta + \zeta, \tag{3.11.7}$$

where $\zeta \in C_2$ and $\zeta(-\beta) = \zeta(\beta) = 0$, but $\zeta(\theta)$ is not identically zero.

The length of this curve is

$$l' = \int_{-\beta}^{\beta} \sqrt{\{(c \sec \theta \tan \theta + \zeta')^2 + (c \sec \theta + \zeta)^2\}}\, d\theta \tag{3.11.8}$$

$$= \int_{-\beta}^{\beta} \sqrt{\{(c \sec^2 \theta + \zeta' \sin \theta + \zeta \cos \theta)^2 + (\zeta' \cos \theta - \zeta \sin \theta)^2\}}\, d\theta$$

$$\geqslant \int_{-\beta}^{\beta} (c \sec^2 \theta + \zeta' \sin \theta + \zeta \cos \theta)\, d\theta.$$

We get equality only if $\zeta' \cos \theta - \zeta \sin \theta = 0$ for all θ in $(-\beta, \beta)$, and this cannot happen, because it would imply $\zeta \cos \theta = \text{constant} = \lambda$, and λ must be zero, because ζ vanishes at $-\beta$ and at β. But $\lambda = 0$ would imply $\zeta = 0$ identically, which is prohibited. Thus

$$l' > \int_{-\beta}^{\beta} (c \sec^2 \theta + \zeta' \sin \theta + \zeta \cos \theta)\, d\theta$$

$$= (c \tan \theta + \zeta \sin \theta)\Big|_{-\beta}^{\beta} = 2c \tan \beta = l,$$

and this completes the proof that the straight line has minimum length in the class of curves considered.

As a second illustration we consider the path of a ray of light in a medium whose refractive index μ is a continuous function of r, the distance from a fixed origin O. The path, in virtue of Fermat's principle (§2.9), makes stationary the integral $\int \mu\, ds$, so the integral we have to consider, expressed in terms of polar coordinates, is

$$\int \mu(r) \sqrt{(r'^2 + r^2)}\, d\theta. \tag{3.11.9}$$

Since the integrand does not contain θ, we have the first integral of Euler's equation $U = \text{constant}$,

$$\frac{\mu(r) r^2}{\sqrt{(r'^2 + r^2)}} = c. \tag{3.11.10}$$

If the ray is at right angles to the radius vector at $r = a$, the value of c is $a\mu(a)$.

Consider in particular the case in which $\mu(r)$ has the form $\sqrt{\left(1 + \dfrac{k^2}{r^2}\right)}$. In this case (3.11.10) becomes

$$r'^2 = \frac{r^2(r^2 - a^2)}{a^2 \mu_0^{\,2}}, \tag{3.11.11}$$

where we have assumed that the ray is at right angles to the radius vector when $r = a$, and μ_0 is written for $\mu(a)$; we notice that $\mu_0 > 1$.

To integrate (3.11.11) we introduce a variable u in place of r, where

(3.11.12) $$r = a \sec u,$$

and then (3.11.11) becomes

(3.11.13) $$\left(\frac{du}{d\theta}\right)^2 = \frac{1}{\mu_0^{\,2}},$$

giving $u = \theta/\mu_0$ if $r = a$ when $\theta = 0$. Thus the ray has the form

(3.11.14) $$r = a \sec (\theta/\mu_0),$$

which is symmetrical about $\theta = 0$ (Fig. 3.11), and we see that $r \to \infty$ θ as $\to \frac{1}{2}\mu_0\pi = \frac{1}{2}\pi + \varepsilon$, say.

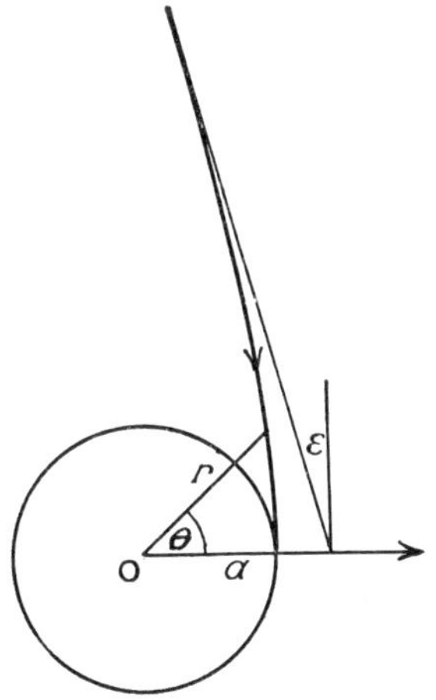

Fig. 3.11

If now a is the Earth's radius, and we assume the formula $\sqrt{\left(1 + \frac{k^2}{r^2}\right)}$ for the index of refraction of the atmosphere (taking the Earth's centre as origin), we have the form of a ray which is tangential to the Earth. The value of μ_0 is about 1·000294, giving for ε the value 1′35″; the sun is still visible after it has actually set, so long as its angular displacement below the horizon does not exceed 1′35″. (This is a good deal smaller than the observed value; the formula we have assumed for μ is not a particularly good approximation to the actual value, and the result we have found is of academic, rather than of practical, interest.)

This is another example of a physical problem of the type mentioned in §1.8, where the first-order conditions alone suffice for the solution (cf. §3.7). In the figure the value of ε is of course greatly exaggerated.

3.12 The Newtonian orbit

A particle moves in a plane under an attraction to the origin O of magnitude μ/r^2 per unit mass ($\mu > 0$). To determine the orbits.

The potential function is $\mathscr{V} = -\mu/r$, and Jacobi's form of the principle of Least Action (§3.6) tells us that the orbits are the extremals for the integral

$$\int \sqrt{\{2(h - \mathscr{V})\}}\, ds, \tag{3.12.1}$$

i.e., using polar coordinates, for

$$\int \sqrt{\left\{2\left(h + \frac{\mu}{r}\right)\left(r'^2 + r^2\right)\right\}}\, d\theta, \tag{3.12.2}$$

where h is the energy constant. The integrand does not contain θ, so we have the first integral of Euler's equation

$$\frac{r^2\sqrt{\left(h + \dfrac{\mu}{r}\right)}}{\sqrt{(r'^2 + r^2)}} = \text{constant}, \tag{3.12.3}$$

or say

$$\frac{hr^4 + \mu r^3}{r'^2 + r^2} = \tfrac{1}{2}\alpha^2, \tag{3.12.4}$$

where the positive constant on the right is called $\frac{1}{2}\alpha^2$, the factor $\frac{1}{2}$ (not obligatory for the calculations) being introduced so that α represents an important physical constant, namely the conserved angular momentum about O. Thus

$$r'^2 = \frac{r^2}{\alpha^2}(2hr^2 + 2\mu r - \alpha^2). \tag{3.12.5}$$

If we put $r = 1/u$ we obtain

$$u'^2 = \frac{2}{\alpha^2}h + \frac{2\mu}{\alpha^2}u - u^2. \tag{3.12.6}$$

The quadratic form in the second member of this equation has real zeros u_1 and u_2. If $h < 0$, $u_1 > u_2 > 0$: if $h = 0$, $u_1 > u_2 = 0$: if $h > 0$, $u_1 > 0 > u_2$.

We can write (3.12.6) in the form

$$u'^2 = (u_1 - u)(u - u_2), \tag{3.12.7}$$

and to integrate this we introduce in place of u a variable φ defined by

$$u = \tfrac{1}{2}(u_1 + u_2) + \tfrac{1}{2}(u_1 - u_2)\cos\varphi, \tag{3.12.8}$$

which leads, on substitution in (3.12.7) to $\varphi'^2 = 1$, $\varphi = \theta - \theta_0$. The orbit is the curve

$$\frac{l}{r} = 1 + e\cos(\theta - \theta_0), \tag{3.12.9}$$

where

$$l = \frac{\alpha^2}{\mu}, \qquad e = \sqrt{\left(1 + \frac{2h\alpha^2}{\mu^2}\right)}. \tag{3.12.10}$$

If $h < 0$, the orbit is an ellipse with one focus at 0. If $h = 0$, it is a parabola with focus at 0. If $h > 0$, it is that branch of a hyperbola for which 0 is the inner focus.

CHAPTER IV

Variable End-points

4.1 Variation from a minimizing curve

We consider the variation in the value of the integral

$$I = \int_X^{\overline{X}} F(x, y, y')\, dx \tag{4.1.1}$$

when we change the path of integration to a neighbouring path. The original curve is assumed to satisfy du Bois-Reymond's equation (2.3.20) derived from the integrand F. The variation contemplated involves a variation of the end-points. For example, instead of seeking a minimizing curve joining the fixed end-points A and B, we might seek a minimizing curve subject to the condition that A lies on a given curve Γ and B lies on a given curve Δ; in this problem we have separated end-conditions (cf. §1.10), but sometimes mixed end-conditions will occur. Moreover, the problem of finding a minimizing curve subject to prescribed end-conditions is only one application, and not the most fundamental, of the theorem that we shall establish.

We consider a family of curves, the typical member K_α having the equation

$$y = \varphi(x, \alpha). \tag{4.1.2}$$

The original curve is the member K_0,

$$y = \varphi(x, 0), \tag{4.1.3}$$

joining A_0 to B_0, and K_0 satisfies du Bois-Reymond's equation. We consider in the first instance the problem with separated end-conditions, A lying on a given curve Γ and B on a given curve Δ.

Now in general we can use the same parameter α occurring in (4.1.2) to define the points of Γ and the points of Δ. Thus Γ is represented parametrically by the formulae

$$x = X(\alpha), \quad y = Y(\alpha) = \varphi\{X(\alpha), \alpha\}, \tag{4.1.4}$$

and similarly for Δ,

$$x = \overline{X}(\alpha), \quad y = \overline{Y}(\alpha) = \varphi\{\overline{X}(\alpha), \alpha\}. \tag{4.1.5}$$

To prove that we can use α as the parameter on Γ, suppose that Γ is the curve

(4.1.6) $$x = p(t), \qquad y = q(t),$$

where $p(t), q(t) \in C_1$, and $\dot{p}, \dot{q}$ do not vanish together. We may suppose, without loss of generality, that $t = 0$ at A_0, the point of intersection of Γ with K_0. Now K_α cuts Γ where

(4.1.7) $$q(t) - \varphi\{p(t), \alpha\} = 0.$$

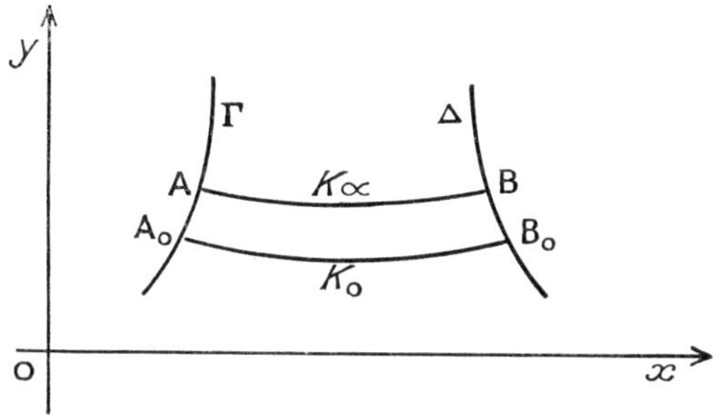

Fig. 4.1

We denote the first member of (4.1.7) by $\lambda(t, \alpha)$. The equation

(4.1.8) $$\lambda(t, \alpha) = 0$$

defines t as a function of α, of class C_1, near $\alpha = 0$ (and $t = 0$ when $\alpha = 0$) unless

(4.1.9) $$\lambda_t(0, 0) = 0.$$

Now

(4.1.10) $$\lambda_t(0, 0) = \dot{q}(0) - \varphi_x\{p(0), 0\}\,\dot{p}(0),$$

and this does not vanish unless K_0 touches Γ at A_0. We shall assume that this *non-tangency condition* is satisfied, and then t is determined as a uniform function of α near $\alpha = 0$. Therefore we can take α instead of t as the parameter defining a point on Γ, and we can write Γ in the form (4.1.4). Similar remarks apply to Δ, assuming that the non-tangency condition is satisfied at B_0.

We shall assume that $\varphi(x, \alpha) \in C_1$ in a domain $\mathscr{D}$ of (x, α) containing the segment $\alpha = 0$, $X(0) \leqslant x \leqslant \overline{X}(0)$, and we shall assume also that $\varphi_\alpha{}'(x, \alpha)$ $(= \varphi_{\alpha x}(x, \alpha))$ is continuous in $\mathscr{D}$. It follows that in $\mathscr{D}$,

(4.1.11) $$\varphi_{x\alpha} = \varphi_{\alpha x}.$$

It will be noticed that for the moment we exclude the possibility that K_0 has a corner.

We write $\eta(x)$ for $\varphi_\alpha(x, 0)$, so that if α is infinitesimal $\alpha\eta(x)$ is the contemporaneous variation from K_0 to K_α. We notice that this notation agrees with that of §2.2 and §2.3, where $\varphi(x, \alpha)$ had the special form $\varphi(x) + \alpha\eta(x)$. We have here an example of a phenomenon mentioned in §1.2; it may not be possible to obtain the varied curve by contemporaneous variations without first extending the range of definition of the original curve.

We write

$$\psi(\alpha) = I(K_\alpha) = \int_{X(\alpha)}^{\bar{X}(\alpha)} F\{x, \varphi(x, \alpha), \varphi'(x, \alpha)\}\, dx, \tag{4.1.12}$$

and to find $\psi'(0)$ we need the theorem on the differentiation of a Riemann integral when the limits, as well as the integrand, involve the parameter α. We have

$$\psi'(0) = F(b)\bar{X}'(0) - F(a)X'(0) \tag{4.1.13}$$

$$+ \int_{X(0)}^{\bar{X}(0)} [F_y\{x, \varphi(x, 0), \varphi'(x, 0)\}\eta(x) + F_{y'}\{x, \varphi(x, 0), \varphi'(x, 0)\}\eta'(x)]\, dx,$$

where a is the element of K_0 at A_0,

$$a = [X(0), \varphi\{X(0), 0\}, \varphi'\{X(0), 0\}], \tag{4.1.14}$$

and b is the element of K_0 at B_0. Since $\eta(x) = \varphi_\alpha(x, 0)$,

$$\eta'(x) = \varphi_{\alpha x}(x, 0) = \varphi_{x\alpha}(x, 0). \tag{4.1.15}$$

4.2 The variable end-point theorem

Now K_0 satisfies du Bois-Reymond's equation

$$F_{y'}\{x, \varphi(x, 0), \varphi'(x, 0)\} = \chi(x) + C, \tag{4.2.1}$$

where

$$\chi(x) = \int_{X(0)}^{x} F_y\{t, \varphi(t, 0), \varphi'(t, 0)\}\, dt. \tag{4.2.2}$$

We can therefore write the integral in the second member of (4.1.13) in the form

$$\begin{aligned} &\int_{X(0)}^{\bar{X}(0)} [\chi'(x)\eta(x) + \{\chi(x) + C\}\eta'(x)]\, dx \\ &= \{\chi(x) + C\}\eta(x) \Big|_{A_0}^{B_0} \\ &= F_{y'}(b)\, \eta\{\bar{X}(0)\} - F_{y'}(a)\eta\{X(0)\}. \end{aligned} \tag{4.2.3}$$

Next we must express the value of η at A_0 in terms of $X'(0)$ and $Y'(0)$. Now, as in (4.1.4),

$$Y(\alpha) = \varphi\{X(\alpha), \alpha\}, \tag{4.2.4}$$

whence

$$Y'(\alpha) = \varphi'\{X(\alpha), \alpha\}X'(\alpha) + \varphi_\alpha\{X(\alpha), \alpha\}, \tag{4.2.5}$$

and, in particular,

$$Y'(0) = \varphi'\{X(0), 0\}X'(0) + \varphi_\alpha\{X(0), 0\}, \tag{4.2.6}$$

which is equivalent to

$$Y'(0) = \eta\{X(0)\} + p_A X'(0), \tag{4.2.7}$$

where p_A is the slope of K_0 at A_0. There is a similar result for B_0.

The formula (4.2.7) is important. It relates the contemporaneous displacement of the end-point A,

$$\partial Y = \eta\{X(0)\}\, d\alpha, \tag{4.2.8}$$

to the actual displacement (dX, dY),

$$dX = X'(0)\, d\alpha, \qquad dY = Y'(0)\, d\alpha, \tag{4.2.9}$$

and is needed often. The geometrical interpretation of (4.2.7), which can be written in the easily-remembered form

$$dY = \partial Y + p\, dX, \tag{4.2.10}$$

is illustrated in Fig. 4.2*a*.

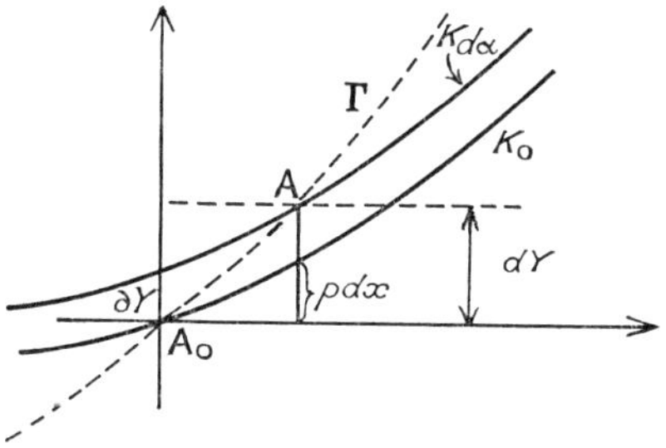

Fig. 4.2*a*

We now return to the formula for $\psi'(0)$. From (4.1.13), in virtue of (4.2.3) and (4.2.7), we have

$$\begin{aligned}\psi'(0) &= F(b)\bar{X}'(0) - F(a)X'(0) + F_{y'}(b)\{\bar{Y}'(0) - p_B\bar{X}'(0)\} \\ &\qquad - F_{y'}(a)\{Y'(0) - p_A X'(0)\} \\ &= \{U(b)\bar{X}'(0) + V(b)\bar{Y}'(0)\} - \{U(a)X'(0) + V(a)Y'(0)\}\end{aligned} \tag{4.2.11}$$

and if we write dI for $\psi'(0)\,d\alpha$ we can express (4.2.11) in the compact and convenient form

$$(4.2.12)\qquad dI = (U\,dx + V\,dy)\Big|_A^B$$

$$= (U_B\,d\overline{X} + V_B\,d\overline{Y}) - (U_A\,dX + V_A\,dY),$$

where U_A ($= U(a)$) and V_A ($= V(a)$) are the values of U and V for the element a of K_0 at A_0, and (dX, dY) is the displacement of A: and similarly U_B ($= U(b)$) and V_B ($= V(b)$) are the values of U and V for the element b of K_0 at B_0, and $(d\overline{X}, d\overline{Y})$ is the displacement of B. The formula (4.2.12), giving the variation in I for a general variation from a minimizing curve, is spoken of as the variable end-point theorem.

Another proof of the theorem will be given later in connexion with the parametric problem (§9.8).

A number of important corollaries follow from the theorem.

COROLLARY 1. If ϖ is the slope of Γ at A_0, so that $dY = \varpi\,dX$,

$$(4.2.13)\quad U_A\,dX + V_A\,dY = (U_A + \varpi V_A)\,dX = \{F + (\varpi - y')F_{y'}\}\,dX$$

where the arguments in F and $F_{y'}$ belong to the element (x, y, y') of K_0 at A_0. Using the analogous notation for B_0, we can write the variable end-point theorem in the form

$$(4.2.14)\qquad dI = \{F + (\varpi - y')F_{y'}\}\,dx\Big|_{A_0}^{B_0}.$$

COROLLARY 2. The proof given above involved the non-tangency condition, i.e. it excluded the possibility that $\varpi = y'$ at A_0 or at B_0. Nevertheless if $\varpi = y'$ we have, from (4.2.13),

$$(4.2.15)\qquad U\,dx + V\,dy = F\,dx,$$

and the theorem is still true if $\varpi = y'$ at A_0 or at B_0.

COROLLARY 3. We can deduce from the variable end-point theorem the corner conditions already established in §2.6. Suppose that a minimizing curve AB has a corner at C (Fig. 4.2b). If we vary to the neighbouring path $AC'B$ we have, applying the theorem separately to the arcs AC and CB,

$$(4.2.16)\quad dI = (U_{C-}\,dx + V_{C-}\,dy) - (U_{C+}\,dx + V_{C+}\,dy),$$

where (dx, dy) is the displacement CC', the suffix $C-$ refers to the element of the minimizing curve immediately to the left of C, and the suffix $C+$ to the element immediately to the right of C. Now I has a stationary value for the curve ACB, so $dI = 0$, and both corner conditions follow since dx and dy are independent.

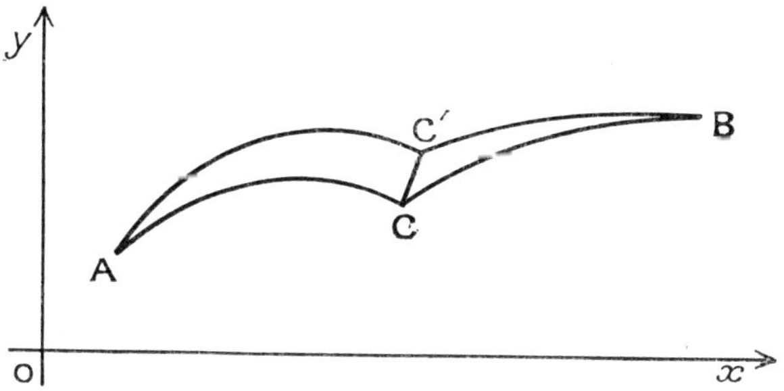

Fig. 4.2*b*

COROLLARY 4. The proof of the variable end-point theorem referred to a minimizing arc without corners, but in fact the restriction to arcs without corners is unnecessary. The theorem is valid if the minimizing curve from which we start has a finite number of corners. Let us suppose, for the sake of simplicity, that the minimizing curve K_0 has just one corner between A_0 and B_0 at C_0 (Fig. 4.2*c*). Then,

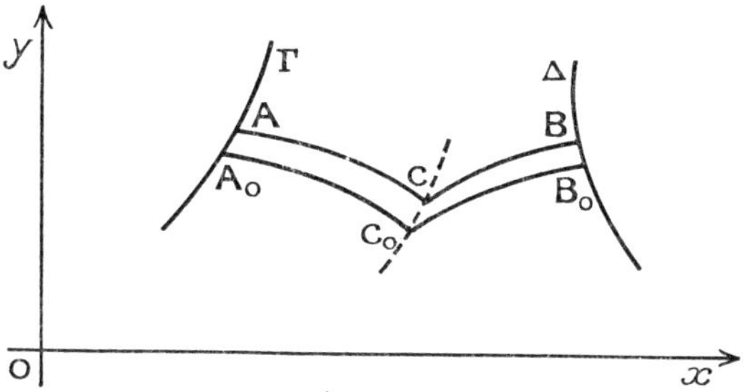

Fig. 4.2*c*

applying the theorem separately to the extremal arcs A_0C_0 and C_0B_0, we have

$$(4.2.17)\quad dI = (U\,dx + V\,dy)_{C_0-} - (U\,dx + V\,dy)_{A_0} + (U\,dx + V\,dy)_{B_0} - (U\,dx + V\,dy)_{C_0+}$$

where the suffix C_0- means that the values of U and V in the brackets are for an element of K_0 immediately to the left of C_0, and the suffix C_0+ similarly refers to an element of K_0 immediately to the right of C_0. But U and V are continuous at a corner, so the terms containing the displacement C_0C disappear, and the variable end-point theorem still holds.

COROLLARY 5. For the line-integral $\int P\,dx + Q\,dy$ considered in §3.2, F has the form $P + Qy'$, and in this case $U = P$ and $V = Q$. The variable end-point theorem takes the form

$$dI = (P\,dx + Q\,dy)\Big|_{A_0}^{B_0}. \tag{4.2.18}$$

Since $\dfrac{\partial Q}{\partial x} - \dfrac{\partial P}{\partial y}$ vanishes on the minimizing curve, the result can also be regarded as a simple corollary to Stokes's theorem.

4.3 The problem of the minimizing curve with variable end-points

We now consider the problem of finding a minimizing curve K_0 for

$$I = \int_X^{\overline{X}} F(x, y, y')\,dx \tag{4.3.1}$$

when A and B are not fixed, but are constrained to lie on given curves Γ and Δ. Wherever A lies on Γ, and wherever B lies on Δ, the minimizing curve will surely be a minimizing curve for the corresponding problem with fixed end-points, and this is an extremal arc through A and B, or a curve with corners built up of extremal arcs. In addition we have, as a necessary condition,

$$dI = 0 \tag{4.3.2}$$

when A moves on Γ and B moves independently on Δ, giving

$$U_A\,dX + V_A\,dY = U_B\,d\overline{X} + V_B\,d\overline{Y} = 0. \tag{4.3.3}$$

In this equation U_A, V_A are the values of U, V for the element of K_0 at A_0, the differentials dX, dY represent a displacement on Γ, and so on.

We can write the conditions (4.3.3) in another form which we shall need later. If the curve Γ is defined by the equation $\gamma(X, Y) = 0$, and the curve Δ by the equation $\delta(\overline{X}, \overline{Y}) = 0$, the conditions (4.3.3) are equivalent to the statement that there exist constants e, e' such that

$$(U_B\,d\overline{X} + V_B\,d\overline{Y}) - (U_A\,dX + V_A\,dY) + e\,d\gamma + e'd\delta = 0 \tag{4.3.4}$$

for *arbitrary* values of the differentials dX, dY, $d\overline{X}$, $d\overline{Y}$.*

* It is assumed that γ is chosen so that $d\gamma \neq 0$. If we replaced γ by γ^2, for example, in (4.3.4), the resulting equation would be false.

The form (4.3.4) can be extended to include the case of *mixed* end-conditions. We state the result here for convenience, postponing the proof to a later stage (Chapter VIII). If K_0 is minimizing, subject to the end-conditions

(4.3.5) $$\psi^r(X, Y, \bar{X}, \bar{Y}) = 0,$$

where $r = 1, 2, \ldots, p$, and $p \leqslant 4$, then there exist constants e^r such that

(4.3.6) $$(U_B\, d\bar{X} + V_B\, d\bar{Y}) - (U_A\, dX + V_A\, dY) + \sum_{r=1}^{p} e^r\, d\psi^r = 0$$

for arbitrary values of dX, dY, $d\bar{X}$, $d\bar{Y}$.

The case of fixed end-points is the trivial case in which $p = 4$ and the end-conditions $\psi^r = 0$ are

(4.3.7) $$X - X_0 = 0, \quad Y - Y_0 = 0, \quad \bar{X} - \bar{X}_0 = 0, \quad \bar{Y} - \bar{Y}_0 = 0.$$

In this case, as we expect, the end-conditions (4.3.6) yield no information; they only determine the values of the constants e^r.

We return to the case of separated end-conditions, and consider the important special case in which $F(x, y, y')$ has the form

(4.3.8) $$f(x, y)\sqrt{(1 + y'^2)},$$

where $f(x, y) > 0$ for all relevant values of (x, y). In this case

$$U = f(x, y) \cos \psi, \quad V = f(x, y) \sin \psi.$$

If A is fixed, and B is constrained to lie on a given curve Δ, the end-condition at B is

(4.3.9) $$\cos \beta\, d\bar{X} + \sin \beta\, d\bar{Y} = 0,$$

where β is the value of ψ at B_0. The minimizing curve cuts Δ normally at B_0. Of course the result is evident also by elementary reasoning; if K_0 did not cut Δ normally we could decrease the value of I by replacing a small segment of K_0 near B_0 by a line normal to Δ.

In the problem considered at the end of §3.2, where the integral I has the form $\int P(x, y)\, dx$, the integrand not containing y', we noticed that, in the *fixed* end-point problem, there is in general no extremal through A and B. But there is one case of the *variable* end-point problem in which the solution is simple, namely that in which X and $\bar{X}$ are fixed, and Y and $\bar{Y}$ are arbitrary. Then the end-conditions (4.3.3) are automatically fulfilled, and therefore the extremal K_0, $y = \varphi(x)$, defined implicitly by the equation $P_y = 0$, gives a stationary value to I. This stationary value is actually a minimum if $P \in C_2$, and if $P_{yy}(x, \eta) > 0$

when x lies in $(X, \overline{X})$ and η is arbitrary. For if k is the curve $y = \varphi(x) + \zeta(x)$, where now $\zeta(x)$ does not necessarily vanish at X and at $\overline{X}$, we have

$$(4.3.10)\quad I(K) - I(K_0) = \int_X^{\overline{X}} \{P(x, \varphi + \zeta) - P(x, \varphi)\}\, dx$$
$$= \int_X^{\overline{X}} \zeta P_y(x, \varphi)\, dx + \frac{1}{2}\int_X^{\overline{X}} \zeta^2 P_{yy}(x, \eta)\, dx,$$

where η lies between $\varphi(x)$ and $\varphi(x) + \zeta(x)$. The first integral on the right in (4.3.10) vanishes, since $P_y(x, \varphi)$ is identically zero, and therefore K_0 is minimizing if $P_{yy}(x, \eta) > 0$.

EXAMPLE 1. $$I = \int \frac{1}{y}\, ds.$$

To find the minimizing curve when $A(X, Y)$ is a fixed point in the upper half-plane, and B lies on the line $x = k$ $(k > X)$. The required curve (Fig. 4.3*a*) is an arc of the circle through A with its centre at $(k, 0)$. We have not proved that this is actually a minimizing curve, but if we are content to assume the *existence* of a minimizing curve, this is it; there is no other competitor.

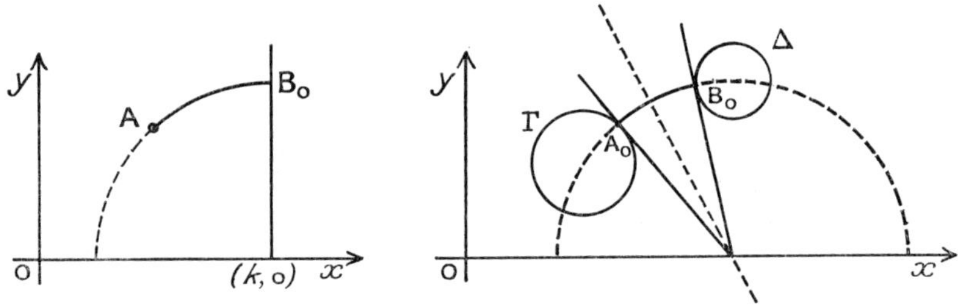

Fig. 4.3*a*

If Γ and Δ are two circles, external to one another, in the upper half-plane, and A lies on Γ and B on Δ, the minimizing curve is an arc of a circle whose centre is the point where the radical axis of the circles meets $y = 0$.

EXAMPLE 2. $$I = \int \frac{1}{\sqrt{y}}\, ds.$$

To find the brachistochrone *with given energy* from a given point A to a given not-horizontal line Δ (cf. §3.7). The required curve is an arc of a cycloid with cusps on the energy level $y = 0$, and the arc cuts the line Δ orthogonally.

The solution is unique. To prove this, let Δ cut the energy level Ox in C, and consider any cycloidal arc K' of the family (Fig. 4.3*b*.) Let the (unique) normal to K' which is parallel to Δ cut Ox in C', and draw through C' a line parallel to CA to meet K' in A'. The position of A' on K' is uniquely determined by this construction, and the uniqueness of the solution of the problem proposed now follows from the properties of similar figures.

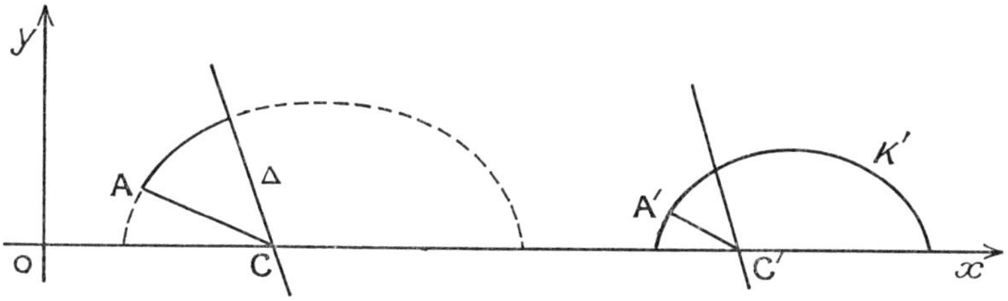

Fig. 4.3*b*

EXAMPLE 3. $$I = \int \sqrt{y}\, ds.$$

To find the minimizing curve from a point on a given vertical line Γ to a given fixed point B. We may take the line Γ to be the axis Oy without loss of generality. The point B is $(\bar{X}, \bar{Y})$, and we will assume $\bar{Y} > \bar{X} > 0$. There are two parabolas through B with Oy as axis and Ox as directrix,

(4.3.11) $$\frac{y}{b} = 1 + \frac{x^2}{4b^2}.$$

The two values of b are given by

(4.3.12) $$4b(\bar{Y} - b) = \bar{X}^2,$$

and we can write the solutions for b in the form

(4.3.13) $$2b = \bar{X}t^2, \qquad 2b = \bar{X}/t^2,$$

where $t > 1$ and

(4.3.14) $$\frac{\bar{Y}}{\bar{X}} = \frac{1}{2}\left(t^2 + \frac{1}{t^2}\right).$$

For the upper parabola K_1, $2b = \bar{X}t^2$, and for the lower parabola K_2, $2b = \bar{X}/t^2$. To determine which of these gives the smaller value to I, let us calculate explicitly the values I_1 and I_2 of I for the arcs K_1 and K_2. If

(4.3.15) $$\frac{y}{b} = 1 + \frac{x^2}{4b^2}$$

then

$$1 + y'^2 = 1 + \frac{x^2}{4b^2} = \frac{y}{b}, \tag{4.3.16}$$

and

$$I = \int \sqrt{y}\, ds = \frac{1}{\sqrt{b}} \int_0^{\bar{X}} y\, dx = \sqrt{b}\left(\bar{X} + \frac{\bar{X}^3}{12b^2}\right). \tag{4.3.17}$$

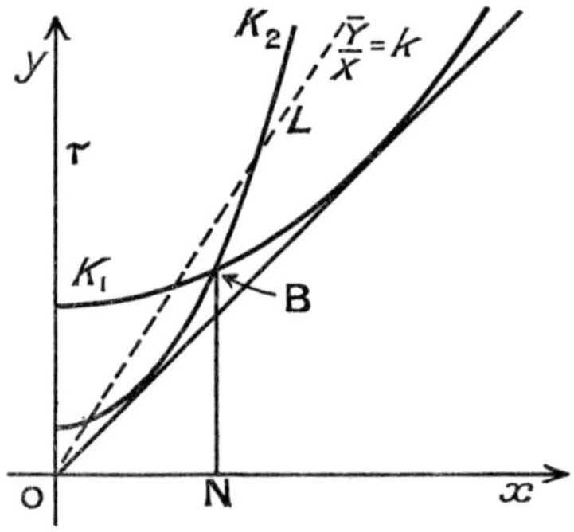

Fig. 4.3*c*

Thus for K_1, when $2b = \bar{X}t^2$, we have

$$I_1 = \frac{1}{3\sqrt{2}} \bar{X}^{3/2}\left(3t + \frac{1}{t^3}\right), \tag{4.3.18}$$

and similarly for K_2

$$I_2 = \frac{1}{3\sqrt{2}} \bar{X}^{3/2}\left(\frac{3}{t} + t^3\right). \tag{4.3.19}$$

Thus

(4.3.20)

$$I_2 - I_1 = \frac{1}{3\sqrt{2}} \bar{X}^{3/2}\left\{t^3 - \frac{1}{t^3} - 3\left(t - \frac{1}{t}\right)\right\} = \frac{1}{3\sqrt{2}} \bar{X}^{3/2}\left(t - \frac{1}{t}\right)^3 > 0,$$

so $I_2 > I_1$, and the *upper* parabola gives the smaller value to I. It is true that we have not proved that this minimizes the integral under the conditions stated; but if we assume the *existence* of a minimizing curve of the form $y = \varphi(x)$, this curve is the parabola K_1.

But now a point of great interest emerges. If we admit to competition a wider class of curves (as in the parametric problem) we can, in some circumstances, find a curve giving a still smaller value to I. Consider Λ the Goldschmidt curve ONB (Fig. 4.3c), and denote the value of I for this curve by I_0. Then

(4.3.21) $$I_0 = \int_0^{\overline{Y}} \sqrt{y}\, dy = \frac{2}{3}\,\overline{Y}^{3/2} = \frac{1}{3\sqrt{2}}\,\overline{X}^{3/2}\left(t^2 + \frac{1}{t^2}\right)^{3/2},$$

and

(4.3.22)
$$I_0 - I_1 = \frac{1}{3\sqrt{2}}\,\overline{X}^{3/2}\left\{\left(t^2 + \frac{1}{t^2}\right)^{3/2} - \left(3t + \frac{1}{t^3}\right)\right\} = \frac{1}{3\sqrt{2}}\,\overline{X}^{3/2} f(t),$$

say, and we are interested in the sign of $f(t)$ for $t \geqslant 1$. Now

(4.3.23) $$f(1) = 2\sqrt{2} - 4 < 0,$$

and

(4.3.24) $$f'(t) = 3\left(1 - \frac{1}{t^4}\right)\{\sqrt{(t^4 + 1)} - 1\} > 0.$$

Thus $f(t)$ steadily increases as t increases, and $f(t)$ is large when t is large, so $I_0 - I_1$ passes just once through the value zero, say at $t = t_0$, as t increases from 1 to ∞. For $t < t_0$, $I_0 < I_1$, and for $t > t_0$, $I_0 > I_1$. Now t_0 is the real positive root of the equation

(4.3.25) $$t^8 - 6t^4 - 3 = 0,$$

and its value is 1·594 . . . For $t = t_0$, $\overline{Y}/\overline{X} = k$, where $k = 1{\cdot}47$ approximately; let the line $y = kx$ be denoted by L (Fig. 4.3c). Then if $\overline{Y}/\overline{X} < k$, i.e. if B lies below L, the Goldschmidt curve Λ gives a smaller value to I than the upper parabola K_1, while if $\overline{Y}/\overline{X} > k$, i.e. if B lies above L, K_1 gives a smaller value than Λ.

4.4 Weierstrass's necessary condition

We now establish a necessary condition for a *strong* relative minimum. When we found necessary conditions for a minimizing curve in §2.3 we used weak variations, namely variations $\alpha\eta(x)$ which are such that both δy and $\delta y'$ tend uniformly to zero with α. Weierstrass observed that if we lift this restriction, and consider a strong variation (in which $\delta y'$ is not necessarily small when δy is small) we can obtain a condition which must be satisfied by any curve giving a strong relative minimum to I.

Let $P(x_0, y_0)$ be a point on an arc without corners of a minimizing curve $y = \varphi(x)$, and let $Q(\xi, \eta)$ be a point of the arc to the right of P (Fig. 4.4a). We denote the segment PQ of the arc by K. Let Γ, $y = \lambda(x)$, be an arbitrary admissible arc through P, and let R be a point on Γ to the right of P whose x-coordinate is α ($\alpha > x_0$). We now construct a one-parameter family of arcs Δ_α joining the points R of Γ to Q the family being so chosen that Δ_α coincides with K when R is at P. For example we can take for Δ_α the arc

$$y = \varphi(x) + \left\{\frac{\lambda(\alpha) - \varphi(\alpha)}{\xi - \alpha}\right\}(\xi - x). \tag{4.4.1}$$

It is clear that if Δ_α is defined by (4.4.1) it has the required properties; Δ_α coincides with K when $\alpha = x_0$, and Δ_α goes through R and Q for all values of α in (x_0, ξ).

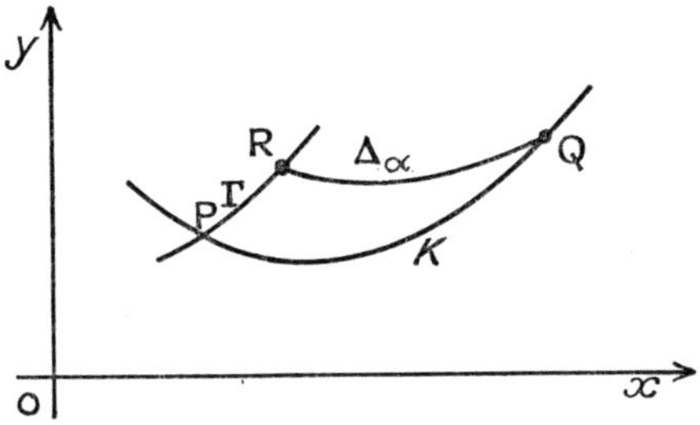

Fig. 4.4a

Now let $\psi(\alpha)$ be the value of I along the path consisting of the segment PR of Γ and the arc Δ_α. A necessary condition for a minimizing curve is $\psi'(x_0) \geqslant 0$. For $\psi'(x_0) < 0$ would imply the existence of a curve of class D_1 joining P to Q and giving to I a smaller value than that given by K. (Of course $\psi'(x_0) < 0$ would also imply that there is a curve of class C_1 giving to I a smaller value than that given by K; this follows from the rounding argument.) Now

$$\psi(\alpha) = I(\Gamma_{PR}) + I(\Delta_\alpha), \tag{4.4.2}$$

and hence, by the variable end-point theorem,

$$\psi'(x_0) = F(x_0, y_0, \varpi) - U(x_0, y_0, p_0) - \varpi V(x_0, y_0, p_0), \tag{4.4.3}$$

where p_0 is the slope of K, and ϖ is the slope of Γ, at P. Hence a necessary condition for a minimizing curve is that, at any element (x, y, y') of an arc of the curve,

$$F(x, y, \varpi) - F(x, y, y') - (\varpi - y')F_{y'}(x, y, y') \geqslant 0 \tag{4.4.4}$$

for all values of ϖ.

The function on the left in (4.4.4) is the *excess function* of Weierstrass, already encountered in §2.6, and we denote it by $E(x, y, y', \varpi)$. The condition

$$E(x, y, y', \varpi) \geqslant 0 \tag{4.4.5}$$

is Weierstrass's necessary condition for a strong relative minimum. It must be satisfied for every element (x, y, y') of the curve for all real values of ϖ.

COROLLARY 1. Since

$$E(x, y, y', \varpi) = \tfrac{1}{2}(\varpi - y')^2 N(x, y, \theta), \tag{4.4.6}$$

where θ lies between y' and ϖ, Weierstrass's condition is certainly satisfied if the problem is regular (§2.7); indeed, we can go further, and observe that in the regular problem $E(x, y, p, \varpi) > 0$ for all unequal values of p and ϖ, so long as (x, y, p) and (x, y, ϖ) lie in R. (We assume, as usual, that R is z-convex.)

COROLLARY 2. We can deduce from Weierstrass's necessary condition another proof of Legendre's necessary condition (§2.11). It is clear, from (4.4.6), that if (x, y, y') is an element of a minimizing curve, Weierstrass's condition implies

$$N(x, y, \theta) \geqslant 0 \tag{4.4.7}$$

for all admissible values of ϖ, and letting $\varpi \to y'$ we find

$$N(x, y, y') \geqslant 0 \tag{4.4.8}$$

since $\theta \to y'$ as $\varpi \to y'$. The condition (4.4.8) is Legendre's necessary condition.

Legendre's condition is a weaker condition than Weierstrass's condition. Legendre's condition is satisfied whenever K provides a weak relative minimum, and it is *a fortiori* satisfied whenever Weierstrass's condition is satisfied. But Legendre's condition may be satisfied when Weierstrass's condition is not.

EXAMPLE 1. Consider the integral

$$I = \int_0^1 (y'^2 + y'^3)\, dx, \tag{4.4.9}$$

where A is (0, 0) and B is $(1, k)$. Here

$$\begin{aligned} E &= (\varpi^2 + \varpi^3) - (y'^2 + y'^3) - (\varpi - y')(2y' + 3y'^2) \\ &= (\varpi - y')^2(1 + \varpi + 2y'), \end{aligned} \tag{4.4.10}$$

and on the line AB

$$E = (\varpi - k)^2(1 + \varpi + 2k). \tag{4.4.11}$$

Weierstrass's necessary condition is not satisfied, and the segment AB is not a minimizing curve. It does not provide even a strong relative minimum. We have noticed this already in the case $k = 0$ (§2.10). Since

$$N = 2 + 6y', \tag{4.4.12}$$

Legendre's necessary condition *is* satisfied on AB if $k > -\frac{1}{3}$, but the segment does not provide a strong relative minimum. (It does in fact provide a weak relative minimum if $k > -\frac{1}{3}$, as we shall see later, in §5.16.)

EXAMPLE 2. Consider the integral

$$I = \int_0^1 (y'^2 - 1)^2\, dx, \tag{4.4.13}$$

where, as before, A is (0, 0) and B is $(1, k)$. Here

$$E = (\varpi - y')^2\{(\varpi + y')^2 + 2(y'^2 - 1)\}, \tag{4.4.14}$$

and on the segment AB

$$E = (\varpi - k)^2\{(\varpi + k)^2 + 2(k^2 - 1)\}. \tag{4.4.15}$$

If $|k| < 1$, Weierstrass's necessary condition is not satisfied, and the line-segment AB is not minimizing. We have noticed already that it

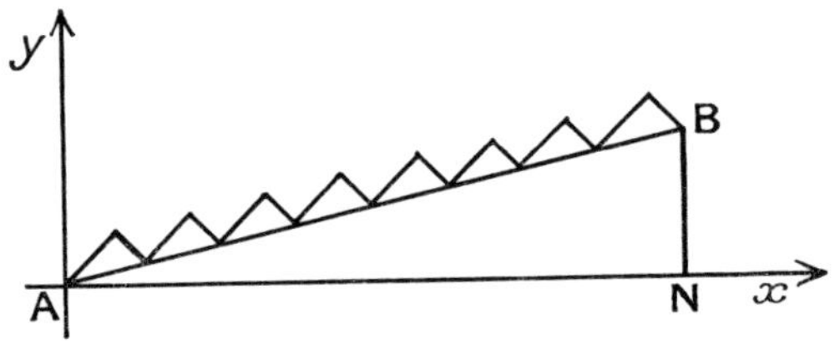

Fig. 4.4*b*

is not minimizing in the sense of an absolute minimum (§3.3), and we now see that it does not provide even a strong relative minimum. This is in fact evident otherwise, since we can construct a curve in the neighbourhood of AB on which $y' = \pm 1$ (Fig. 4.4*b*) and for this curve $I = 0$. Since

$$N = 12(y'^2 - \tfrac{1}{3}), \tag{4.4.16}$$

Legendre's condition is satisfied if $k^2 > \frac{1}{3}$.

EXAMPLE 3. Consider a problem in which

$$F = f(x, y)\sqrt{(1 + y'^2)}, \tag{4.4.17}$$

where $f(x, y) > 0$ for all values of (x, y). Here

$$N = \frac{f(x, y)}{(1 + y'^2)^{3/2}}. \tag{4.4.18}$$

The problem is regular, $N > 0$ for all values of (x, y, y'). Thus $E > 0$ for all values of (x, y) and for all unequal values of y' and ϖ, so the necessary conditions of Legendre and of Weierstrass are amply satisfied. In these circumstances we hardly need to calculate E: actually the value is

(4.4.19)

$$E(x, y, y', \varpi) = \frac{f(x, y)}{\sqrt{(1 + y'^2)}}\{\sqrt{[(1 + \varpi^2)(1 + y'^2)]} - (1 + \varpi y')\},$$

and $E > 0$, in virtue of Cauchy's inequality, if $\varpi \neq y'$.

EXAMPLE 4. In Weierstrass's problem (§3.5)

$$F = x^2y'^2. \tag{4.4.20}$$

Here

$$N = 2x^2, \quad E = x^2(\varpi - y')^2, \tag{4.4.21}$$

and $N > 0$, $E > 0$, if $x \neq 0$ and $\varpi \neq y'$. In §3.5 we considered the particular problem when the end-points are $A(\frac{1}{2}, 0)$ and $B(1, 1)$, and we noticed that there is a unique extremal through A and B. We now see that Weierstrass's necessary condition for a strong relative minimum is satisfied on this extremal. Actually of course we know much more! For we saw that the extremal makes I an absolute minimum, and therefore *a fortiori* it gives a strong relative minimum. Weierstrass's condition gives us no new information in this case.

CHAPTER V

The Fundamental Sufficiency Theorem

5.1 Fields of extremals

We consider the problem of minimizing

$$\int_X^{\bar{X}} F(x, y, y')\, dx, \tag{5.1.1}$$

the end-points being fixed. A field Φ is a simply-connected domain of the (x, y)-plane which is simply covered by a one-parameter family of extremals K_α,

$$y = \varphi(x, \alpha). \tag{5.1.2}$$

The functions φ and φ' have continuous second derivatives in the appropriate region $\mathscr{R}$ of (x, α), which will be defined by equations of the form

$$\alpha_1 < \alpha < \alpha_2, \qquad X(\alpha) < x < \bar{X}(\alpha). \tag{5.1.3}$$

To say that Φ is simply covered by the family means that one and only one of the extremals passes through each point of Φ, and this is true if, as we assume, $\varphi_\alpha(x, \alpha)$ does not vanish in $\mathscr{R}$. Then we can solve the equation (5.1.2) for α as a function of (x, y),

$$\alpha = \lambda(x, y), \tag{5.1.4}$$

and $\lambda \in C_2$ in Φ. Of course (5.1.4) is equivalent to (5.1.2), and the extremals of the family are the curves $\lambda(x, y) =$ constant.

The slope of the extremal of the family through a given point (x, y) of Φ is

$$\varphi'(x, \alpha) = \varphi'\{x, \lambda(x, y)\} = p(x, y), \tag{5.1.5}$$

where $p \in C_2$, and this function $p(x, y)$ is the *slope function* of the field.

Now in the variable end-point theorem

$$dI = U\, dx + V\, dy \Big|_A^B \tag{5.1.6}$$

we assume that the original curve is an extremal, but not necessarily the curve to which it is varied, i.e. in that theorem we contemplate a family of curves $y = \varphi(x, \alpha)$ in which $y = \varphi(x, \alpha)$ is an extremal for

$\alpha = 0$, but not for all values of α. We now turn to the important and interesting case where the curves $y = \varphi(x, \alpha)$ are extremals for all values of α in some domain of α containing $[\alpha_1, \alpha_2]$.

We denote by $I(K_{AB})$ the value of the integral $\int F(x, y, y')\, dx$ taken along an arc AB of an extremal K_α of the field, and we consider how $I(K_{AB})$ varies as A traces out an arc A_1A_2 of a path Γ, and B traces out an arc B_1B_2 of a path Δ (Fig. 5.1). At each stage the

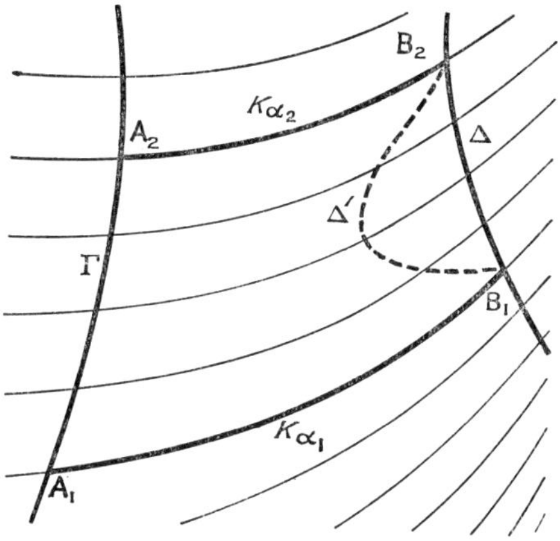

Fig. 5.1

integral is along an arc AB of an extremal of the field, A_1 and B_1 lying on K_{α_1}, and A_2 and B_2 lying on K_{α_2}. We can express the change in $I(K_{AB})$ in terms of the integral $\int U\, dx + V\, dy$ taken along Γ and along Δ; but the coefficients U and V in this line-integral are functions of (x, y, p), and p is a known function of (x, y), so these coefficients are now known functions of (x, y) only, say

(5.1.7) $U\{x, y, p(x, y)\} = u(x, y), \quad V\{x, y, p(x, y)\} = v(x, y),$

and the functions u and v are of class C_2 in Φ. We denote the line-integral $\int u\, dx + v\, dy$, taken along a curve $\mathscr{C}$ in the field, by $H(\mathscr{C})$. The curves $\mathscr{C}$ admitted have continuously turning tangents, except at a finite number of corners; they are not necessarily curves of the form $y = f(x)$.

Now

(5.1.8) $$dI(K_{AB}) = u\, dx + v\, dy \Big|_A^B,$$

whence

(5.1.9) $$I(K_{A_2B_2}) - I(K_{A_1B_1}) = H(\Delta_{B_1B_2}) - H(\Gamma_{A_1A_2}),$$

where $\Delta_{B_1B_2}$ is the arc of Δ from B_1 to B_2, and $\Gamma_{A_1A_2}$ is the arc of Γ from A_1 to A_2; as we have noticed, these curves Γ and Δ may have a finite number of corners.

The formula (5.1.9) is fundamental, and we deduce from it some important and interesting results.

5.2 Hilbert's invariant integral

The first point that emerges is that $H(\Delta_{B_1B_2})$ is a function of the end-points B_1 and B_2 only, independent of the path Δ in the field from B_1 to B_2. For we can change the path from B_1 to B_2 (say from Δ to Δ' in Fig. 5.1) while leaving the other parts of the contour $A_1B_1B_2A_2A_1$ unaltered; three terms in the equation (5.1.9) are unchanged, and therefore the value of the fourth term is unchanged. Thus

$$H(\Delta_{B_1B_2}) = H(\Delta'_{B_1B_2}). \tag{5.2.1}$$

The value of the integral H taken round the closed contour $\Delta_{B_1B_2} + \Delta'_{B_2B_1}$ is zero.

In fact the integral H, taken round any closed contour in the field, has the value zero. To complete the proof we must first show that the integral vanishes for a contour consisting in part of arcs of extremals of the field. This follows from the important observation that along an arc of an extremal of the field $H = I$. This is true because on such an arc $dy = p\,dx$, and

$$\begin{aligned} H &= \int \{F(x, y, p) - pF_{y'}(x, y, p)\}\,dx + F_{y'}(x, y, p)\,dy \\ &= \int F(x, y, p)\,dx = I. \end{aligned} \tag{5.2.2}$$

The fundamental result (5.1.9) can be written as a theorem about the integral H for the closed contour $\mathscr{F}$ made up of

$$K_{A_1B_1} + \Delta_{B_1B_2} + K_{B_2A_2} + \Gamma_{A_2A_1}, \tag{5.2.3}$$

namely

$$H(\mathscr{F}) = 0. \tag{5.2.4}$$

It is now easy to see that H vanishes for any closed contour, with only a finite number of corners, in the field. We express this result in the form

$$\oint u\,dx + v\,dy = 0. \tag{5.2.5}$$

Thus H has the same value for all curves $\mathscr{C}_{PQ}$ joining two given points P and Q in the field; it is *Hilbert's invariant integral.* It follows that the Pfaffian form $u\,dx + v\,dy$ is a perfect differential $d\psi$, and

$$H(\mathscr{C}_{PQ}) = \psi(Q) - \psi(P), \tag{5.2.6}$$

where $\psi(P)$ is the value of ψ at P, and $\psi(Q)$ is the value of ψ at Q.

The curves $\psi =$ constant are called *transversals* of the field. If P and Q lie on the same transversal the integral H taken along the transversal from P to Q (or indeed along any curve in the field from P to Q) is zero. The slope of the transversal at (x, y) is

$$-\frac{u}{v} = -\frac{F(x, y, p) - pF_{y'}(x, y, p)}{F_{y'}(x, y, p)}, \tag{5.2.7}$$

where p is the slope function. In the particular case where F has the form $f(x, y)\sqrt{(1 + y'^2)}$ the slope of the transversal is $-1/p$, and the transversals are the orthogonal trajectories of the extremals of the field.

If in (5.1.8) the curves Γ and Δ are transversals

$$I(K_{A_1B_1}) = I(K_{A_2B_2}). \tag{5.2.8}$$

Some concrete illustrations of fields may help to clarify the ideas.

EXAMPLE 1.

$$F = F(y').$$

The extremals are the straight lines. A very simple way of constructing a field is to take a family of parallel lines not in the direction Oy, and then the field is the whole plane. Or we may take the pencil of lines through a point (x_0, y_0) of the plane, and then the field can be any simply-connected region in the domain $x > x_0$. The invariant integral is $\int d\psi$, where

$$d\psi = \{F(p) - pF'(p)\}\,dx + F'(p)\,dy. \tag{5.2.9}$$

In the first case mentioned, where the extremals of the field are the lines parallel to $y = mx$,

$$\psi = \{F(m) - mF'(m)\}x + F'(m)y. \tag{5.2.10}$$

In the second case, suppose Φ is the first quadrant, $x > 0, y > 0$, and the extremals are the radii through the origin. Then the slope function p is y/x, and

$$d\psi = \left\{F\left(\frac{y}{x}\right) - \frac{y}{x}F'\left(\frac{y}{x}\right)\right\}dx + F'\left(\frac{y}{x}\right)dy = d\left\{xF\left(\frac{y}{x}\right)\right\}, \tag{5.2.11}$$

so

$$\psi = xF\left(\frac{y}{x}\right), \tag{5.2.12}$$

and the transversals are the curves

$$xF\left(\frac{y}{x}\right) = \text{constant.} \tag{5.2.13}$$

As a concrete illustration, if $F = y'^2$,

$$u = -y^2/x^2, \qquad v = 2y/x, \qquad \psi = y^2/x, \tag{5.2.14}$$

and the transversals (Fig. 5.2*a*) are the parabolas

$$y^2 = kx. \tag{5.2.15}$$

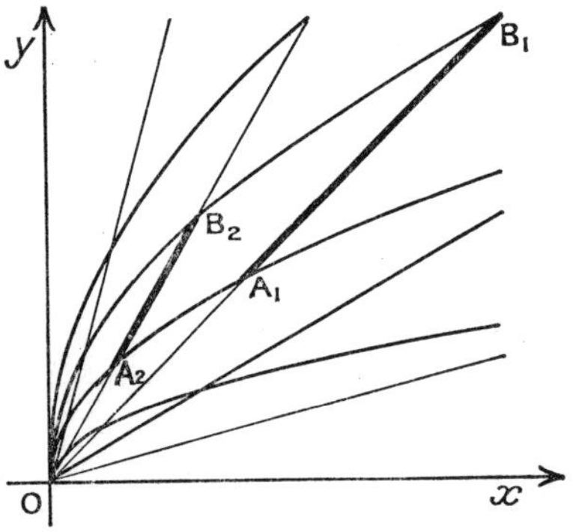

Fig. 5.2*a*

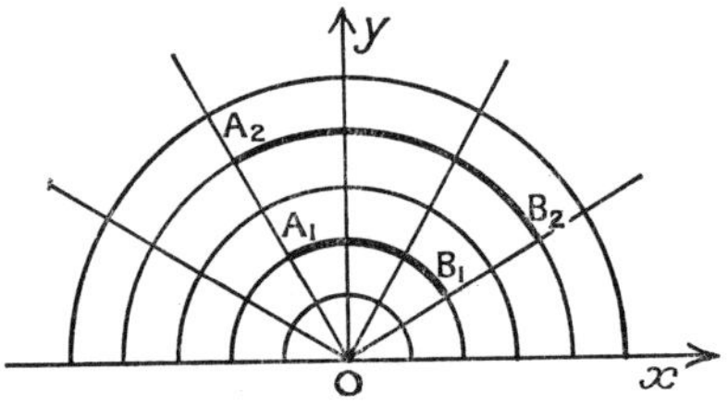

Fig. 5.2*b*

EXAMPLE 2. $\qquad F = \dfrac{1}{y}\sqrt{(1 + y'^2)}.$

The extremals in the upper half-plane $y > 0$ are the semi-circles with centres on Ox (§3.7), and we obtain a field by taking the semi-circles with centres at O. The transversals are the orthogonal trajectories, i.e. the radii through O (Fig. 5.2*b*), and we can foresee that ψ will turn out to be a function of x/y. The slope function p is $-x/y$,

$$U = \frac{1}{y\sqrt{(1 + y'^2)}}, \qquad V = \frac{y'}{y\sqrt{(1 + y'^2)}}, \tag{5.2.16}$$

giving

$$u = \frac{1}{r}, \qquad v = -\frac{x}{yr}, \tag{5.2.17}$$

where $r = \sqrt{(x^2 + y^2)}$, so

$$u\,dx + v\,dy = \frac{y\,dx - x\,dy}{yr} = d\left(\sinh^{-1}\frac{x}{y}\right), \tag{5.2.18}$$

$$\psi = \sinh^{-1}\frac{x}{y}. \tag{5.2.19}$$

The theorem (5.2.8) is obvious in this case from the theory of similar figures.

5.3 The Pfaffian form $u\,dx + v\,dy$

We found in the preceding paragraph that $u\,dx + v\,dy$ is a perfect differential $d\psi$, and it is interesting to verify this fact independently. We have to prove that $\dfrac{\partial v}{\partial x} - \dfrac{\partial u}{\partial y}$ vanishes identically.

For each extremal K_α, $y'' = \varphi''(x, \alpha)$ exists. In terms of the slope function p,

$$y'' = \frac{\partial p}{\partial x} + p\frac{\partial p}{\partial y}. \tag{5.3.1}$$

The result (5.3.1) is evident, but it is easy to construct a formal proof if desired. We have

$$p = \varphi'(x, \lambda), \tag{5.3.2}$$

and

$$\begin{aligned}\frac{\partial p}{\partial x} + p\frac{\partial p}{\partial y} &= \varphi''(x, \lambda) + \varphi_\alpha'(x, \lambda)\lambda_x + \varphi'(x, \lambda)\varphi_\alpha'(x, \lambda)\lambda_y \\ &= \varphi''(x, \lambda) + \varphi_\alpha'(x, \lambda)\{\lambda_x + \varphi'(x, \lambda)\lambda_y\}.\end{aligned} \tag{5.3.3}$$

But also

$$\varphi(x, \lambda) = y \tag{5.3.4}$$

identically, whence

$$\varphi'(x, \lambda) + \varphi_\alpha(x, \lambda)\lambda_x = 0, \tag{5.3.5}$$

$$\varphi_\alpha(x, \lambda)\lambda_y - 1, \tag{5.3.6}$$

and therefore

$$\varphi_\alpha(x, \lambda)\{\lambda_x + \varphi'(x, \lambda)\lambda_y\} = 0. \tag{5.3.7}$$

But $\varphi_\alpha(x, \lambda)$ does not vanish anywhere in the field, so

$$\lambda_x + \varphi'(x, \lambda)\lambda_y = 0, \tag{5.3.8}$$

and in virtue of (5.3.8) the equation (5.3.3) leads to (5.3.1).

Now

$$u = F(x, y, p) - pF_{y'}(x, y, p), \qquad v = F_{y'}(x, y, p), \tag{5.3.9}$$

and therefore

$$\text{(5.3.10)} \quad \frac{\partial v}{\partial x} - \frac{\partial u}{\partial y} = F_{y'x} + F_{y'y'}\frac{\partial p}{\partial x} - F_y$$

$$- F_{y'}\frac{\partial p}{\partial y} + \frac{\partial p}{\partial y}F_{y'} + p\left(F_{y'y} + F_{y'y'}\frac{\partial p}{\partial y}\right),$$

the arguments in the derivatives of F being (x, y, p) throughout. We can write the second member of (5.3.10) in the form

$$\text{(5.3.11)} \qquad F_{y'x} + F_{y'y}y' + F_{y'y'}y'' - F_y$$

where y', y'' refer to the extremal through (x, y), and the arguments in the derivatives of F are (x, y, y'). But (5.3.11) is identically zero, in virtue of Euler's equation (2.2.12), and the required result is established.

5.4 Jacobi's necessary condition for a minimizing curve

We now consider a problem in which the extremals through A have an envelope D. This happens, for example, for the integrals $\int \sqrt{y}\, ds$ and $\int y\, ds$ discussed in §3.8 and §3.9. A point on an extremal through A where it touches the envelope D is said to be *conjugate* to A.

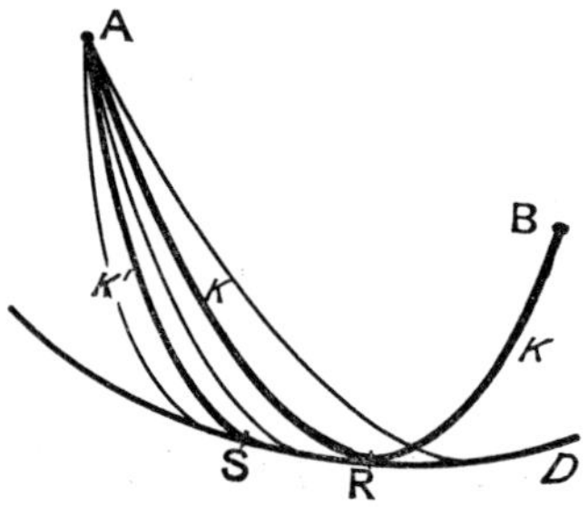

Fig. 5.4

Jacobi's necessary condition is that a minimizing arc K_{AB} (the suffixes denoting the end-points of the arc) cannot contain a point conjugate to A.

To establish Jacobi's condition, let us suppose that the extremal arc K_{AB} touches D at a point R between A and B. We construct the *semi-field* of extremals through A by deleting the part of each extremal beyond its point of contact with D. Let S be a point of D *before* (i.e. to the left of) R (Fig. 5.4). Let K' be the extremal through A touching D at S. (It can happen that D has a cusp at R, and that there is no point S on D before R. In this exceptional case the present proof does not apply.)

Then the integral I along the composite arc

$$K'_{AS} + D_{SR} + K_{RB} \tag{5.4.1}$$

has the same value as it has along the extremal arc K_{ARB}.

To prove this, we notice first that Hilbert's line-integral is invariant for all paths $\mathscr{C}_{AP}$ in the semi-field joining A to a point P lying in, or on the frontier of, the semi-field, and that this invariance still holds if a segment of $\mathscr{C}_{AP}$ coincides with a segment of D, on the frontier of the semi-field. Therefore

$$I(K_{AR}) = H(K_{AR}) = H(K'_{AS}) + H(D_{SR}). \tag{5.4.2}$$

But

$$H(K'_{AS}) = I(K'_{AS}), \tag{5.4.3}$$

since $H = I$ on an extremal, and

$$H(D_{SR}) = I(D_{SR}) \tag{5.4.4}$$

since $y' = p$ on D as well as on an extremal arc. Thus

$$I(K_{ARB}) = I(K'_{AS}) + I(D_{SR}) + I(K_{RB}), \tag{5.4.5}$$

which is the result stated. Bliss describes this as "one of the most interesting and most beautiful theorems in the domain of geometrical analysis."

We easily deduce Jacobi's condition. For suppose that K_{ARB} *is* a minimizing arc. Then the composite arc

$$K'_{AS} + D_{SR} + K_{RB} \tag{5.4.1}$$

is also a minimizing arc, at least for positions of S on D sufficiently near to R. But Euler's equation is a necessary condition for a minimizing arc, and the arc D_{SR} does not satisfy Euler's equation; for the solution of Euler's equation through R, with the given value of y', is unique, and this solution is the extremal K, not the envelope D. Therefore K_{ARB} is not a minimizing arc. Jacobi's condition must be satisfied even for a weak relative minimum.

5.5 The fundamental sufficiency theorem

We have now four necessary conditions that must be satisfied by a minimizing curve. These are (1) du Bois-Reymond's equation and Euler's equation, (2) Legendre's condition, (3) Weierstrass's condition, (4) Jacobi's condition. And in a number of special cases we have been able to construct an *ad hoc* proof that the curve we have found is actually a minimizing curve. But there is a certain sense of frustration at this point, because so far we have not established any general theorem involving *sufficient* conditions. We now turn to a famous theorem of Weierstrass which is the fundamental theorem of this class.

We consider an extremal arc K joining A to B, and we assume that it is *embedded* in a field Φ, i.e. the extremal K is itself one of the extremals of the field. Let Γ be any curve $y = \varphi(x)$ of class D_1 joining A to B and lying in Φ.

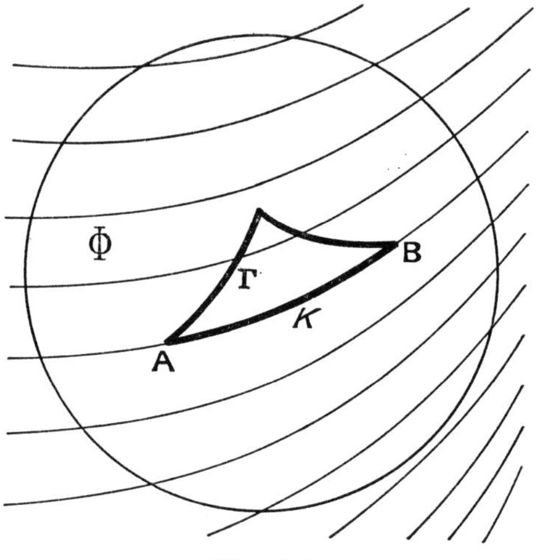

Fig. 5.5

Let us consider the difference $I(\Gamma) - I(K)$. Now

(5.5.1) $$\begin{aligned} I(\Gamma) - I(K) &= I(\Gamma) - H(K) \\ &= I(\Gamma) - H(\Gamma) \end{aligned}$$

so the difference is expressed as an integral along Γ, namely

(5.5.2)

$$\int_\Gamma F(x, y, \varpi)\, dx - \{F(x, y, p) - pF_{y'}(x, y, p)\}\, dx - F_{y'}(x, y, p)\, dy$$

where ϖ is the slope of Γ at (x, y). Now $dy = \varpi\, dx$, so

(5.5.3)

$$I(\Gamma) - I(K) = \int_{\Gamma} \{F(x, y, \varpi) - F(x, y, p) - (\varpi - p)F_{y'}(x, y, p)\}\, dx.$$

The integrand in the second member of (5.5.3) is formed from the excess function $E(x, y, y', \varpi)$ by replacing y' by the slope function $p(x, y)$. We write

(5.5.4) $$E\{x, y, p(x, y), \varpi\} = \mathscr{W}(x, y, \varpi),$$

so that $\mathscr{W}$ is a function of the three independent variables (x, y, ϖ). We notice that $\mathscr{W}$ vanishes if $\varpi = p$, i.e. for any element of an extremal of the field. Now (5.5.3) can be written

(5.5.5) $$I(\Gamma) - I(K) = \int_{\Gamma} \mathscr{W}(x, y, \varpi)\, dx,$$

and we deduce immediately the following result:

The fundamental sufficiency theorem. If

(5.5.6) $$\mathscr{W}(x, y, \varpi) \geqslant 0$$

when (x, y) lies in Φ, and (x, y, ϖ) is any admissible element different from (x, y, p), then

(5.5.7) $$I(\Gamma) \geqslant I(K),$$

i.e. K gives a minimum value to I in the family of curves of class D_1 joining A to B and lying in Φ. If the condition (5.5.6) holds without the equality sign, then

(5.5.8) $$I(\Gamma) > I(K),$$

unless Γ is identical with K.

COROLLARY 1. *A fortiori* K is a minimizing curve if

(5.5.9) $$E(x, y, p, \varpi) > 0$$

for all (x, y) in Φ and all values of ϖ different from p.

This condition is certainly satisfied in the regular problem if we assume, as usual, that R is z-convex. For, as we have noticed already (§4.4),

(5.5.10) $$E(x, y, p, \varpi) = \tfrac{1}{2}(\varpi - p)^2 N(x, y, \theta),$$

where θ is a number lying between p and ϖ. Thus, if

(5.5.11) $$N(x, y, \theta) > 0$$

for all (x, y) in Φ and for all values of θ, then K is a minimizing curve. (The simple special case when the integrand is a function of y' has already been noticed in §3.3.)

COROLLARY 2. The fundamental sufficiency theorem is valid if, instead of a field in which K is embedded, we use the semi-field through A (§3.8). (We notice again, in connexion with this Corollary, that care is needed if, as for the integrals $\int y\,ds$ and $\int \sqrt{y}\,ds$ previously discussed, the extremals through A have an envelope D. In these cases, to construct the semi-field through A, we must erase the parts of the extremals beyond the points conjugate to A.)

To sum up, the position we have arrived at is this. To test the minimizing property of the extremal arc K_{AB} we construct a field Φ (which may be the semi-field through A) in which K is embedded. If $\mathscr{W}(x, y, \varpi) > 0$ in Φ, then K_{AB} gives a smaller value to I than any other curve of class D_1 joining A to B and lying in Φ. The condition $\mathscr{W}(x, y, \varpi) > 0$ is certainly satisfied if $E(x, y, p, \varpi) > 0$ for all values of p and ϖ, and this is true *a fortiori* in the regular problem.

In the following sections we shall apply the fundamental sufficiency theorem to the discussion of minimizing and maximizing curves in some concrete cases.

5.6 A notation for the various conditions

It is sometimes convenient to have names for the various conditions that have appeared.

We denote Weierstrass's sufficient condition

(5.6.1) $$\mathscr{W}(x, y, \varpi) > 0,$$

where (x, y) is a point of the field and ϖ is arbitrary, by W: the condition

(5.6.2) $$E(x, y, p, \varpi) > 0$$

for arbitrary values of p and ϖ, by W_+: and the condition

(5.6.3) $$N(x, y, z) > 0$$

for all (x, y, z) in R (i.e. the regular problem) by L_+.

We use the suffix *minus* to indicate a condition which is concerned with the elements of the curve being considered. Thus Weierstrass's necessary condition

(5.6.4) $$E(x, y, y', \varpi) \geqslant 0,$$

where (x, y, y') is an element of the curve, and ϖ is arbitrary, is denoted by W_-. Legendre's necessary condition

(5.6.5) $$N(x, y, y') \geqslant 0,$$

where again (x, y, y') is an element of the curve, is denoted by L_-.

We notice that

$$(5.6.6) \qquad L_+ \Rightarrow W_+ \Rightarrow W \Rightarrow W_- \Rightarrow L_-,$$

so that L_+ and L_- are the most exacting and the least exacting of these five conditions. If the problem is regular (i.e. if L_+ holds) we need not in general trouble to calculate E and $\mathscr{W}$.

We may use the symbols W_-', L_-' to denote W_-, L_- with the equality sign excluded.

5.7 Problems in which the integrand is a function of y'

The integral to be minimized is

$$(5.7.1) \qquad \int_X^{\bar{X}} F(y')\,dx.$$

The extremals are straight lines. If L is the segment AB we can easily construct a field in which L is embedded; perhaps the simplest way is to take the lines parallel to L. Alternatively we can take the pencil of lines through a point C on BA produced, or we can use the semi-field, the pencil of lines through A (cf. §5.2, Example 1).

Suppose that AB is a segment of the line

$$(5.7.2) \qquad y = mx + h.$$

The slope function for the field of parallel lines is $p = m$: for the pencil through C it is $p = (y - h)/x$ (where we have supposed $0 < X$, and taken C as the point $(0, h)$ in which BA produced cuts Oy): for the semi-field through A it is

$$p = (y - Y)/(x - X).$$

We recall that

$$(5.7.3) \qquad E = F(\varpi) - F(y') - (\varpi - y')F'(y'),$$

and that $\mathscr{W}(x, y, \varpi)$ is obtained from E by substituting for y' the slope function p of the field; and $N = F''(y')$.

Let us consider some simple special cases as follows: (i) $F = y'^2$, (ii) $F = y'^2 + y'^4$, (iii) $F = y'^2 + y'^3$, (iv) $F = (y'^2 - 1)^2$.

In (i) $\mathscr{W} = (\varpi - p)^2$ and $N = 2$, and in (ii) $\mathscr{W} = (\varpi - p)^2 \times \{1 + (\varpi + p)^2 + 2p^2\}$ and $N = 2 + 12y'^2$. In both cases the problem is regular, $N > 0$ for all values of y'; the condition L_+ is satisfied. It does not matter which field we choose to construct, and we do not need to calculate $\mathscr{W}$. The line-segment AB is a minimizing curve. (Actually we can dispense with the fundamental sufficiency theorem in these cases, because the minimizing property of the line-segment is evident from the elementary theorem of §3.3.)

In (iii) the line-segment is not a minimizing curve. Indeed it does not provide even a strong relative minimum, since Weierstrass's necessary condition W_- is not satisfied (§4.4, Example 1).

In (iv), which we have mentioned already (§3.3, Example 2 and §4.4, Example 2), we have

$$\mathscr{W} = (\varpi - p)^2\{(\varpi + p)^2 + 2(p^2 - 1)\}, \quad N = \tfrac{1}{2}(y'^2 - \tfrac{1}{3}). \tag{5.7.4}$$

If A is the origin of coordinates, and AB makes an angle β with Ox, we know that the line-segment *is not* minimizing, and indeed does not provide even a strong relative minimum, if $0 \leqslant \beta < \pi/4$, and *is* minimizing if $\beta \geqslant \pi/4$. To re-examine the case $\beta \geqslant \pi/4$ in the light of the fundamental sufficiency theorem, let us choose for the extremals of the field the lines parallel to AB. Then the slope function p is

$$p = k = \tan\beta, \tag{5.7.5}$$

and

$$\mathscr{W} = (\varpi - k)^2\{(\varpi + k)^2 + 2(k^2 - 1)\}, \tag{5.7.6}$$

and $\mathscr{W} > 0$ since $k \geqslant 1$. It follows from the fundamental sufficiency theorem that the line-segment AB is a minimizing curve.

5.8 The integral $\int f(x, y)\, ds$

Here

$$F = f(x, y)\sqrt{(1 + y'^2)}, \tag{5.8.1}$$

and (as in §4.4, Example 3) we assume $f(x, y) > 0$. Let us suppose that the extremal arc K_{AB} is embedded in a field Φ. We have

$$\begin{aligned} \mathscr{W}(x, y, \varpi) &= E(x, y, p, \varpi) \\ &= \frac{f(x, y)}{\sqrt{(1 + p^2)}}\{\sqrt{[(1 + \varpi^2)(1 + p^2)]} - (1 + \varpi p)\}, \end{aligned} \tag{5.8.2}$$

and

$$N = \frac{f(x, y)}{(1 + y'^2)^{3/2}}\cdot \tag{5.8.3}$$

The condition L_+ is satisfied, and *a fortiori* W_+ is satisfied (as is evident also from Cauchy's inequality). The extremal arc K_{AB} is a minimizing curve.

The geometrical interpretation of E and of N is not without interest. If $y' = \tan\psi$, $p = \tan\theta$, $\varpi = \tan\lambda$, we have

$$E = \frac{f(x, y)}{\cos\lambda}\{1 - \cos(\theta - \lambda)\} \tag{5.8.4}$$

and

(5.8.5) $$N = f(x, y)\cos^3 \psi.$$

A particular case, which has been discussed already in §3.6, is that in which $F = y^n\sqrt{(1 + y'^2)}$. The points A and B lie in the upper half-plane. For the cases $n = -1$, $n = -\frac{1}{2}$, there is a unique extremal through A and B, and it is easy to construct a field in which this extremal is embedded (§3.7). The unique extremal through A and B gives a smaller value to I than does any other curve of class D_1 joining A to B and lying in the upper half-plane.

(i) Consider more particularly the brachistochrone problem, $n = -\frac{1}{2}$. The extremals are represented parametrically by the equations

(5.8.6) $$\begin{cases} x - a = -\frac{1}{2}b(2\psi + \sin 2\psi), \\ \quad\;\; y = \frac{1}{2}b(1 + \cos 2\psi), \end{cases}$$

where $\frac{1}{2}\pi > \psi > -\frac{1}{2}\pi$. One curve of this family goes through A and B; the points A and B serve to determine unique values of a and b. A field can be constructed very simply by fixing a and allowing different values for b. Thus, all the conditions of the fundamental sufficiency theorem are fulfilled, and the cycloidal arc is surely a minimizing arc if A and B are any two points in the upper half-plane.

The matter needs further consideration in the important special case when A lies on the energy level $y = 0$; the particle starts from rest. The integral is an improper integral, since the integrand is infinite at A. We now consider how to complete the proof in this case. (We write the proof for the case when B lies between A and the vertex of the cycloidal arc.)

Let M be the vertex of the cycloidal arc E through A and B, with cusp at A, and let Γ be any other curve $y = \varphi(x)$ in the upper half-plane joining A to B. The tangent to Γ at A must not be horizontal, and we will assume that the angle of slope ψ of Γ near A lies between β and $\frac{1}{2}\pi$, where $0 < \beta < \frac{1}{2}\pi$. Let K be the extremal of the field through a point P of Γ, and let N be the vertex of K, so that N lies on the vertical line through M. We consider now the integral taken along the composite arc $\Gamma_{AP} + K_{PN}$, say

(5.8.7) $$f(P) = I(\Gamma_{AP}) + I(K_{PN}).$$

We shall prove (i) that $f(P)$ varies continuously, and (ii) that $f(P)$ steadily increases, as P moves along Γ from A to B. It will follow that $f(B) > f(A)$, and this implies $I(\Gamma_{AB}) > I(E_{AB})$ since

(5.8.8) $$f(B) - f(A) = I(\Gamma_{AB}) - I(E_{AB}).$$

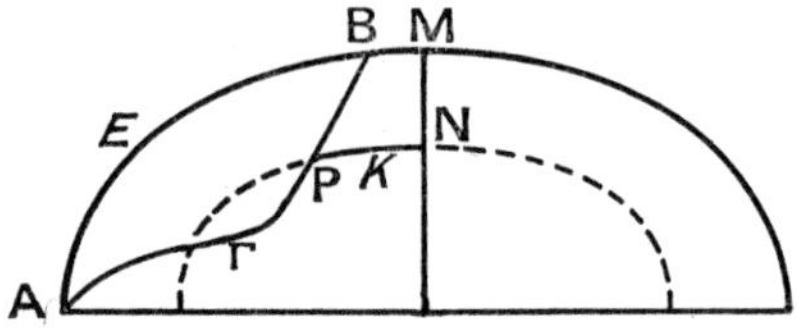

Fig. 5.8*a*

To prove (i), there is no difficulty except at A. The assumption that $\psi > \beta$ when P is sufficiently near to A ensures the convergence of the integral $\int ds/\sqrt{y}$ along Γ. Indeed, if $P(h,k)$ is sufficiently near to A,

(5.8.9) $$I(\Gamma_{AP}) = \int_{\Gamma_{AP}} \frac{1}{\sqrt{y}}\,ds = \int_{\Gamma_{AP}} \frac{1}{\sqrt{y}}\frac{dy}{\sin\psi} < \frac{1}{\sin\beta}\int_0^k \frac{1}{\sqrt{y}}\,dy = \frac{2\sqrt{k}}{\sin\beta},$$

which tends to zero as P tends to A. Further, as in (3.7.13),

(5.8.10) $$I(K_{PN}) = 2\alpha\sqrt{c},$$

where c is the parameter (replacing the parameter b of (5.8.6)) of the cycloid K_{PN}, and α is the angle of slope of this cycloid at P. As P tends to A, $c \to b$ and $\alpha \to \frac{1}{2}\pi$.

Thus as P tends to A, $I(\Gamma_{AP}) \to 0$ and $I(K_{PN}) \to \pi\sqrt{b}$, so

(5.8.11) $$f(P) \to \pi\sqrt{b} = f(A),$$

and this establishes the continuity of $f(P)$ at A.

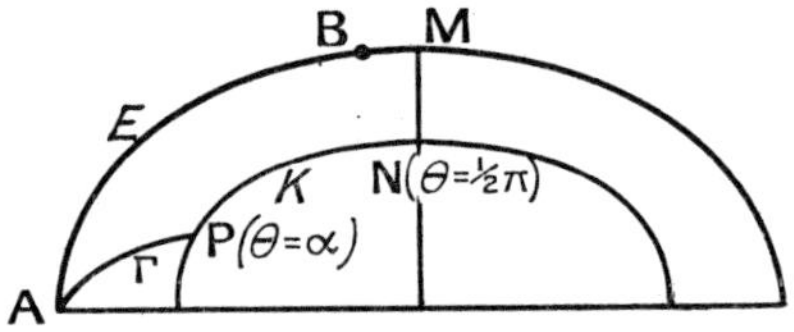

Fig. 5.8*b*

To prove (ii), let P, P' be two points on Γ_{AB}, the order being $APP'B$ Then, denoting by N' the vertex of the extremal K' through P',

(5.8.12) $$\begin{aligned} f(P') - f(P) &= I(\Gamma_{AP'}) + I(K'_{P'N'}) - \{I(\Gamma_{AP}) + I(K_{PN})\} \\ &= I(\Gamma_{PP'}) + I(K'_{P'N'}) - I(K_{PN}) \end{aligned}$$

Now from the fundamental property of the invariant integral H

(5.8.13) $$H(K'_{P'N'}) + H(T_{N'N}) + H(K_{NP}) + H(\Gamma_{PP'}) = 0,$$

where T denotes the vertical line MN. But $H(T_{N'N})$ is zero, since T is a transversal of the field, and thus

(5.8.14) $$I(K'_{P'N'}) - I(K_{PN}) = H(K'_{P'N'}) - H(K_{PN}) = -H(\Gamma_{PP'}).$$

Therefore

$$(5.8.15)\quad f(P') - f(P) = I(\Gamma_{PP'}) - H(\Gamma_{PP'}) = \int_{\Gamma_{PP'}} \mathscr{W}(x, y, \varpi)\, dx > 0,$$

and this completes the proof.

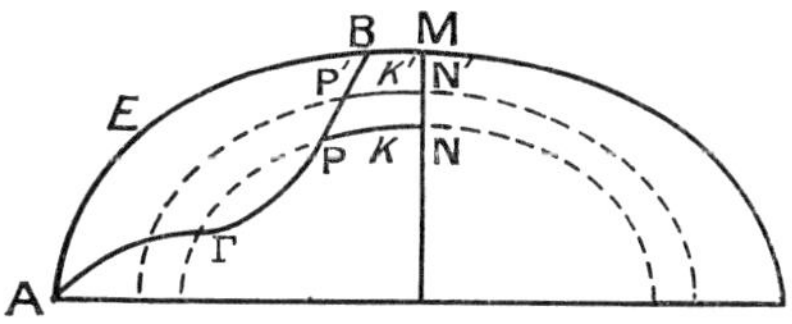

Fig. 5.8*c*

(ii) For the case $n = \frac{1}{2}$,

$$(5.8.16)\qquad F = \sqrt{\{y(1 + y'^2)\}},$$

the extremals through A have an envelope D, and if B lies above D there are two extremals through A and B. We construct the semi-field through A by deleting the parts of the extremals beyond the points of contact with D (Fig. 5.8*d*). Thus the upper parabola through

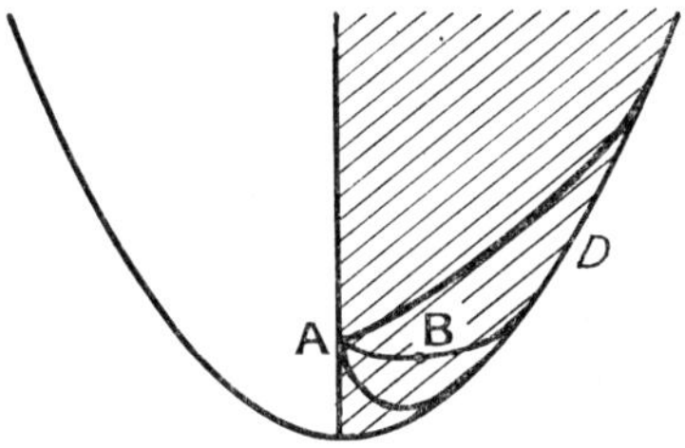

Fig. 5.8*d*

A and B is embedded in the semi-field, and the conditions of the fundamental sufficiency theorem are fulfilled. The upper parabola K_1 through A and B gives to I a smaller value than any other curve of class D_1 joining A and B *and lying above* D. But we must not lose sight of the fact that there may be a curve joining A to B and going below D that gives a still smaller value to I; and in fact in some cases such a curve does exist. We will return to this topic later (§5.17).

The lower parabola K_2 through A and B has a point conjugate to A on AB, so Jacobi's necessary condition is violated, and K_2 does not give even a weak relative minimum.

5.9 Problems arising from Hamilton's principle

We have already discussed a simple problem arising from Hamilton's principle in §3.4; we now reconsider such problems in the light of the fundamental sufficiency theorem. For the simplest dynamical system, a particle moving on a straight line in a field of force, the integral to be discussed has the form

$$I = \int_X^{\bar{X}} \{\tfrac{1}{2}y'^2 - \mathscr{V}(y)\}\, dx. \tag{5.9.1}$$

In this formula x is the time, y is the displacement of the particle (from a fixed origin O on the line) at time x, and $\mathscr{V}(y)$ is the potential function of the field per unit mass. Hamilton's principle assures us that the motion is such that I has a stationary value. The question we wish now to consider is, "Is this value actually a minimum?"

Euler's equation is the familiar equation of motion

$$y'' = -d\mathscr{V}/dy, \tag{5.9.2}$$

and the integrand does not contain x, so we have the first integral $U =$ constant,

$$\tfrac{1}{2}y'^2 + \mathscr{V} = C, \tag{5.9.3}$$

which is of course the integral of energy. Since $N = 1$, the condition L_+ is satisfied, and therefore *a fortiori* the condition W_+, and we need not trouble to calculate the excess function E or the function $\mathscr{W}$ (though, as a matter of interest, we easily find that $E = \tfrac{1}{2}(\varpi - y')^2$ and $\mathscr{W} = \tfrac{1}{2}(\varpi - p)^2$). Thus if we construct a field in which the extremal K_{AB} is embedded, this extremal gives a smaller value to I than any other curve in the field.

In this problem

$$U = -(\tfrac{1}{2}y'^2 + \mathscr{V}), \qquad V = y', \tag{5.9.4}$$

and the theory of the invariant integral tells us that

$$u\, dx + v\, dy = -(\tfrac{1}{2}p^2 + \mathscr{V})\, dx + p\, dy, \tag{5.9.5}$$

where p is the slope function of the field, is a perfect differential $d\psi$.

5.10 The integral $\int(\tfrac{1}{2}y'^2 + cy)\, dx$

In the simple problem of a uniform field, already mentioned in §3.4, $\mathscr{V} = -cy$, and the integral arising from Hamilton's principle is

$$I = \int_X^{\bar{X}} (\tfrac{1}{2}y'^2 + cy)\, dx. \tag{5.10.1}$$

The extremals are, as in (3.4.6),

(5.10.2) $$y = a + bx + \tfrac{1}{2}cx^2,$$

and, as we saw, there is a unique extremal K_0 through A and B. We can easily construct a field in which K_0 is embedded; perhaps the simplest way is to construct the extremals for different values of a, keeping b fixed. Since L_+ is satisfied the integral is a minimum for the actual motion—a conclusion that we have already arrived at independently, by an elementary argument, in §3.4.

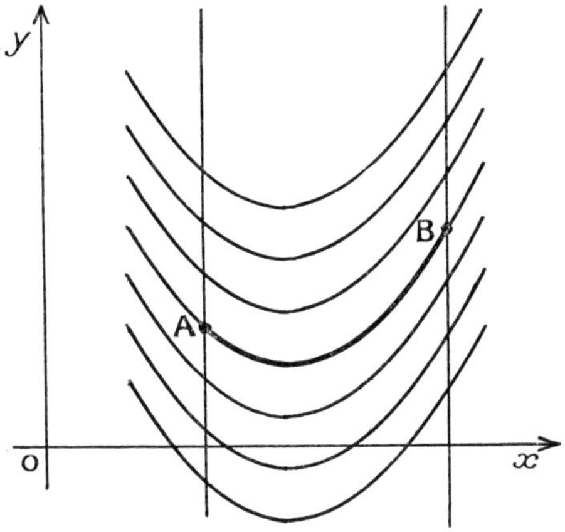

Fig. 5.10

The slope function of this field is

(5.10.3) $$p = b + cx,$$

and therefore the invariant integral is $\int d\psi$, where

(5.10.4) $$d\psi = \{-\tfrac{1}{2}(b + cx)^2 + cy\}\, dx + (b + cx)\, dy,$$

(5.10.5) $$\psi = -\frac{1}{6c}(b + cx)^3 + (b + cx)y.$$

Alternatively, as an illustration, we may use the semi-field through A. Taking A as origin, which involves no loss of generality, the extremals are

(5.10.6) $$y = bx + \tfrac{1}{2}cx^2$$

with b as parameter, and the slope function is

(5.10.7) $$p = \frac{y}{x} + \frac{1}{2}cx.$$

One member of the pencil goes through $(\bar{X}, \bar{Y})$, and there is no envelope. The invariant integral is

$$H = \int \left\{ -\frac{1}{2}\left(\frac{y}{x} + \frac{1}{2}cx\right)^2 + cy \right\} dx + \left(\frac{y}{x} + \frac{1}{2}cx\right) dy \Big\} = \int d\psi \tag{5.10.8}$$

where

$$\psi = \frac{y^2}{2x} + \frac{1}{2}cxy - \frac{1}{24}c^2x^3. \tag{5.10.9}$$

5.11 The integral $\int \frac{1}{2}(y'^2 - y^2)\,dx$

Another familiar problem of elementary dynamics, slightly more intricate than that of the uniform field, is the problem of the harmonic oscillator. The particle is attracted to a point O, the force of attraction being proportional to the distance from O. Here, with an appropriate choice of the unit of time,

$$\mathscr{V} = \tfrac{1}{2}y^2, \tag{5.11.1}$$

and the integral to be discussed is

$$I = \int \tfrac{1}{2}(y'^2 - y^2)\,dx. \tag{5.11.2}$$

Euler's equation is

$$y'' + y = 0. \tag{5.11.3}$$

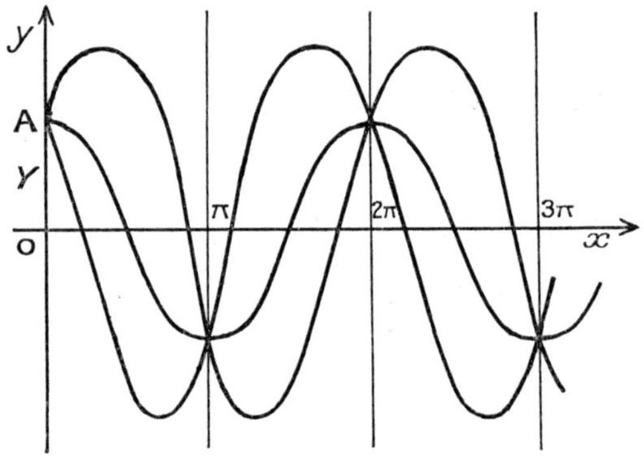

Fig. 5.11*a*

We can put $X = 0$ without loss of generality, and the extremals through $A(0, Y)$ are the curves

$$y = Y\cos x + a\sin x, \tag{5.11.4}$$

where the parameter a is the value of y' at A.

If $\bar{X} < \pi$, all is well. There is a unique extremal from $(0, Y)$ to $(\bar{X}, \bar{Y})$, it is embedded in the semi-field through A, and it is a minimizing curve.

Next, suppose $\bar{X} > \pi$. If $\bar{X}$ is not an integral multiple of π, there is a unique extremal through $(0, Y)$ and $(\bar{X}, \bar{Y})$; but it is not minimizing. In fact all the extremals go through $(\pi, -Y)$, and we should expect this point to have much the same significance as a conjugate point in Jacobi's necessary condition. Let us consider some particular cases.

(i) Let A be the origin and B be $(c, 0)$. The extremals through A are the curves

(5.11.5) $$y = a \sin x,$$

and, unless c is a multiple of π, there is a unique extremal through A and B, namely $y = 0$; the particle rests at O. If $c < \pi$ this does give a genuine minimum, as we noticed above.

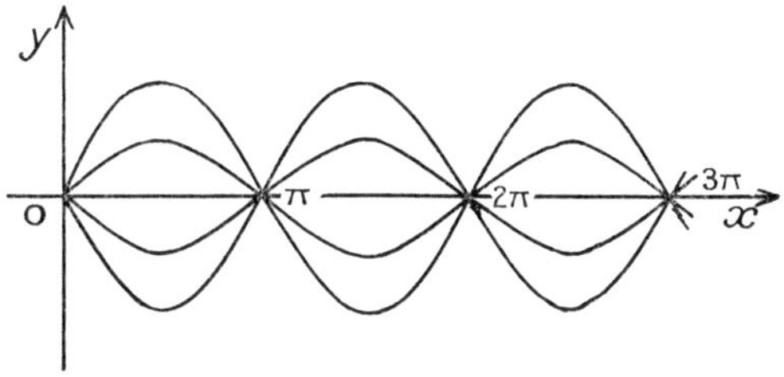

Fig. 5.11*b*

Next, let us suppose that c is greater than π, but that c is not an integral multiple of π. Then the extremal $y = 0$ does not give even a relative minimum for I, and there is no absolute minimum. To prove this, consider the curve Γ

(5.11.6) $$y = a \sin \frac{n\pi x}{c}$$

which passes through A and B. Then

(5.11.7)

$$I(\Gamma) = \tfrac{1}{2}a^2 \int_0^c \left\{ \left(\frac{n\pi}{c}\right)^2 \cos^2 \frac{n\pi x}{c} - \sin^2 \frac{n\pi x}{c} \right\} dx = \tfrac{1}{4}a^2 c \left\{ \left(\frac{n\pi}{c}\right)^2 - 1 \right\}.$$

If $n = 1$, $I < 0$ (since $\pi < c$), and if a is small, y and y' are small, so we have here a weak variation. Thus $I(\Gamma) < I(L)$, where L is the line AB, and L does not give even a weak relative minimum. If a is large, I has a large negative value.

If n is large, I is large and positive, and this can be achieved even if a is small. This is a strong variation. For example if we take $a = \dfrac{1}{\sqrt{n}}$ we have

$$I(\Gamma) = \frac{1}{4}\left(\frac{n\pi^2}{c} - \frac{c}{n}\right), \tag{5.11.8}$$

and $I \to \infty$ with n, although the maximum value of $|y|$ is $1/\sqrt{n}$ and tends to zero. A similar phenomenon has been noticed already, in connexion with the geodesic problem, in §1.7.

(ii) Next, let A be the origin, and let B be $(\frac{1}{2}\pi, 1)$. The extremal K_0 through A and B is

$$y = \sin x. \tag{5.11.9}$$

We can set up the semi-field with the extremals

$$y = a \sin x, \tag{5.11.10}$$

containing the extremal K_0, and covering the strip $0 < x \leqslant \frac{1}{2}\pi$, and (since L_+ is satisfied) the extremal K_0 gives a proper absolute minimum. Hence we derive a simple theorem in the theory of inequalities:

"If $y(0) = 0$ and $y(\frac{1}{2}\pi) = 1$, then

$$\int_0^{\frac{1}{2}\pi} y^2\,dx \leqslant \int_0^{\frac{1}{2}\pi} y'^2\,dx, \tag{5.11.11}$$

with equality only if $y = \sin x$."

The slope function for the semi-field is

$$p = y \cot x \tag{5.11.12}$$

and the invariant integral is

(5.11.13)

$$H = \int -(\tfrac{1}{2}y^2 \cot^2 x + \tfrac{1}{2}y^2)\,dx + y \cot x\,dy = \int d(\tfrac{1}{2}y^2 \cot x),$$

$$\psi = \tfrac{1}{2}y^2 \cot x. \tag{5.11.14}$$

(iii) Finally, let A be the origin, and B be $(\pi, 0)$. The extremals

$$y = a \sin x \tag{5.11.15}$$

form a *quarter-field*, i.e. all the extremals go through A and B, and precisely one of these extremals goes through each point of the strip $0 < x < \pi$. On each of these extremals $I = 0$, and this is less than the value for any curve joining A to B which is not an extremal. Thus we have another theorem in the theory of inequalities:

"If $y(0) = y(\pi) = 0$,

(5.11.16) $$\int_0^\pi y^2\,dx \leqslant \int_0^\pi y'^2\,dx,$$

with equality only if $y = a \sin x$ for some value of a."

(iv) The inequalities established in (ii) and (iii) are Wirtinger's inequalities. It may be of interest to give an independent proof. Take for example the inequality established in (ii). We have

(5.11.17) $$\frac{d}{dx}(y^2 \cot x) = -y^2 \operatorname{cosec}^2 x + 2yy' \cot x$$

and therefore

(5.11.18) $$\int_0^{\frac{1}{2}\pi} (-y^2 \operatorname{cosec}^2 x + 2yy' \cot x)\,dx = 0$$

provided that $y^2/x \to 0$ as $x \to 0$; it will suffice, for example, if $y = O(x)$. Thus

(5.11.19)

$$\int_0^{\frac{1}{2}\pi} (y'^2 - y^2)\,dx = \int_0^{\frac{1}{2}\pi} \{(y'^2 - y^2) - (-y^2 \operatorname{cosec}^2 x + 2yy' \cot x)\}\,dx$$
$$= \int_0^{\frac{1}{2}\pi} (y' - y \cot x)^2\,dx,$$

and therefore

(5.11.20) $$\int_0^{\frac{1}{2}\pi} (y'^2 - y^2)\,dx > 0$$

unless $y = a \sin x$.

The corresponding problem in which the particle is *repelled* from O with a force proportional to the distance from O deserves a brief mention. The integral arising from Hamilton's principle is

(5.11.21) $$\int \tfrac{1}{2}(y'^2 + y^2)\,dx.$$

Euler's equation is

(5.11.22) $$y'' - y = 0,$$

and the extremals (taking $X = 0$, as we may do without loss of generality) are the curves

(5.11.23) $$y = Y \cosh x + a \sinh x.$$

A unique extremal K_0 goes through $(\bar{X}, \bar{Y})$, the parameter a being determined by the equation

$$\bar{Y} = Y \cosh \bar{X} + a \sinh \bar{X}. \tag{5.11.24}$$

This extremal K_0 is embedded in the field whose extremals are defined, for different values of a, by (5.11.23). The value of the integral (5.11.21) along K_0, namely

$$\{(Y^2 + \bar{Y}^2) \cosh \bar{X} - 2Y\bar{Y}\}/(2 \sinh \bar{X}) \tag{5.11.25}$$

is less than the value along any other curve. In this case, of course, the minimizing property of K_0 is easily established without appeal to the fundamental sufficiency theorem (cf. (3.1.5)).

5.12 The integral $\int \left(\frac{1}{2} y'^2 + \frac{1}{y}\right) dx$

This is the problem of a Newtonian attraction to O; with an appropriate choice of the time-scale we have $\mathscr{V} = -1/y$ for $y > 0$. Taking $X = 0$, which involves no loss of generality, the integral is

$$\int_0^{\bar{X}} \left(\frac{1}{2} y'^2 + \frac{1}{y}\right) dx. \tag{5.12.1}$$

Euler's equation is, for $y > 0$,

$$y'' = -\frac{1}{y^2}, \tag{5.12.2}$$

and we have the first integral

$$\tfrac{1}{2} y'^2 = \frac{1}{y} + C. \tag{5.12.3}$$

If $C \geqslant 0$ the particle moves to infinity. Let us be content to discuss the case $C < 0$ for which y is bounded. We write $C = -\dfrac{1}{2a}$, where $a > 0$, and then

$$\tfrac{1}{2} y'^2 = \frac{1}{y} - \frac{1}{2a} = \frac{2a - y}{2ay}. \tag{5.12.4}$$

To find the extremals we introduce a parameter θ and write (cf. Fig. 5.12*a*)

$$y = a(1 + \cos \theta). \tag{5.12.5}$$

We may suppose, without loss of generality, that $\theta' > 0$. If we substitute $a(1 + \cos \theta)$ for y in (5.12.4) we find

$$a^{3/2}(1 + \cos \theta)\theta' = 1, \tag{5.12.6}$$

whence

$$x = a^{3/2}\{(\theta + \sin \theta) - (\alpha + \sin \alpha)\} \tag{5.12.7}$$

where $\theta = \alpha$ initially, so

(5.12.8) $$Y = a(1 + \cos\alpha) = 2a\cos^2\tfrac{1}{2}\alpha,$$

and $-\pi < \alpha < \theta < \pi$. If $\alpha < 0$ the particle is projected away from O. The equations (5.12.5) and (5.12.7) are the parametric equations of an extremal. The curves are somewhat like cycloids (Fig. 5.12*b*). The

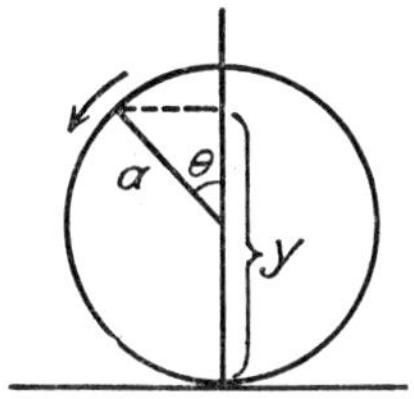

Fig. 5.12*a*

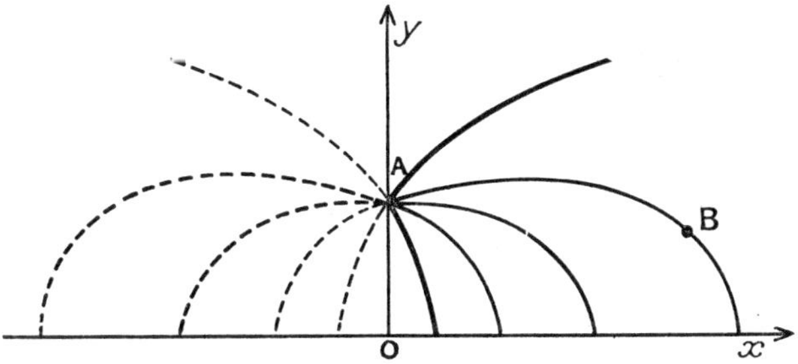

Fig. 5.12*b*

curves for α and $-\alpha$ are mirror images in $x = 0$. The slope of an extremal with parameter α at the point θ is

(5.12.9) $$\frac{dy}{dx} = -\frac{\sin\theta}{\sqrt{a(1+\cos\theta)}} = -\sqrt{\left(\frac{2}{Y}\right)}\cos\tfrac{1}{2}\alpha\tan\tfrac{1}{2}\theta,$$

and at A

(5.12.10) $$\frac{dy}{dx} = -\sqrt{\left(\frac{2}{Y}\right)}\sin\tfrac{1}{2}\alpha,$$

which lies between the limits $\sqrt{\left(\frac{2}{Y}\right)}$ (as $\alpha \to -\pi$) and $-\sqrt{\left(\frac{2}{Y}\right)}$ (as $\alpha \to \pi$). For the limiting case when C has the value zero,

(5.12.11) $$\tfrac{1}{2}y'^2 = \frac{1}{y},$$

and the characteristics are the curves

(5.12.12) $$2y^3 = 9(x \pm b)^2,$$

where $b = \sqrt{(2Y^3/9)}$. These limiting curves are shown by a firm line in Fig. 15.12*b*. In the sector bounded by the limiting curves we have a semi-field, and the extremals are minimizing curves compared with other curves in the sector.

It is almost evident on physical grounds that one and only one extremal of the family goes through each point of the sector, but a formal proof is easily constructed by proving that for any fixed positive value of x, $dy/d\alpha < 0$ for all values of y. We have

(5.12.13) $$dy = (1 + \cos\theta)\,da - a\sin\theta\,d\theta,$$

and from the equations $dY = dx = 0$ (since we are considering a fixed value of x) we have also

$$0 = \frac{da}{a} - \frac{\sin \alpha \, d\alpha}{1 + \cos \alpha}, \tag{5.12.14}$$

$$0 = \frac{3}{2}\frac{da}{a} + \frac{(1 + \cos \theta)\, d\theta - (1 + \cos \alpha)\, d\alpha}{(\theta + \sin \theta) - (\alpha + \sin \alpha)}. \tag{5.12.15}$$

From these three equations, eliminating da and $d\theta$, we find

$$\frac{dy}{d\alpha} = \frac{1}{2} a \tan\frac{\alpha}{2} \tan\frac{\theta}{2} \{f(\theta) - f(\alpha)\}, \tag{5.12.16}$$

where

$$f(\theta) = 2\frac{(1 + \cos \theta)^2}{\sin \theta} + 3(\theta + \sin \theta). \tag{5.12.17}$$

We notice that

$$f'(\theta) = -\frac{(1 + \cos \theta)^2}{1 - \cos \theta} < 0, \tag{5.12.18}$$

and the graph of $f(\theta)$ is as shown in Fig. 5.12c. Taking separately the

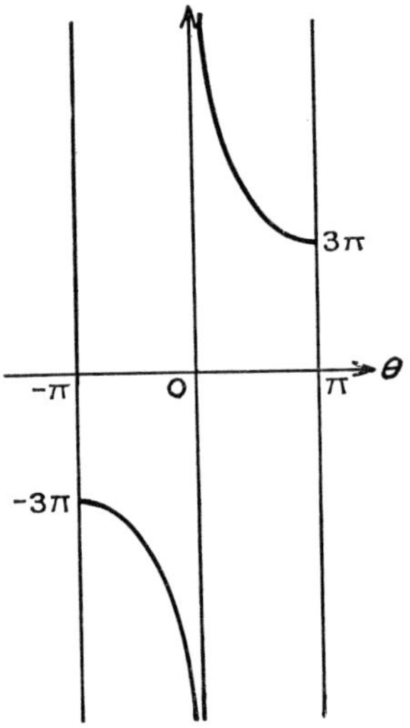

Fig. 5.12c

three cases

$$\begin{cases} \alpha < \theta < 0, & f(\theta) - f(\alpha) < 0, \\ \alpha < 0 < \theta, & f(\theta) - f(\alpha) > 0, \\ 0 < \alpha < \theta, & f(\theta) - f(\alpha) < 0, \end{cases} \tag{5.12.19}$$

and in each case therefore, from (5.12.16), $dy/d\alpha < 0$, and this completes the proof.

5.13 The integral $\int y^2(1 + y'^2)\,dx$

We take the (fixed) end-points as $A(-1, \beta)$ and $B(1, \gamma)$. We suppose A and B to lie on the same side of the x-axis, say in the upper half-plane, and we assume for definiteness that B is higher than A, so that $0 < \beta < \gamma$. Euler's equation can be written

$$y\left\{\frac{d}{dx}(yy') - 1\right\} = 0. \tag{5.13.1}$$

The extremals are the rectangular hyperbolas

$$(x - a)^2 - y^2 = k, \tag{5.13.2}$$

and the straight lines $y = 0$ and $y' = \pm 1$. If $k > 0$ we have a "steep" hyperbola, with $|y'| > 1$, and if $k < 0$ we have a "gentle" hyperbola, with $|y'| < 1$. We consider curves joining A to B and lying in the region $y \geqslant 0$. The fact that V is continuous at a corner shows that a corner on a minimizing curve must lie on $y = 0$. Since $N = 2y^2$, the condition L_+ is satisfied in the upper half-plane $y > 0$, so an extremal that can be embedded in a field is surely a minimizing curve.

If the hyperbola (5.13.2) goes through A and B we have

$$(-1 - a)^2 - \beta^2 = k, \qquad (1 - a)^2 - \gamma^2 = k, \tag{5.13.3}$$

whence

$$a = -\tfrac{1}{4}(\gamma^2 - \beta^2), \tag{5.13.4}$$

and

$$k = \left\{1 - \left(\frac{\gamma + \beta}{2}\right)^2\right\}\left\{1 - \left(\frac{\gamma - \beta}{2}\right)^2\right\}. \tag{5.13.5}$$

If we distinguish the various cases by reference to a subsidiary diagram in which β and γ are rectangular coordinates, we see that the domain $0 < \beta < \gamma$ is divided into four regions (Fig. 5.13a) with the following properties. In the region 1, $k > 0$ and $a < -1$; in the region 2, $k < 0$ and $a < -1$; in the region 3, $k < 0$ and $a > -1$; in the region 4, $k > 0$ and $a > -1$. For (β, γ) in the region 1, there is a steep hyperbolic arc through A and B; for (β, γ) in the region 2 or the region 3, there is a gentle hyperbolic arc through A and B. The troublesome case arises when (β, γ) is in the region 4; then there are two disjoint arcs of a steep hyperbola, one through A and one through B (Fig. 5.13c).

Consider for definiteness a point (β, γ) in the region 3. The minimizing curve is the gentle hyperbolic arc shown. To construct a field in the region $-1 \leqslant x \leqslant 1, y > 0$, we use the hyperbolas (5.13.2) for positive values of k, and the straight lines with $y' = \pm 1$, as in Fig. 5.13b. The hyperbolic arc AB is a minimizing curve.

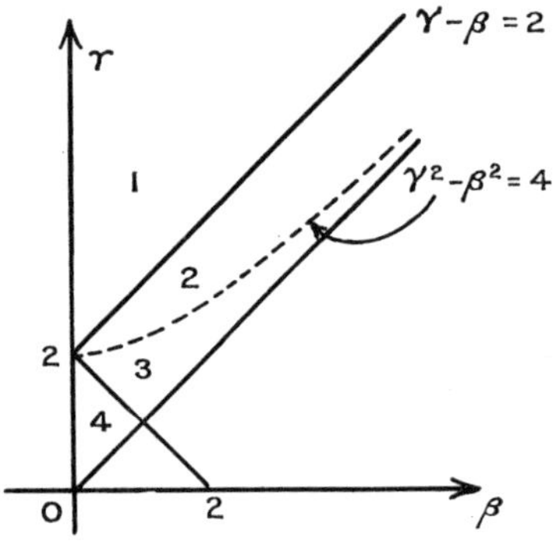

Fig. 5.13a

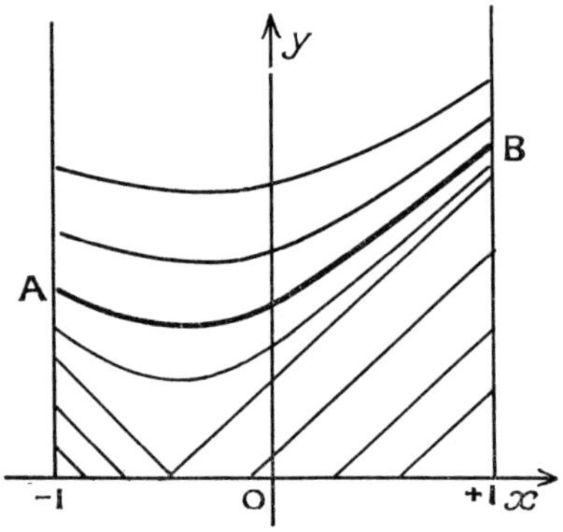

Fig. 5.13b

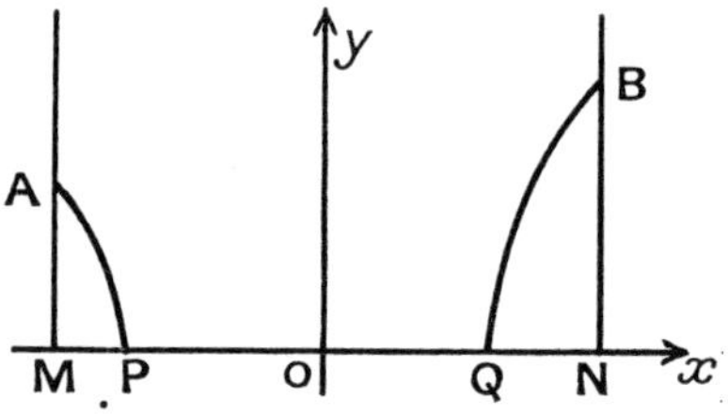

Fig. 5.13c

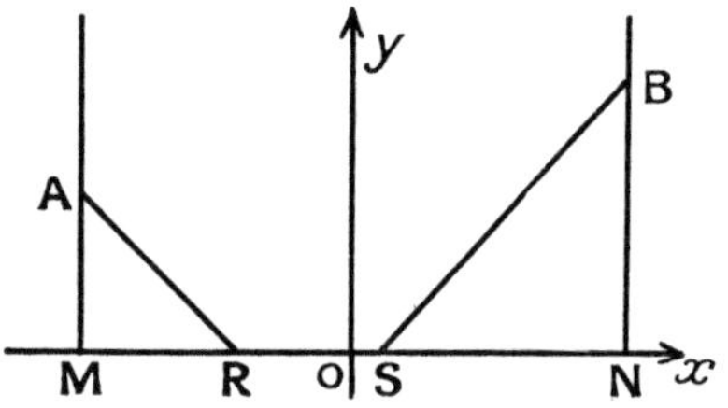

Fig. 5.13d

A word may be added about the troublesome case, $\beta + \gamma < 2$. For the composite curve $APQB$ (Fig. 5.13c) consisting of two hyperbolic arcs (not necessarily arcs of the same hyperbola) and the line-segment PQ, the integral is convergent, in spite of the fact that the tangents to the arcs at P and Q are vertical; but in fact the broken line $ARSB$ (Fig. 5.13d) gives a still smaller value to I. Perhaps the simplest proof of this comes from considering how the integral along a hyperbolic arc AP of this type varies if A is supposed fixed, and the distance MP $(= \xi)$ is supposed variable, $0 < \xi \leqslant \beta$. For the moment we take M as origin, and the arc as

(5.13.6) $$(x - b)^2 - y^2 = c^2, \qquad (b > c > 0).$$

Then

(5.13.7) $$\xi = b - c, \quad \beta^2 = b^2 - c^2 = \xi(b + c), \quad c = \frac{1}{2}\left(\frac{\beta^2}{\xi} - \xi\right).$$

The integral along the arc AP is

$$I(\xi) = \int_0^{b-c} \{2(x-b)^2 - c^2\}\,dx \tag{5.13.8}$$

$$= \tfrac{1}{3}(b-c)(2b^2 + 2bc - c^2)$$

$$= \frac{1}{4}\frac{\beta^4}{\xi} + \frac{1}{2}\beta^2\xi - \frac{1}{12}\xi^3.$$

$$= \frac{1}{12\xi}\{12\beta^4 - (3\beta^2 - \xi^2)^2\}, \tag{5.13.9}$$

and the integral has its least value, $\frac{2}{3}\beta^3$, when $\xi = \beta$, i.e. for the line-segment AR. The fact that the integral for the broken line $ARSB$ is less than the integral for the composite arc $APQB$ now follows easily.

5.14 The integral $\int\sqrt{\{y(1-y'^2)\}}\,dx$

This integral has already appeared in §3.10, and we are now in a position to prove the statement made there, that the parabolic extremal gives a maximum value to I in comparison with other curves of class D_1 in the appropriate region $y \geqslant 0$, $|y'| \leqslant 1$. For this problem

$$U = \sqrt{\left(\frac{y}{1-y'^2}\right)}, \qquad V = -y'\sqrt{\left(\frac{y}{1-y'^2}\right)}, \tag{5.14.1}$$

and

$$E = \sqrt{\left(\frac{y}{1-y'^2}\right)}[\sqrt{\{(1-\varpi^2)(1-y'^2)\}} - (1-\varpi y')], \tag{5.14.2}$$

and $E < 0$ if $y > 0$, $-1 < y' < 1$, $-1 < \varpi < 1$, $\varpi \neq y'$. If A and B lie in the upper half-plane there is a unique extremal through A and B of the form

$$4b(b-y) = (x-a)^2, \tag{5.14.3}$$

and we easily construct a field in which this extremal is embedded by taking the extremals (5.14.3) with a fixed and for varying values of b. It is clear therefore that the extremal arc is maximizing in the family of curves of class D_1 in the sector $x \geqslant y \geqslant 0$. For this field the slope function is

$$p = -\frac{x-a}{r+y}, \tag{5.14.4}$$

where $r^2 = (x-a)^2 + y^2$. The Hilbert integral is

$$H = \frac{1}{\sqrt{2}}\int \sqrt{(r+y)}\,dx + \sqrt{(r-y)}\,dy, \tag{5.14.5}$$

and the Pfaffian form

$$(5.14.6)\qquad \frac{1}{\sqrt{2}}\{\sqrt{(r+y)}\,dx+\sqrt{(r-y)}\,dy\}$$
$$= d\left\{\frac{\sqrt{2}}{3}(r-y)^{3/2}+\sqrt{2}y(r-y)^{1/2}\right\}.$$

The parabolic arc is still maximizing in the important special case when A and B lie *on* the x-axis; let us suppose for definiteness that A is $(0, 0)$ and B is $(\bar{X}, 0)$. We can use the field just introduced, or, alternatively, we can use the semi-field through A, which is defined, as in (3.10.7), by the equation

$$(5.14.7)\qquad y = x - \frac{x^2}{4b}, \qquad (b > 0),$$

and for the extremal through B the value of b is $\frac{1}{4}\bar{X}$. We have here the anomalous case in which all the extremals of the semi-field have the same tangent at A. The slope function of the semi-field is

$$(5.14.8)\qquad p = -\frac{x-2y}{x},$$

and the Pfaffian form $u\,dx + v\,dy$ is

$$(5.14.9)\qquad \frac{x}{2\sqrt{(x-y)}}\,dx + \frac{x-2y}{2\sqrt{(x-y)}}\,dy,$$

and this, as we expect, is a perfect differential

$$(5.14.10)\qquad d\{\tfrac{1}{3}(x+2y)\sqrt{(x-y)}\}.$$

The value of the integral along the extremal from A to B is $\frac{1}{3}\bar{X}^{3/2}$, and this is the maximum value of I for curves in the sector $x \geqslant y \geqslant 0$. The minimum value of I, namely zero, is given by the line-segment AB (and also, if we admit curves of class D_1, by a broken line such as the broken line AMB in Fig. 3.10). For this problem the domain R is defined by

$$(5.14.11)\qquad y > 0, \qquad -1 < y' < 1,$$

and the maximizing curve has end-points whose elements lie on the frontier of R. The elements of the minimizing curves lie wholly or partly on the frontier of R.

5.15 The construction of a field in a neighbourhood of a given extremal

In order to apply the fundamental sufficiency theorem to a concrete problem we need to construct a field in which one extremal is the extremal under examination, and this we have done in a number of particular examples. We now turn to the less ambitious problem of finding sufficient conditions for a *relative* minimum. In this context we shall consider the arc AB of a regular extremal K_0; the elements of K_0 all satisfy the condition $N(x, y, y') > 0$ (cf. §2.7). Now, by a known property of differential equations, a regular extremal can be embedded in a two-parameter family of extremals $y = \psi(x, a, b)$, the arc K_0 itself being the member of this family defined by particular values, say (a_0, b_0), of (a, b). Our object is to pick out from this two-parameter family a one-parameter family simply covering a neighbourhood of the arc AB of K_0. The fundamental result that we need is contained in the following lemma.

LEMMA. *If the arc AB of the regular extremal K_0 contains no point conjugate to A, then there is a positive number ε such that K_0 can be embedded in a field covering the region Φ,*

(5.15.1) $$X \leqslant x \leqslant \overline{X}, \quad |\delta y| < \varepsilon.$$

It is to be understood that the arc AB in this enunciation is taken closed, so $N(x, y, y') > 0$ for all elements of the arc, including those at the ends; and B itself, as well as the points of K_0 between A and B, is precluded from being conjugate to A. The first condition is the condition we have called L_-' in §5.6, i.e. it is Legendre's necessary condition strengthened by the exclusion of the equality sign. The second condition is Jacobi's necessary condition.

To begin with, let us consider the pencil of extremals through a point $R(\xi, \eta)$. Let these extremals be the curves K_α, $y = \varphi(x, \alpha)$, where $\varphi \in C_2$, and α lies in a certain interval (α_1, α_2); the parameter α might be, for example, the slope of the extremal at R. Let us suppose that this family of extremals has an envelope D. Then, by a well-known result in the theory of envelopes, the points of contact of K_α with D are given by the roots (other than ξ) of the equation

(5.15.2) $$\varphi_\alpha(x, \alpha) = 0.$$

On an arc of K_α containing no point conjugate to R, $\varphi_\alpha(x, \alpha)$ does not vanish.

We can express the condition (5.15.2), giving the points on K_α conjugate to R, in another and (for our present purpose) more convenient form. The extremals, determined by the integration of Euler's equation, are defined by the two-parameter family

(5.15.3) $$y = \psi(x, a, b),$$

where $\psi \in C_2$, and (a, b) lies in a certain domain. For the one-parameter family through (ξ, η),

$$\eta = \psi(\xi, a, b), \tag{5.15.4}$$

and we can regard this equation (5.15.4) as defining b as a function of a. If the particular extremal K_0 under examination is

$$y = \psi(x, a_0, b_0), \tag{5.15.5}$$

b is defined by (5.15.4) as a function of a, of class C_2, taking the value b_0 at a_0, and defined for values of a near a_0, provided that

$$\psi_b(\xi, a_0, b_0) \neq 0, \tag{5.15.6}$$

and we shall assume that this condition is fulfilled.

Let us now express the equation (equivalent to (5.15.2)) for the points on K_0 conjugate to R in terms of the function ψ. We have

$$\psi_a(x, a_0, b_0) + \psi_b(x, a_0, b_0)b_0' = 0, \tag{5.15.7}$$

subject to

$$\psi_a(\xi, a_0, b_0) + \psi_b(\xi, a_0, b_0)b_0' = 0, \tag{5.15.8}$$

where b_0' is the value of db/da at $a = a_0$. Thus the points on K_0 conjugate to R are given by the values of x (other than ξ) which satisfy

$$u(x, \xi) \equiv \begin{vmatrix} \psi_a(x, a_0, b_0) & \psi_b(x, a_0, b_0) \\ \psi_a(\xi, a_0, b_0) & \psi_b(\xi, a_0, b_0) \end{vmatrix} = 0, \tag{5.15.9}$$

a fact which we have noticed already in another context in §2.13. We notice that the equation (5.15.9) has the form

$$u(x, \xi) \equiv l\psi_a(x, a_0, b_0) + m\psi_b(x, a_0, b_0) = 0, \tag{5.15.10}$$

and on an arc of K_0 containing no point conjugate to R, $u(x, \xi)$ does not vanish.

We suppose now that K_0 is a regular extremal through A and B, and that the arc AB contains no point conjugate to A. Consider a variable point P on K_0, and let the points on K_0 conjugate to P be $Q_1, Q_2, \ldots$ When P is at A, the points $Q_1, Q_2, \ldots$ lie outside the arc AB, and as P moves to the left from A, say to R, the points conjugate to R will still lie outside the arc AB provided that R is not too far from A. Thus if R is the point (ξ, η), $u(x, \xi)$ does not vanish for $X \leqslant x \leqslant \overline{X}$.

To prove formally that such a point R exists we notice first that $u'(\theta, \theta)$ does not vanish at any point $x = \theta$ of the regular extremal K_0

(§2.13), and in particular that $u'(X, X) \neq 0$. We now choose a number ε such that $u'(x, \xi)$ is different from zero for every pair (x, ξ) in the region

(5.15.11) $$X - \varepsilon \leqslant x \leqslant X + \varepsilon, \qquad X - \varepsilon \leqslant \xi \leqslant X.$$

Then $u(x, \xi)$ vanishes on the line $x = \xi$ (when $X - \varepsilon \leqslant \xi \leqslant X$) and has its derivative $u'(x, \xi)$ different from zero (and therefore always of the same sign) throughout the interval $\xi \leqslant x \leqslant X + \varepsilon$, so $u(x, \xi)$ does not vanish in $\xi < x \leqslant X + \varepsilon$. But also $u(x, X)$ does not vanish in the region $X + \varepsilon \leqslant x \leqslant \bar{X}$, and $u(x, \xi)$ has the same property if ξ is sufficiently near to X. Thus we can find a value ξ less than X such that $u(x, \xi)$ is different from zero in the closed interval $[X, \bar{X}]$.

Let us suppose for definiteness that $u(x, \xi) > 0$ in $[X, \bar{X}]$. We now consider the one-parameter family of extremals K_α,

$$y = \varphi(x, \alpha) = \psi(x, a_0 + l\alpha, b_0 + m\alpha),$$

so that the extremal K_0 is embedded in the family and corresponds to $\alpha = 0$. Now

(5.15.12) $$\varphi_\alpha(x, 0) = l\psi_a(x, a_0, b_0) + m\psi_b(x, a_0, b_0) = u(x, \xi),$$

and therefore

(5.15.13) $$\varphi_\alpha(x, 0) > 0$$

in $X \leqslant x \leqslant \bar{X}$. But $\varphi_\alpha(x, \alpha)$ is a continuous function of its two arguments, and we can find a positive number η such that

(5.15.14) $$\varphi_\alpha(x, \alpha) > 0$$

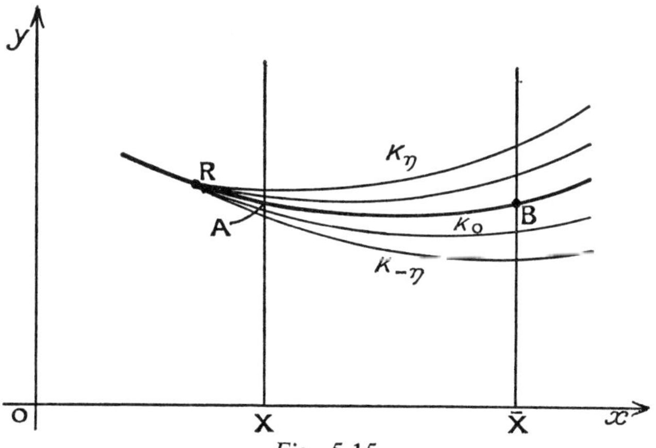

Fig. 5.15

in the region

(5.15.15) $$X \leqslant x \leqslant \bar{X}, \quad |\alpha| < \eta.$$

The members of the family $y = \varphi(x, \alpha)$, for $-\eta < \alpha < \eta$, are the extremals of a field in a neighbourhood of the arc AB of K_0. For consider the region Φ_1 bounded by the vertical lines $x = X$, $x = \overline{X}$, and by the extremals K_η and $K_{-\eta}$ (Fig. 5.15). For any fixed value of x in $[X, \overline{X}]$, $\varphi(x, \alpha)$ increases steadily as α increases from $-\eta$ to $+\eta$, and precisely one extremal of the family passes through each point of Φ_1. But Φ_1 contains a region Φ of the form (5.15.1), and this completes the proof of the lemma.

COROLLARY. An immediate corollary is that, if the *problem* is regular (§2.7), and if K_{AB} is an extremal arc containing no point conjugate to A, then K_{AB} *gives for I a strong relative minimum* (cf. §3.3). For the arc K_{AB} satisfies the conditions of the lemma, and we can construct a field Φ in the neighbourhood of K_{AB} in which K_{AB} is embedded. Then K_{AB} is a minimizing curve in comparison with other curves in Φ in virtue of Corollary 1, §5.5.

5.16 Sufficient conditions for a weak relative minimum

We have the following simple theorem:

THEOREM. *If K_{AB} is an extremal arc which is regular, and which contains no point conjugate to A, then K_{AB} gives a weak relative minimum for I.*

To prove this result, we begin by constructing a field Φ in the neighbourhood of K_{AB}, as in the lemma of §5.15. Then we choose a neighbourhood Θ of the elements (x, y, y') of K_{AB} with the following properties: (i) Θ is z-convex, (ii) if $(x, y, z) \in \Theta$ then $(x, y) \in \Phi$, (iii) if $(x, y, z) \in \Theta$, then $N(x, y, z) > 0$. Then K_{AB} gives a smaller value to I than any other curve Γ_{AB} whose elements lie in Θ, since

$$E(x, y, p, \varpi) = \tfrac{1}{2}(\varpi - p)^2 N(x, y, q) > 0, \tag{5.16.1}$$

where p is the slope function of the field Φ, and q lies between p and ϖ. The result follows from (5.5.3). These are weak variations, since the variation of y' is small as well as the variation of y.

We consider some simple applications of the theorem just proved.

EXAMPLE 1. Consider again the integral

$$\int_0^1 (y'^2 + y'^3)\, dx, \tag{5.16.2}$$

where A is (0, 0) and B is (1, 0) as in §2.10. On the segment AB, $N = 2$, so the condition L_-' is fulfilled. The segment furnishes a weak relative minimum (as indeed we have noticed already). Of course in this simple case, where the extremals are straight lines, there is no question of the extremals through A having an envelope, and moreover we do not need the lemma of §5.15 for the construction of a field—for example, we can use the lines parallel to AB.

If A is $(0, 0)$ and B is $(1, k)$, the value of N on the segment AB is $2 + 6k$, and the segment provides a weak relative minimum if $k > -\frac{1}{3}$ (cf. §4.4).

EXAMPLE 2. Let

$$I = \int_0^1 (y'^2 - 1)^2 \, dx, \tag{5.16.3}$$

where A is $(0, 0)$ and B is $(1, k)$, where $k \geqslant 0$. The line AB makes an angle β with Ox, where $\tan \beta = k$. We have discussed this integral already (§§3.3, 4.4, 5.7). We know that L, the line-segment AB, is a minimizing curve if $k \geqslant 1$. We know also that L is not a minimizing curve, and indeed that it does not give even a strong relative minimum, if $0 \leqslant k < 1$ (§4.4, Example 2).

The question that remains unanswered is this: "Does L give a *weak* relative minimum if $0 \leqslant k < 1$, i.e. if $0 \leqslant \beta < \pi/4$?" The answer is affirmative if $\pi/6 < \beta < \pi/4$, negative if $0 \leqslant \beta \leqslant \pi/6$.

To prove these statements we notice first that for an element of L,

$$N = 12(k^2 - \tfrac{1}{3}), \tag{5.16.4}$$

and we then consider three cases as follows.

(*a*) If $\pi/6 < \beta < \pi/4$ (i.e. if $1/\sqrt{3} < k < 1$), $N > 0$ on L. It follows from the theorem above that L gives a weak relative minimum. Again, as in Example 1 above, we do not need to appeal to the lemma of §5.15 for the construction of a field in the neighbourhood of L; for example we can use the lines parallel to L.

(*b*) If $0 \leqslant \beta < \pi/6$ (i.e. if $0 \leqslant k < 1/\sqrt{3}$), $N < 0$ on L. Legendre's necessary condition is not satisfied, and L does not provide even a weak relative minimum. It does provide a weak relative maximum. Any weak variation will make $\delta I < 0$.

The results in (*a*) and (*b*) are easily established independently, without appeal to the theorem. If $y = kx + \zeta$, where $\zeta \in C_1$ and $\zeta(0) = \zeta(1) = 0$,

$$\delta I = I - I_0 = \int_0^1 \zeta'^2\{\zeta'^2 + 4k\zeta' + 6(k^2 - \tfrac{1}{3})\} \tag{5.16.5}$$

and for weak variations this has the sign of $(k^2 - \frac{1}{3})$.

(*c*) Finally let us consider the critical case $\beta = \pi/6$, $k = 1/\sqrt{3}$. Here $N = 0$ on L, and Legendre's necessary condition is satisfied. But L gives neither a weak relative minimum nor a weak relative maximum. If we take the varied curve to be $y = kx + \alpha\eta$, where $\eta \in C_1$ and $\eta(0) = \eta(1) = 0$, we have

$$\delta I = \int_0^1 \left(\alpha^4\eta'^4 + \frac{4}{\sqrt{3}}\, \alpha^3\eta'^3\right) dx. \tag{5.16.6}$$

This is positive for a variation symmetrical about $x = \frac{1}{2}$ (for example $\eta = x(1 - x)$), since any such variation makes $\int_0^1 \eta'^3\, dx = 0$. But for $\eta = x^2(1 - x)$,

$$\delta I = \frac{2}{35}\alpha^3\left(-\frac{4}{\sqrt{3}} + \alpha\right), \tag{5.16.7}$$

which is negative for small positive values of α. Thus some weak variations make δI positive and some make δI negative, and in this case L gives neither a weak relative minimum nor a weak relative maximum.

5.17 The absolute minimum for $\int \sqrt{y}\, ds$

In some problems, for example the problem of the brachistochrone, we found that there is a unique extremal through the given points A and B in the upper half-plane, and we proved that the arc K_{AB} of this extremal gives to I a smaller value than any other curve joining A to B and lying in the upper half-plane.

A different situation arises in the problem of the minimal surface of revolution, and in the problem of the orbits of a particle moving in a uniform field of force. In these problems the pencil of extremals through A has an envelope D. If B lies above D, there are two extremals through A and B, and, as we saw, the upper extremal K_1 gives a minimum *for curves lying above* D. But if we consider the whole class of curves lying in the region $y \geqslant 0$, including those going below D, there may be curves giving a still smaller value to I.

If B lies below D there is no extremal through A and B, and there is no minimizing curve $y = \varphi(x)$, with $\varphi \in D_1$. There is however, as we saw, a minimizing curve in the corresponding parametric problem. This is the Goldschmidt curve Λ consisting of the three straight lines AM, MN, NB. The value of the integral for the Goldschmidt curve is the infimum m for I for curves of the form $y = \varphi(x)$, but the infimum is not actually attained in the class D_1.

Now it is easy to see that the Goldschmidt curve Λ gives a relative minimum in all cases, even when B lies above D. To prove this, consider a curve Γ joining A to B, and lying in the region $y \geqslant 0$, and having length greater than $Y + \overline{Y}$. This condition is certainly satisfied by curves in the neighbourhood of Λ; and in the case of the integral $\int \sqrt{y}\, ds$, where the extremals are parabolas, it is satisfied by *all* curves in the region $y \geqslant 0$ if B lies below D, because if B lies below D the length AB is greater than $Y + \overline{Y}$. Let AC be an arc of Γ of length Y, and DB an arc of Γ of length $\overline{Y}$ (Fig. 5.17). Let a point at distance s from A on the arc AC have ordinate y, and let a point at distance s from A on the line AM have ordinate z. Then $y > z$, and if $I = \int y^n\,ds$, with $n > 0$, we have

(5.17.1) $$I(\Gamma_{AC}) - I(\Lambda_{AM}) = \int_0^Y (y^n - z^n)\,ds > 0.$$

Similarly

(5.17.2) $$I(\Gamma_{DB}) - I(\Lambda_{NB}) > 0.$$

Finally

(5.17.3) $$I(\Gamma_{CD}) - I(\Lambda_{MN}) = I(\Gamma_{CD}) > 0,$$

and, by adding the three results,

(5.17.4) $$I(\Gamma_{AB}) > I(\Lambda_{AB}),$$

and this completes the proof.

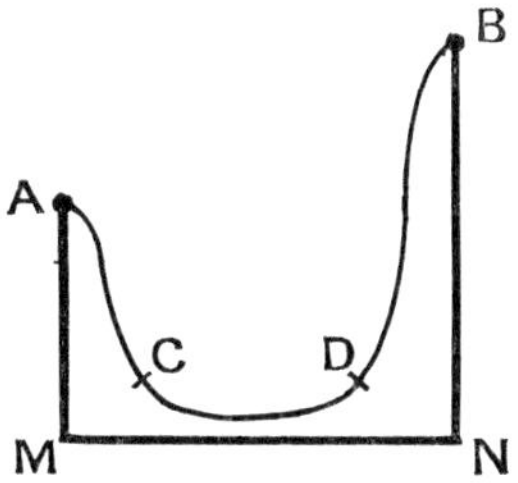

Fig. 5.17

We have here an illustration of a remark made in §1.3. The domain R of (x, y, y') for this problem is the domain $y > 0$, and the segment MN is a curve whose elements are not interior points of R but lie on the frontier of R. When we consider variation to a neighbouring curve, the variation is restricted by the requirement that no element of the new curve lies in the region $y < 0$.

We therefore have the following situation. For $\int \sqrt{y}\,ds$ and for $\int y\,ds$ both the upper extremal K_1 and the Goldschmidt curve Λ give strong relative minima, and the question we wish to examine is this, "Which of these gives the smaller value to I?". The answer to this question is of the same general form in both cases. We choose for detailed examination the integral $\int \sqrt{y}\,ds$ for which the calculations are rather simpler.

5.18 Calculation of the integrals

The extremals, as in (3.8.5), are the parabolas

(5.18.1) $$\frac{y}{b} = 1 + \left(\frac{x-a}{2b}\right)^2, \qquad (b > 0),$$

and two of these pass through A and B if B lies above D. The one in which we are primarily interested is the upper parabola K_1, i.e.

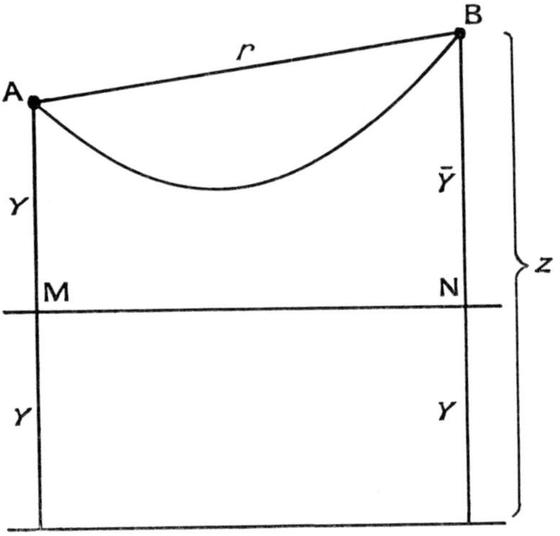

Fig. 5.18*a*

the parabola with the larger value of b.

Since

$$y' = \frac{x-a}{2b}, \quad 1 + y'^2 = \frac{y}{b}, \tag{5.18.2}$$

we have

$$I = \int_X^{\overline{X}} \sqrt{\{y(1+y'^2)\}}\,dx = \frac{1}{\sqrt{b}}\int_X^{\overline{X}} y\,dx \tag{5.18.3}$$

$$= \sqrt{b}\left\{\overline{X} - X + \frac{(\overline{X}-a)^3 - (X-a)^3}{12b^2}\right\}$$

We have to express this in terms of $(X, Y, \overline{X}, \overline{Y})$, and to do this we must determine a and b. Now

$$4b(Y-b) = (X-a)^2, \tag{5.18.4}$$

$$4b(\overline{Y}-b) = (\overline{X}-a)^2, \tag{5.18.5}$$

whence

$$4b(\overline{Y}-Y) = (\overline{X}-X)(\overline{X}+X-2a). \tag{5.18.6}$$

Now (5.18.6) can also be written in the forms

$$X - a = \frac{2b(\overline{Y} - Y)}{\overline{X} - X} - \tfrac{1}{2}(\overline{X} - X), \tag{5.18.7}$$

$$\overline{X} - a = \frac{2b(\overline{Y} - Y)}{\overline{X} - X} + \tfrac{1}{2}(\overline{X} - X), \tag{5.18.8}$$

and substituting for $(X - a)$ from (5.18.7) in (5.18.4) we get the equation for b, namely

$$\frac{4r^2}{(\overline{X} - X)^2}\, b^2 - 2zb + \tfrac{1}{4}(\overline{X} - X)^2 = 0, \tag{5.18.9}$$

where (Fig. 5.18*a*)

$$r^2 = (\overline{X} - X)^2 + (\overline{Y} - Y)^2, \qquad z = Y + \overline{Y}. \tag{5.18.10}$$

The solution is

$$b = \frac{(\overline{X} - X)^2}{4r^2}\{z \pm \sqrt{(z^2 - r^2)}\} \tag{5.18.11}$$

$$= \frac{(\overline{X} - X)^2}{8r^2}\{\sqrt{(z + r)} \pm \sqrt{(z - r)}\}^2,$$

and we can also write this in the form

$$b = \frac{(\overline{X} - X)^2}{2}\,\frac{1}{\{\sqrt{(z + r)} \mp \sqrt{(z - r)}\}^2}. \tag{5.18.12}$$

We know that $z > r$, since B lies above D, and it is the larger value of b in which we are interested, so we take the upper sign in (5.18.11) and (5.18.12).

In the formula (5.18.3) for I we need $(\overline{X} - a)^3 - (X - a)^3$, and from (5.18.7) and (5.18.8) we have

$$(\overline{X} - a)^3 - (X - a)^3 = \frac{12b^2(\overline{Y} - Y)^2}{\overline{X} - X} + \tfrac{1}{4}(\overline{X} - X)^3, \tag{5.18.13}$$

so

$$I = \sqrt{b}(\overline{X} - X) + \frac{1}{12b^{3/2}}\left\{\frac{12b^2(\overline{Y} - Y)^2}{\overline{X} - X} + \tfrac{1}{4}(\overline{X} - X)^3\right\} \tag{5.18.14}$$

$$= \frac{\sqrt{b}r^2}{\overline{X} - X} + \frac{1}{48}\left(\frac{\overline{X} - X}{\sqrt{b}}\right)^3.$$

We now substitute for $\sqrt{b}$ in the second member of (5.18.14) (using the formula (5.18.11) in the first term and the formula (5.18.12) in the second), and we find for the value of I for the upper extremal K_1

$$(5.18.15) \quad I_1 = \frac{r}{2\sqrt{2}}\{\sqrt{(z+r)} + \sqrt{(z-r)}\} + \frac{1}{48}[\sqrt{2}\{\sqrt{(z+r)} - \sqrt{(z-r)}\}]^3$$

$$= \frac{1}{4\sqrt{2}}(\theta^2 - \varphi^2)(\theta + \varphi) + \frac{1}{12\sqrt{2}}(\theta - \varphi)^3$$

$$= \frac{1}{3\sqrt{2}}(\theta^3 - \varphi^3),$$

where we write, for the moment, θ for $\sqrt{(z+r)}$ and φ for $\sqrt{(z-r)}$. Thus

$$(5.18.16) \qquad I_1 = \frac{1}{3\sqrt{2}}\{(z+r)^{3/2} - (z-r)^{3/2}\}.$$

It is easily verified that the value I_2 of I for the lower parabola K_2 is

$$(5.18.17) \qquad I_2 = \frac{1}{3\sqrt{2}}\{(z+r)^{3/2} + (z-r)^{3/2}\}.$$

Let us now turn to the Goldschmidt curve Λ. The value I_0 of I for Λ is

$$(5.18.18) \quad I_0 = \int_0^Y \sqrt{y}\,dy + \int_0^{\overline{Y}} \sqrt{y}\,dy = \tfrac{2}{3}(Y^{3/2} + \overline{Y}^{3/2}).$$

We wish to determine, when B is above D (i.e. $z > r$) whether I_1 or I_0 is the greater.

Let us first consider points *on* D; for these points $z = r$,

$$(5.18.19) \qquad I_1 = \tfrac{2}{3}z^{3/2},$$

and

$$(5.18.20) \qquad I_1 - I_0 = \tfrac{2}{3}\{(Y + \overline{Y})^{3/2} - Y^{3/2} - \overline{Y}^{3/2}\}.$$

This vanishes (as it must) when $\overline{Y} = 0$. Moreover

$$(5.18.21) \qquad \frac{\partial}{\partial \overline{Y}}(I_1 - I_0) = \sqrt{(Y + \overline{Y})} - \sqrt{\overline{Y}} > 0,$$

so $I_1 > I_0$ on D, except at the vertex, where $I_1 = I_0$.*

* Alternatively, to prove that $I_1 > I_0$ on D except at the vertex, we can appeal to the elementary result that, if p and q are real non-zero numbers, $(p^2 + q^2)^3 > (p^3 + q^3)^2$.

On the axis $x = X$, $r = |\overline{Y} - Y|$, and

$$(5.18.22) \qquad I_1 - I_0 = \tfrac{2}{3}|\overline{Y}^{3/2} - Y^{3/2}| - \tfrac{2}{3}(Y^{3/2} + \overline{Y}^{3/2}) < 0.$$

If now we consider points B on a horizontal line $y = \overline{Y}$ we have, since z is now fixed,

$$(5.18.23) \qquad \frac{\partial}{\partial r}(I_1 - I_0) = \frac{\partial I_1}{\partial r} = \frac{1}{2\sqrt{2}}\{\sqrt{(z + r)} + \sqrt{(z - r)}\} > 0$$

for points above D. As B moves along $y = \overline{Y}$, from a point P on the line $x = X$ to a point Q on D, $I_1 - I_0$ steadily increases. Now $I_1 - I_0 < 0$ at P and $I_1 - I_0 > 0$ at Q, so there is just one point R between P and Q at which $I_1 = I_0$. The locus of R is the curve Γ given by

$$(5.18.24) \qquad (z + r)^{3/2} - (z - r)^{3/2} = (2Y)^{3/2} + (2\overline{Y})^{3/2}.$$

In this equation $(\overline{X}, \overline{Y})$ are to be regarded as current coordinates (A being fixed), and the equation can also be written in the form

$$(5.18.25) \qquad (z + r)^{3/2} - (z - r)^{3/2} = 2\sqrt{2}\{Y^{3/2} + (z - Y)^{3/2}\}.$$

The form of the curve Γ is shown in Fig. 5.18*b*.

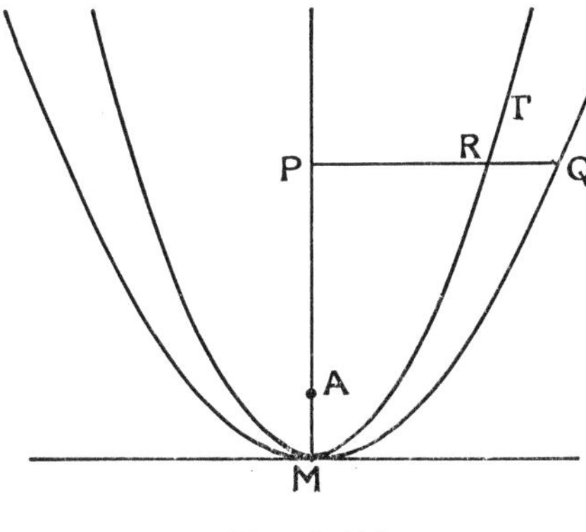

Fig. 5.18*b*

We can now answer the question proposed. If B lies above Γ, K_1 gives a smaller value to I than Λ: if B lies between Γ and D, Λ gives a smaller value to I than K_1: if B lies below D, only Λ comes in question, and this gives the infimum value for I.

5.19 Variable end-points

The theory developed above in relation to the fundamental sufficiency theorem refers in the first instance to the fixed end-point problem. The theory can be modified in sufficiently simple cases to embrace also problems with variable end-points.

As a concrete illustration, consider again the Example 1 of §4.3. The integral is $\int(1/y)ds$, the end-point $A(X, Y)$ is fixed, and the end-point B is to lie on the line Λ, $x = k$. We found that the circular arc K_0 (which has its centre at $(k, 0)$, passes through A, and cuts Λ orthogonally at B_0) gives a stationary value to I. It is now easy to see that this value is a minimum.

Let us consider the semi-field through A. The extremals are the circles of the coaxal system through (X, Y) and $(X, -Y)$, and the transversals are the orthogonal trajectories, i.e. the circles of the coaxal system for which these points are inverse points. Let us denote the transversal that touches Λ at B_0 by Γ (Fig. 5.19). If B is

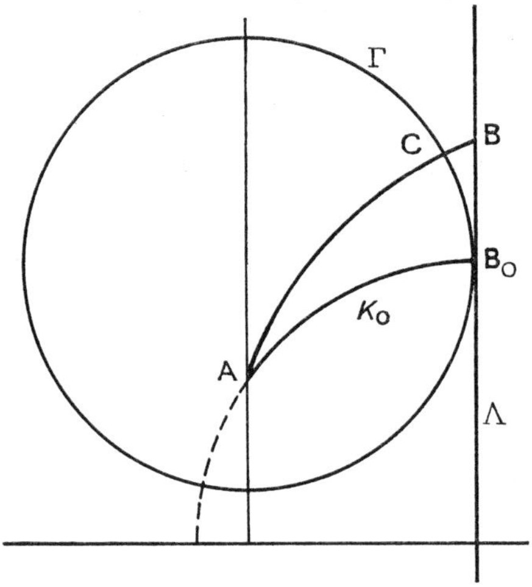

Fig. 5.19

any point of Λ in the upper half-plane other than B_0, the extremal K_{AB} cuts Γ at a point C to the left of Λ, and

(5.19.1) $$I(K_{AB}) > I(K_{AC}).$$

But $I(K_{AC}) = I(K_0)$ in virtue of (5.2.8). Thus $I(K_{AB}) > I(K_0)$, and therefore K_0 is a genuinely minimizing curve. (In performing the calculations we can put $X = 0$ without loss of generality. The slope function of the semi-field is $(-x^2 + y^2 - Y^2)/2xy$, and

(5.19.2) $$\psi = \cosh^{-1}\frac{x^2 + y^2 + Y^2}{2Yy}.)$$

CHAPTER VI

The Isoperimetrical Problem

6.1 Steiner's problem

The classical isoperimetrical problem, to find the plane closed curve of given length which shall enclose the greatest possible area, was known in the ancient world. The problem was proposed by a Greek mathematician, Zenodorus, who lived in Alexandria in the time of the Ptolemies. He found the correct answer: the curve is a circle.

To express the matter more precisely, consider the class of simple closed rectifiable curves C of length l. The area A enclosed by one of these curves is bounded; it is clear, for example, that $A < \frac{1}{4}l^2$. Let M be the supremum (least upper bound) of the area A enclosed by a curve of this class. Then, as we shall prove later, $M = l^2/4\pi$. It will follow that

(6.1.1) $$A \leqslant l^2/4\pi,$$

a result known as the *isoperimetrical inequality*. The supremum value $l^2/4\pi$ for the area is actually attained by the circle of circumference l, and by no other curve of length l.

In this context we are dealing with closed curves of length l, but we are not concerned with the position and orientation of the curves in the plane. Thus, for our present purpose, any two congruent curves, whatever their position and orientation, are to be regarded as the same curve.

The isoperimetrical inequality (6.1.1) holds for all positive values of l, not merely for one particular value, and this implies a second theorem which is closely related to the first. The infimum (greatest lower bound) of the perimeters of simple closed rectifiable curves which enclose a prescribed area A is $\sqrt{(4\pi A)}$, and this infimum is attained by the circle of area A, and by no other curve of area A.

The isoperimetrical problem is one which has always captured the imagination of mathematicians. More especially it is associated with the name of Jakob Steiner, the great geometer who was professor at Berlin from 1834 to 1863. Steiner devised a number of ingenious synthetic methods for attacking the isoperimetrical problem and a number of related problems. We begin this Chapter with an account of one of the problems discussed by Steiner: to prove that a polygon with $2m$ sides (where m is a prescribed positive integer), and with prescribed perimeter l, has greatest area when it is regular.

We need the following simple lemma.

LEMMA. *In the triangle ABC the vertices B and C are fixed, the side BC having length a, and the sum* $c + b$ *(i.e.* $BA + AC$*) has the prescribed value k, where* $0 < a < k$. *Then the area of the triangle is a maximum when* $BA = AC = \frac{1}{2}k$.

To prove the lemma, we can appeal to the fact that A lies on a certain ellipse with B and C as foci. The triangle has greatest height when A is at one end of the minor axis of this ellipse. Alternatively, with the notation indicated in Fig. 6.1a (in which N is the foot of the perpendicular from A on to BC) we have

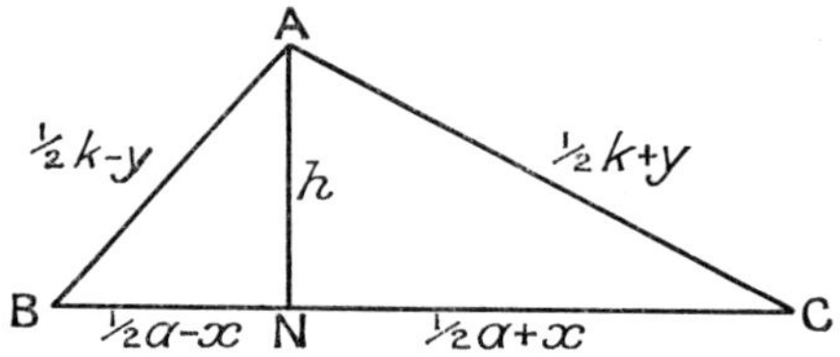

Fig. 6.1a

(6.1.2) $$h^2 = (\tfrac{1}{2}k + y)^2 - (\tfrac{1}{2}a + x)^2 = (\tfrac{1}{2}k - y)^2 - (\tfrac{1}{2}a - x)^2,$$

so $ax = ky$, say

(6.1.3) $$\frac{x}{k} = \frac{y}{a} = \lambda, \qquad 0 \leqslant \lambda < \tfrac{1}{2},$$

and then

(6.1.4) $$h^2 = (\tfrac{1}{2}k + \lambda a)^2 - (\tfrac{1}{2}a + \lambda k)^2 = (\tfrac{1}{4} - \lambda^2)(k^2 - a^2).$$

It follows that h is greatest when $\lambda = 0$. (A related result may be noticed in passing. If B and C are fixed as before, and the *area* of the triangle is prescribed, so that h is given, then $BA + AC$ is a minimum when $BA = AC$. For

(6.1.5) $$k^2 = a^2 + \frac{h^2}{\frac{1}{4} - \lambda^2},$$

and k is least when $\lambda = 0$.) Or again we can appeal to the formula $\sqrt{\{s(s-a)(s-b)(s-c)\}}$ for the area of the triangle, where $s = \frac{1}{2}(a + b + c)$. In this case s and a are prescribed, and we need the maximum value of $(s - b)(s - c)$. Now the sum of the factors $(s - b)$ and $(s - c)$ has the fixed value a, so their product is greatest when they are equal, i.e. when $b = c$.

COROLLARY 1. If BH and AK are segments, each of given length, lying on fixed parallel lines (cf. Fig. 6.1b), the sum $BA + KH$ is

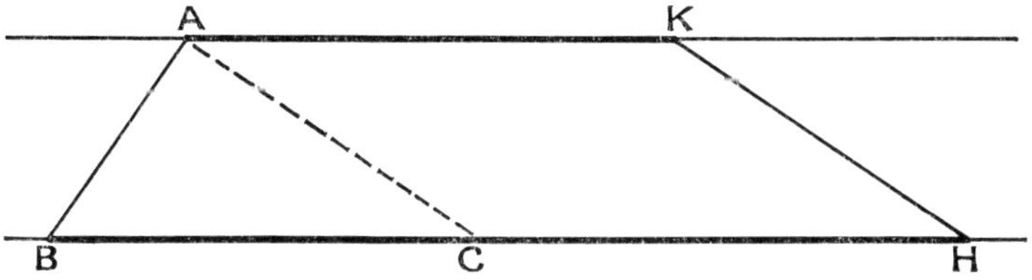

Fig. 6.1b

least when there is symmetry, and $BA = KH$.

COROLLARY 2. A triangle whose perimeter is prescribed has maximum area when it is equilateral. If we denote the supremum of the areas of triangles with perimeter l by M, and if we assume the existence of a triangle with perimeter l and area M, then this triangle must be equilateral. This follows from the Lemma, since any two sides must be equal. If however we use the formula $\sqrt{\{s(s - a)(s - b)(s - c)\}}$ for the area it is at once clear that the supremum is attained. We need the greatest attainable value of $(s - a)(s - b)(s - c)$. Now the factors $(s - a)$, $(s - b)$, and $(s - c)$, are three positive numbers whose sum has the fixed value $s\,(= \frac{1}{2}l)$. The supremum of the product of three positive numbers whose sum has the prescribed value s is $(s/3)^3$, and this value is attained when each of the three numbers has the value $s/3$. (This is merely another aspect of the well-known theorem that the arithmetic mean is not less than the geometric mean.) The supremum value for the area is $l^2/(12\sqrt{3})$, and this value is attained if and only if the triangle is equilateral.

We now turn to Steiner's problem about the polygon with prescribed perimeter l and with $2m$ sides. The area A is bounded (for example, as we have noticed, $A < \frac{1}{4}l^2$), and we denote the supremum by M. Let us assume, to begin with, that a polygon of area M exists. The steps of the argument are then as follows.

(i) The polygon of maximum area must be convex, i.e. the polygon and its interior must form a convex region. (A region is convex if, when P and Q are any two points of the region, all points of the linear segment PQ belong to the region.) If we consider a polygon which is not convex, we can find two vertices P and Q such that PQ is not a side, and such that the polygon lies entirely on one side of PQ. We can increase the area of such a polygon, without changing its perimeter, by reflecting one of the sets of vertices between P and Q in PQ (Fig. 6.1c). Therefore such a polygon cannot have

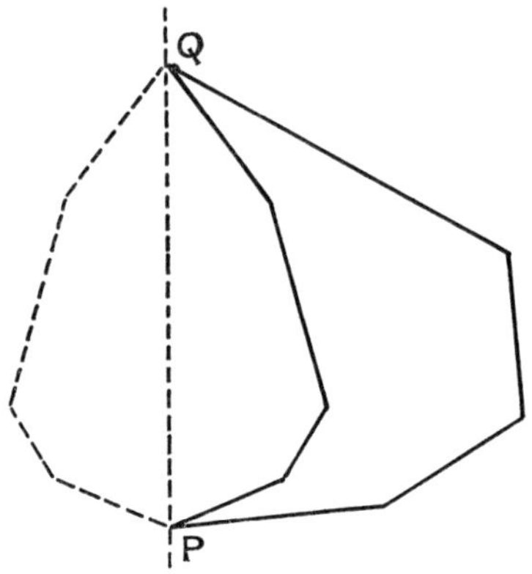

Fig. 6.1c

the maximum area for polygons with the given perimeter.

(ii) The maximum polygon must be equilateral. For suppose on the contrary that two adjacent sides, say A_1A_2 and A_2A_3, are unequal. Keeping all the vertices fixed except A_2, we can increase the area of the polygon (without changing its perimeter) if we replace the vertex A_2 by the point P which is on the same side of A_1A_3 as A_2, and which is such that

(6.1.6) $$A_1P = PA_3 = \tfrac{1}{2}(A_1A_2 + A_2A_3).$$

This follows from the lemma. Thus, since the original polygon has maximum area, the hypothesis $A_1A_2 \neq A_2A_3$ is false, and each side of the polygon has length $l/2m$.

(iii) If the vertices are $A_1, A_2, \ldots, A_{2m}$, the line A_1A_{m+1} divides the polygon into two equal areas. For otherwise we could increase the area (without changing the perimeter) by replacing the part with the smaller area by the reflexion in A_1A_{m+1} of the part with the larger area.

(iv) The maximum polygon is inscribed in a circle. At this stage we can deal with half the polygon in virtue of (iii). We prove that, if $1 < \nu < m + 1$, the angle $A_1A_\nu A_{m+1}$ is a right angle. If this were not so, we could increase the area of the half-polygon $A_1A_2 \ldots A_{m+1}$ by fixing A_1A_ν and rotating $A_\nu A_{m+1}$ about A_ν until the angle is a right angle. (During this process the polygon $A_1A_2 \ldots A_\nu$ is supposed rigid, and so is the polygon $A_\nu A_{\nu+1} \ldots A_{m+1}$.) Thus, if $A_1 A_\nu A_{m+}$ were not a right angle, we could increase the area of the polygon without changing its perimeter, and this is impossible. Thus the polygon of maximum area is inscribed in a circle, and, since it is equilateral, it is regular.

(v) So far we have assumed the existence of a polygon of area M, i.e. we have assumed that the supremum is actually attained. To prove this, let the coordinates of A_r be (x_r, y_r), and let us represent any polygon $A_1A_2 \ldots A_{2m}$ by a point $(x_1, y_1, x_2, y_2, \ldots, x_{2m}, y_{2m})$ in a Euclidian space of $4m$ dimensions. We can confine our attention to the cube $|x_r| \leqslant \frac{1}{4}l$, $|y_r| \leqslant \frac{1}{4}l$, and then the points representing polygons with perimeter l form a bounded closed set, and the area is a continuous function on this set. Since the set is bounded and closed the supremum is attained at a point of the set. Thus the assumption that a polygon of area M exists is justified.

Since the polygon represented by a point in the $4m$-fold may cross itself or degenerate, the definition of area requires some care. We define the area A as the sum of the (signed) areas of the triangles OA_1A_2, $OA_2A_3, \ldots, OA_{2m}A_1$: thus

(6.1.7) $$A = \tfrac{1}{2} \sum_{r=1}^{2m} (x_r y_{r+1} - y_r x_{r+1}),$$

where the symbols (x_{2m+1}, y_{2m+1}) mean the same as (x_1, y_1). The area so defined is not necessarily positive. It is positive for a simple polygon for which the sense of description $A_1A_2 \ldots A_{2m}A_1$ is the positive sense. For a polygon which crosses itself the area may be positive or negative. It is easily seen that the formula (6.1.7) is invariant for changes of origin, and for rotation of the axes, in the plane. The reader may find it interesting to see how the formula works out in practice for polygons which cross themselves, such as the hexagons shown in Fig. 6.1*d*.

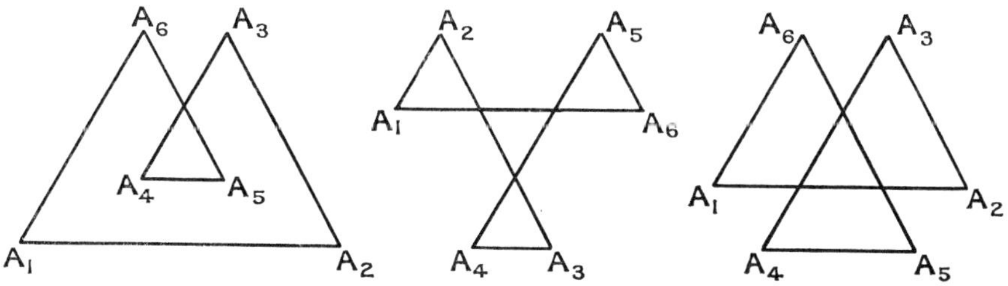

Fig. 6.1*d*

6.2 The classical isoperimetrical problem

The classical isoperimetrical problem, to find the simple closed curve of given length which shall enclose the greatest possible area, may be regarded as a limiting case of Steiner's problem with polygons of $2m$ sides and perimeter l. As the integer m tends to infinity the regular polygon tends to the circle whose circumference is of length l.

If C is a simple closed rectifiable curve, we shall denote the closed region consisting of the curve and its interior by R. We shall denote the length of the curve by $p(C)$ or $p(R)$, and the area enclosed by the curve by $A(C)$ or $A(R)$.

If we start, as before, with the assumption that a maximizing curve of the given length l exists, the proof that this curve must be a circle follows on lines very similar to those for the polygons. The steps of the argument, sketched briefly, are as follows.

(i) The maximizing curve must be convex; any chord of the curve consists entirely of points of R, i.e. of points lying on or inside the curve. In other words, the region R is a convex region.

(ii) If the chord PQ bisects the perimeter, it must also bisect the area.

(iii) Let P, Q be two points on the curve bisecting the perimeter, i.e. each of the arcs PQ is of length $\frac{1}{2}l$. If we consider one of the arcs PQ, and N is any interior point on this arc, the angle PNQ must be a right angle. Thus the maximizing curve, if it exists, must be a circle.

(iv) So far the argument is very similar to that for the polygons. But when we come to the question of *existence* the type of proof used in §6.1 is not applicable, and we need a different kind of attack.

The area enclosed by simple closed curves of length l is bounded, and we denote the supremum of the area by M. Our object is to prove that the supremum is attained, i.e. that there exists a curve of length l and area M.

Let $\{C_n\}$ be a sequence of simple closed curves of length l such that

$$A(C_n) \to M \tag{6.2.1}$$

as $n \to \infty$. Associated with each C_n we can find an inscribed polygon P_n, with an even number of sides, say $2m$ sides, such that

$$\left(1 + \frac{1}{n}\right)A(C_n) \geqslant A(P_n) \geqslant \left(1 - \frac{1}{n}\right)A(C_n), \tag{6.2.2}$$

so that $A(P_n) \to M$ as $n \to \infty$. Let Q_n be the polygon similar to P_n but with perimeter l. Since $p(P_n) \leqslant p(C_n) = l$ we have

$$M \geqslant A(Q_n) \geqslant A(P_n), \tag{6.2.3}$$

so $A(Q_n) \to M$ as $n \to \infty$. Now let K_n be the regular polygon with

$2m$ sides and with perimeter l. Then

$$M \geqslant A(K_n) \geqslant A(Q_n), \tag{6.2.4}$$

and therefore, since $A(Q_n) \to M$,

$$A(K_n) \to M \tag{6.2.5}$$

as $n \to \infty$. But $m \to \infty$ with n, and K_n converges to the circle K with circumference l. Hence $A(K) = M$, and the supremum is actually attained by the circle with circumference l. The value of M is therefore $l^2/4\pi$.

Another attack on the classical isoperimetrical problem depends on the idea of *symmetrization*, which was also used by Steiner. In this discussion we confine our attention to convex curves C; the region R consisting of C and its interior is a convex region. As before, we denote the supremum of the area enclosed by a closed curve of length l by M. It is clear that $M \geqslant l^2/4\pi$, since for the circle $A = l^2/4\pi$. We shall prove that $M = l^2/4\pi$, and that this value is attained by the circle of circumference l, and by no other curve of length l.

Let C be a convex curve and λ a line in its plane. The *symmetrized image* C' of C in the line λ is constructed as follows. Take a line μ perpendicular to λ, and suppose that μ cuts C in the points P and Q. Let P' and Q' be the points on μ such that $P'Q' = PQ$, and such that P' and Q' are equidistant from λ (Fig. 6.2*a*). The convex curve C' built up

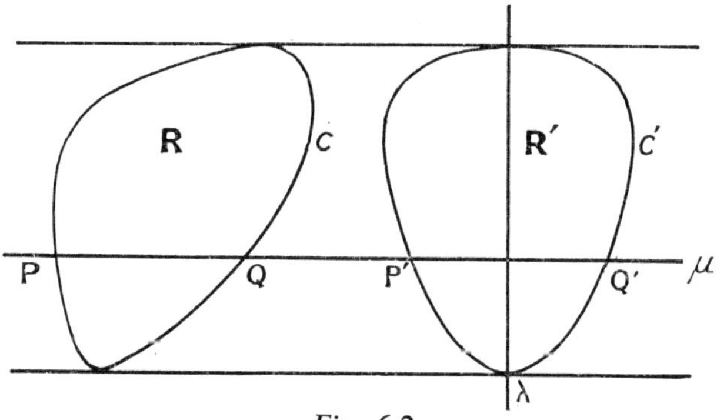

Fig. 6.2*a*

by the points P' and Q' is symmetrical with respect to λ, and is called the symmetrized image of C. The region R' consisting of C' and its interior is called the symmetrized image of R.

The symmetrized image has the following properties,

$$A(C') = A(C), \tag{6.2.6}$$

$$p(C') \leqslant p(C). \tag{6.2.7}$$

The property (6.2.6) is evident. To prove (6.2.7), take lines $\mu_1, \mu_2, \ldots, \mu_n$ (in this order) perpendicular to λ, and let μ_r cut C in P_r and Q_r, and C' in P_r' and Q_r'. Now, by *Corollary* 1 to the *Lemma* in §6.1,

$$P_1'P_2' + Q_2'Q_1' \leqslant P_1P_2 + Q_2Q_1, \tag{6.2.8}$$

with similar results for all the pairs μ_r, μ_{r+1}. Thus if K is a polygon $P_1P_2P_3 \ldots P_{n-1}P_nQ_nQ_{n-1} \ldots Q_2Q_1P_1$ constructed in this way and inscribed in C, and if K' is the corresponding polygon $P_1'P_2'P_3' \ldots P_{n-1}' P_n'Q_n'Q_{n-1}' \ldots Q_2'Q_1'P_1'$ inscribed in C', then

$$p(K') \leqslant p(K). \tag{6.2.9}$$

Let K' be a polygon of this type inscribed in C', and such that

$$p(K') \geqslant p(C') - \varepsilon. \tag{6.2.10}$$

Then

$$p(C') \leqslant p(K') + \varepsilon \leqslant p(K) + \varepsilon \leqslant p(C) + \varepsilon, \tag{6.2.11}$$

and (6.2.7) follows, since ε is arbitrary.

Next we need the following Lemma.

LEMMA. *If C is a convex curve which is such that all of its symmetrized images are circles, then C is a circle.*

To prove the lemma, we notice first that all the circles which are symmetrized images of C have the same radius, because they all have the same area. Let us denote this radius by ρ.

Let G be the mean centre of the region R (consisting of C and its interior); G is the centre of gravity of R considered as a plane material disc of uniform surface density. Let μ be a chord through G cutting C in P and Q, and consider the symmetrized image C' of C in a line λ perpendicular to μ. Then the mean centre of R' (consisting of C' and its interior) also lies on μ. For if ξ is the length of a chord of C parallel to μ, and at height y above μ, we have $\int_R \xi y\, dy = 0$, since G lies on μ. It follows that the mean centre of R' also lies on μ. Thus μ goes through the centre of the circle C', and therefore the chord PQ is of length 2ρ.

Now consider the symmetrized image C'' of C in a line parallel to μ. The line through G perpendicular to μ must go through the centre of C'', by the same argument as before. Moreover, if E and F are points of C'', the only chord EF whose projection on μ has length 2ρ is the diameter of C'' parallel to μ, and therefore the lines through P and Q perpendicular to μ must be tangents to C''. Therefore $PG = GQ = \rho$. But μ is an arbitrary line through G, so all radii of C through G are of length ρ, and C is therefore a circle. This completes the proof of the lemma.

We now use the lemma to prove that if C is a convex closed curve of length l which is not a circle, then $A(C) < M$. Since C is not a circle there exists a symmetrized image C' which is not a circle (Fig. 6.2*a*), and such that

$$A(C') = A(C), \qquad p(C') \leqslant p(C). \tag{6.2.12}$$

Let Γ (Fig. 6.2*b*) be the curve similar to C' but of length l. If S is the closed region consisting of Γ and its interior

$$(6.2.13) \qquad A(S) \geqslant A(R') = A(R), \qquad p(S) = l.$$

Let MN be the axis of symmetry of S, and O the mid-point of MN. We form the region T (Fig. 6.2*c*) from S by reflecting the half of S on

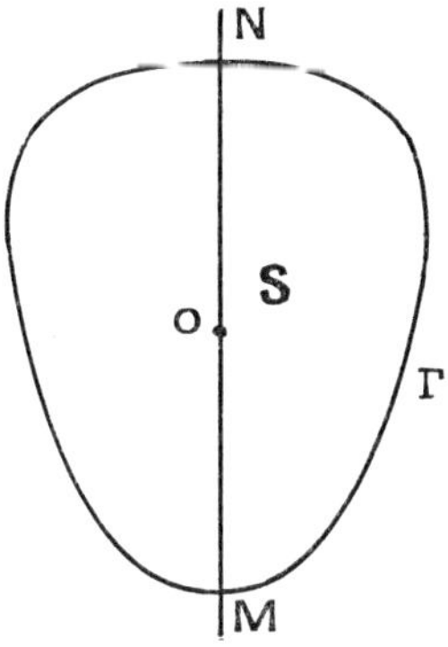

Fig. 6.2*b*

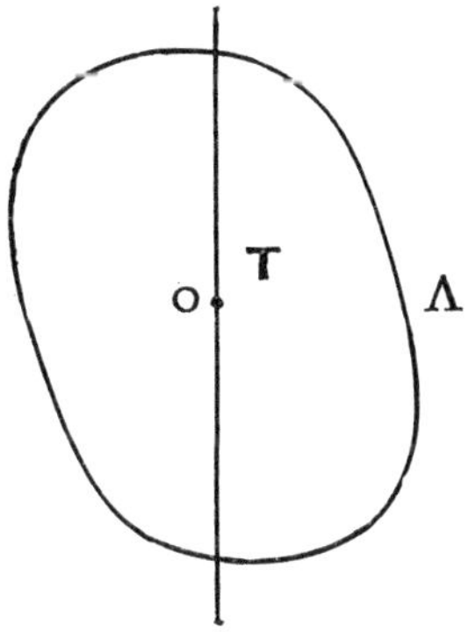

Fig. 6.2*c*

one side of MN in a line through O perpendicular to MN. Then

$$(6.2.14) \qquad A(T) = A(S), \qquad p(T) = p(S),$$

and T is convex and *centrally symmetric*, i.e. every chord through O of the perimeter Λ of T is bisected at O. If P is a point of Λ, the radius OP has a minimum length a (when P is at A) and a maximum length b (when P is at B), where $0 < a < b$ (Fig. 6.2*d*). (The figures are drawn

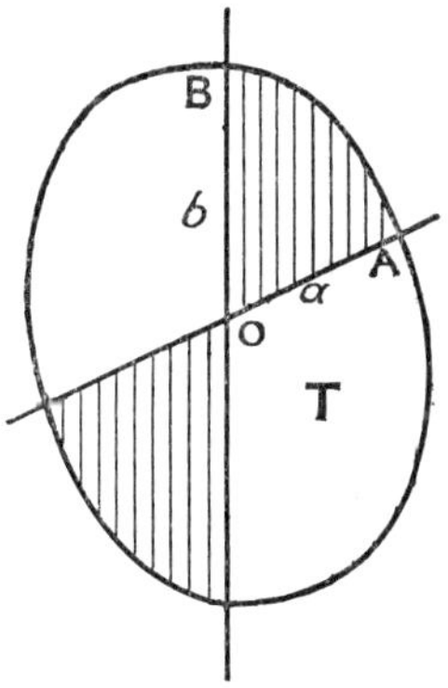

Fig. 6.2*d*

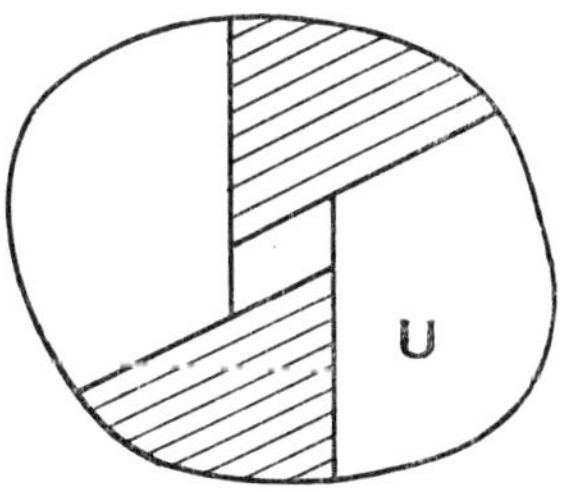

Fig. 6.2*e*

for the simple case in which the longest chord of C' is the axis of symmetry.)

We now use the device illustrated in Fig. 6.2*e* to construct the region U from the region T. The shaded areas in Fig. 6.2*d*, treated as rigid laminas, have been turned over and rotated, the orientation of the unshaded areas being unchanged. The region U is a convex centrally-symmetric region, with the same perimeter as T and with larger area than T,

$$p(U) = p(T) = l, \qquad A(U) > A(T) \geqslant A(R). \tag{6.2.15}$$

Thus we have constructed a region U with the correct perimeter l and with area larger than the area of R, so $A(R)$ must be less than M. If, among all convex regions with perimeter l, R has the greatest possible area, then R must be a circular disc. The curve giving the greatest possible area, if there is one, is unique. We notice that

$$A(U) - A(T) = (b - a)^2 \sin \psi, \tag{6.2.16}$$

where ψ is the acute angle between OA and OB. Since U is convex, it lies entirely on one side of the line through A perpendicular to OA, so $\cos \psi < a/b$. Thus

$$\sin \psi > 1 - \cos \psi > 1 - (a/b), \tag{6.2.17}$$

whence

$$A(U) - A(T) = (b - a)^2 \sin \psi > (b - a)^3/b. \tag{6.2.18}$$

Finally, we prove that $M = l^2/4\pi$. Suppose, on the contrary, that $M > l^2/4\pi$. Then there exists a curve C of length l enclosing an area greater than $l^2/4\pi$. This curve cannot be a circle, so, proceeding as before, we can produce from C a convex region, say U_1, with perimeter l and area greater than $l^2/4\pi$. From U_1, which is itself centrally symmetric, we produce the region U_2 by the same device by which Fig. 6.2*e* was produced from Fig. 6.2*d*. Proceeding in this way, we produce a sequence of centrally symmetric regions $U_1, U_2, U_3, \ldots$, all with perimeter l, and with area increasing with n. Thus $A(U_n)$ increases monotonically with n, and, since the area is bounded, $A(U_n)$ tends to a limit Δ as n tends to infinity.

If a_r, b_r are the least and greatest radii of U_r,

$$A(U_{n+1}) - A(U_n) > (b_n - a_n)^3/b_n, \tag{6.2.19}$$

and since the first member of (6.2.19) tends to zero as n tends to infinity $b_n - a_n \to 0$. Now

$$\pi a_n^2 < A(U_n) < \pi b_n^2, \tag{6.2.20}$$

so both a_n and b_n tend to the limit $\sqrt{(\Delta/\pi)}$. Moreover

$$2\pi a_n < l,$$

since the circumference of a circle is less than the length of a convex curve lying outside the circle, so

$$2\pi\sqrt{(\Delta/\pi)} \leqslant l, \tag{6.2.21}$$

i.e.

$$\Delta \leqslant l^2/4\pi. \tag{6.2.22}$$

But the sequence $A(U_n)$ is monotonic increasing, so

(6.2.23) $$A(U_1) < \Delta \leqslant l^2/4\pi,$$

giving a contradiction, since $A(U_1) > l^2/4\pi$. Therefore the hypothesis $M > l^2/4\pi$ is untenable and the proof that $M = l^2/4\pi$ is complete.

There is a corresponding result in three dimensions; the type of reasoning we have used can be adapted to space of more than two dimensions. The volume V enclosed by a simple closed surface of prescribed area Δ is greatest for the sphere. The isoperimetrical inequality for three dimensions is

(6.2.24) $$V^2 \leqslant \Delta^3/36\pi.$$

We conclude this paragraph with still another proof of the isoperimetrical inequality for two dimensions. This proof, due to Hurwitz, depends on well-known theorems in the theory of Fourier Series. We consider closed curves of length l defined parametrically by $x(t)$, $y(t)$, where t $(= 2\pi s/l)$ is proportional to the arc-length s, and t runs from 0 to 2π. We confine attention to curves for which $x(t)$ and $y(t)$ are of class D_1, and the curves are closed, so that $x(2\pi) = x(0)$, $y(2\pi) = y(0)$. Let (a_n, b_n) be the Fourier coefficients of $x(t)$,

(6.2.25) $$x(t) \sim \tfrac{1}{2}a_0 + \sum_{n=1}^{\infty} (a_n \cos nt + b_n \sin nt),$$

and let (c_n, d_n) be the Fourier coefficients of $y(t)$,

(6.2.26) $$y(t) \sim \tfrac{1}{2}c_0 + \sum_{n=1}^{\infty} (c_n \cos nt + d_n \sin nt).$$

Then the Fourier coefficients of $\dot{x}(t)$ are $(nb_n, -na_n)$, and those of $\dot{y}(t)$ are $(nd_n, -nc_n)$. Thus, from the theorems of Riesz-Fischer and of Parseval, we have

(6.2.27) $$\frac{1}{\pi}\int_0^{2\pi} (\dot{x}^2 + \dot{y}^2)\, dt = \sum_{n=1}^{\infty} n^2(a_n^2 + b_n^2 + c_n^2 + d_n^2),$$

and

(6.2.28) $$\frac{1}{\pi}\int_0^{2\pi} x\dot{y}\, dt = \sum_{n=1}^{\infty} n(a_n d_n - b_n c_n).$$

But

(6.2.29) $$\dot{x}^2 + \dot{y}^2 = (l/2\pi)^2, \quad \int_0^{2\pi} (\dot{x}^2 + \dot{y}^2)\, dt = l^2/2\pi, \quad \int_0^{2\pi} x\dot{y}\, dt = A,$$

so

$$\frac{l^2}{4\pi} - A = \tfrac{1}{2}\pi \sum_{n=1}^{\infty} \{n^2(a_n^2 + b_n^2 + c_n^2 + d_n^2) - 2n(a_n d_n - b_n c_n)\}$$

(6.2.30) $$= \tfrac{1}{2}\pi \sum_{n=1}^{\infty} \{(na_n - d_n)^2 + (nb_n + c_n)^2 + (n^2 - 1)(c_n^2 + d_n^2)\} \geqslant 0,$$

which establishes the isoperimetrical inequality (6.1.1). Moreover, to get equality in (6.2.30), we need

(6.2.31) $a_1 = d_1,\quad b_1 = -c_1,\quad a_n = b_n = c_n = d_n = 0$ for $n > 1$,

so the curve is

(6.2.32)
$$\begin{cases} x = \tfrac{1}{2}a_0 + a_1 \cos t + b_1 \sin t, \\ y = \tfrac{1}{2}b_0 - b_1 \cos t + a_1 \sin t, \end{cases}$$

i.e. it is the circle

(6.2.33)
$$(x - \tfrac{1}{2}a_0)^2 + (y - \tfrac{1}{2}b_0)^2 = a_1^2 + b_1^2.$$

6.3 A "physical" solution of the classical isoperimetrical problem

There are various ways of deducing the solution of the classical isoperimetrical problem from physical considerations, and such proofs, though lacking in rigour, are of great interest. One of the simplest proofs of this class is as follows.

Let a closed curve of the given length l be drawn on a horizontal table, and let a cylinder be constructed with vertical generators through points of the curve. The cylinder is to be thought of as perfectly flexible, the length of the curve of section being invariable, and the generators always vertical. Now let a definite quantity of water be poured into the cylinder, and let the cylinder settle into its equilibrium form. The section will so adjust itself that the potential energy of the water is a minimum. This implies that, in the equilibrium position, the centre of gravity of the water will be as low as possible, and therefore that the water surface will be as low as possible. Therefore (since the volume of water is prescribed) the area of the cross-section of the cylinder must be as large as possible.

But in equilibrium the cross-section must be a circle. For the pressure is the same at all points in any horizontal plane of section, and therefore the curvature of the curve of section, which is determined by the pressure, must be the same at all points. This proves the result.

6.4 The isoperimetrical problem with fixed end-points

We now turn to the analytical theory, and consider first curves of the form $y = \varphi(x)$ joining the fixed end-points A and B. In the isoperimetrical problem we are concerned, not with the whole class κ of curves $y = \varphi(x)$ of class D_1 joining A to B, but only with the sub-class of curves for which the integral J,

(6.4.1)
$$J = \int_X^{\overline{X}} G(x, y, y')\, dx,$$

has the prescribed value l. Let us call this sub-class κ'. Our problem is to find, among the curves of this class κ', one which minimizes the integral I,

$$I = \int_X^{\overline{X}} F(x, y, y')\, dx. \tag{6.4.2}$$

The given functions F and G are of simple type; for our present purpose, of finding necessary conditions for a minimizing curve in the class κ', it will suffice to assume that these functions are of class C_2 in an appropriate domain R of (x, y, y').

One point must be noticed at the outset. It may happen that the integral J (for curves $y = \varphi(x)$ of class D_1) is bounded. Suppose for example that there is an infimum value m, and that this value is attained for just one curve K_0, $y = \varphi_0(x)$. Then if the prescribed value l is less than m the class κ' is empty, and the problem evaporates; and if $l = m$ the class κ' has just the one member K_0, and the problem is trivial. For example, in the eponymous case where J is the length of the curve, the class κ' is empty if $l < m$, where m denotes the distance AB; and if $l = m$ the class κ' has just one member, namely the straight line AB.

If J is bounded below, with infimum m, we shall assume that $l > m$, and that the class κ' has infinitely many members.

6.5 Euler's rule

We begin by establishing the fundamental theorem, known as *Euler's rule*. It provides a necessary condition for a minimizing curve in the class κ'. The rule is as follows.

Euler's rule. We consider the problem of finding a curve $y = \varphi(x)$, of class D_1, through A and B, to minimize the integral

$$\int_X^{\overline{X}} (F - \lambda G)\, dx, \tag{6.5.1}$$

where λ is a constant. In general the curves so found are of the form

$$y = \varphi(x; a, b, \lambda), \tag{6.5.2}$$

where a and b are parameters. *The required curve, minimizing I in κ', must be of this form,* a, b, and λ being so chosen that the curve passes through A and B and satisfies the isoperimetrical condition $J = l$.

To prove the rule, suppose that the curve K, $y = \varphi(x)$, belongs to κ' and minimizes I in κ'. We know that K is not a minimizing

12

curve, in the sense of an absolute minimum, for the integral $J = \int_X^{\bar{X}} G(x, y, y')\,dx$, because $l > m$; and we shall assume further that K is not even a curve for which J has a stationary value. To establish a necessary condition for a weak relative minimum we employ the technique already used in the ordinary problem. We choose a one-parameter family κ'' from κ', and we write a necessary condition for K to be a relative minimum in the one-parameter family.

We take two independent functions $\eta(x)$, $\zeta(x)$, of class D_1, each of which vanishes at X and at $\bar{X}$. We consider a family of curves $K_{\alpha\beta}$ belonging to κ', and defined, for sufficiently small values of α and β, by the equation

$$y = \varphi(x) + \alpha\eta(x) + \beta\zeta(x). \tag{6.5.3}$$

This is a one-parameter family, because α and β are not independent; they are related by the condition

$$\chi(\alpha, \beta) = 0, \tag{6.5.4}$$

where

$$\chi(\alpha, \beta) \equiv \int_X^{\bar{X}} G(x, \varphi + \alpha\eta + \beta\zeta, \varphi' + \alpha\eta' + \beta\zeta')\,dx - l. \tag{6.5.5}$$

Now $\chi(0, 0) = 0$, so α and β vanish together, and $\chi(\alpha, \beta) \in C_2$ in some neighbourhood of (0, 0). The equation (6.5.4) defines β as a function of α in some neighbourhood of $\alpha = 0$, provided that

$$\chi_\beta(0, 0) \neq 0. \tag{6.5.6}$$

But

$$\chi_\beta(0, 0) = \int_X^{\bar{X}} (\zeta G_y + \zeta' G_{y'})\,dx, \tag{6.5.7}$$

where the arguments in G_y and $G_{y'}$ are (x, φ, φ'), and we choose ζ such that the second member of (6.5.7) does not vanish, which is possible because J is not stationary for $y = \varphi(x)$. Thus β is a known function of α near $\alpha = 0$.

If now we write

$$\psi(\alpha, \beta) = \int_X^{\bar{X}} F(x, \varphi + \alpha\eta + \beta\zeta, \varphi' + \alpha\eta' + \beta\zeta')\,dx \tag{6.5.8}$$

we have a problem of restricted minima in two variables. The point (0, 0) gives a minimum value to $\psi(\alpha, \beta)$ under the restriction $\chi(\alpha, \beta) = 0$. A necessary condition, familiar in the ordinary theory of minima, is

$$\frac{\psi_\alpha(0, 0)}{\chi_\alpha(0, 0)} = \frac{\psi_\beta(0, 0)}{\chi_\beta(0, 0)}. \tag{6.5.9}$$

The equation (6.5.9), written out in full, is

$$(6.5.10) \qquad \frac{\int_X^{\bar{X}} (\eta F_y + \eta' F_{y'})\,dx}{\int_X^{\bar{X}} (\eta G_y + \eta' G_{y'})\,dx} = \frac{\int_X^{\bar{X}} (\zeta F_y + \zeta' F_{y'})\,dx}{\int_X^{\bar{X}} (\zeta G_y + \zeta' G_{y'})\,dx},$$

where the arguments in F_y, $F_{y'}$, G_y, $G_{y'}$ are the elements (x, φ, φ') of the curve $y = \varphi(x)$.

We now make a definite choice for ζ, arbitrary save for the restriction that $\int_X^{\bar{X}} (\zeta G_y + \zeta' G_{y'})\,dx$ does not vanish, and we write

$$(6.5.11) \qquad \frac{\int_X^{\bar{X}} (\zeta F_y + \zeta' F_{y'})\,dx}{\int_X^{\bar{X}} (\zeta G_y + \zeta' G_{y'})\,dx} = \lambda.$$

Then for all choices of η

$$(6.5.12) \qquad \int_X^{\bar{X}} \{\eta(F_y - \lambda G_y) + \eta'(F_{y'} - \lambda G_{y'})\}\,dx = 0.$$

This is (cf. §2.3) precisely the necessary condition for the vanishing of the first variation of

$$\int_X^{\bar{X}} (F - \lambda G)\,dx,$$

and thus Euler's rule is established.

In the proof of Euler's rule we can use, if preferred, a more general two-parameter family $y = \varphi(x, \alpha, \beta)$ instead of the special two-parameter family (6.5.3) in which α and β appear linearly. In the alternative proof the function $\varphi_\alpha(x, 0, 0)$ plays much the same part as $\eta(x)$ in the proof given above, and similarly $\varphi_\beta(x, 0, 0)$ replaces $\zeta(x)$.

If K is a minimizing curve in the class κ' the function $F - \lambda G$ must satisfy du Bois-Reymond's equation for some value of the constant λ; and on an arc between corners Euler's equation (formed for $F - \lambda G$) is satisfied. From the point of view of concrete applications this is often sufficient to solve the problem. There is a further development of the theory, similar to that for the unrestricted problem, in which we establish further necessary conditions, and finally sufficient conditions, for a minimizing curve. This further development, however, we do not pursue in this book.

The extension to the case where there are several isoperimetrical conditions

$$\int_X^{\bar{X}} G^k(x, y, y')\, dx = l^k, \qquad k = 1, 2, \ldots, m, \tag{6.5.13}$$

is as follows. We form the Euler equation for

$$F^* = F - \sum_{k=1}^{m} \lambda^k G^k, \tag{6.5.14}$$

where the multipliers $\lambda^1, \lambda^2, \ldots, \lambda^m$ are constants to be determined. The solutions have the form

$$y = \varphi(x; a, b, \lambda^1, \lambda^2, \ldots, \lambda^m). \tag{6.5.15}$$

The two end-conditions and the m isoperimetrical conditions give $(m + 2)$ relations which may, in sufficiently simple cases, suffice to determine the $(m + 2)$ unknowns. To establish the rule we consider an $(m + 1)$-parameter family of curves

$$y = \varphi(x) + \sum_{r=1}^{m+1} \alpha_r \eta_r(x), \tag{6.5.16}$$

and the problem is reduced to finding a necessary condition that a function $\psi(\alpha_1, \alpha_2, \ldots, \alpha_{m+1})$, where the variables $\alpha_1, \alpha_2, \ldots, \alpha_{m+1}$ are subject to m equations of condition $\chi_r(\alpha_1, \alpha_2, \ldots, \alpha_{m+1}) = 0$, should be a minimum at $\alpha_1 = \alpha_2 = \ldots = \alpha_{m+1} = 0$. We now use the method of the Lagrange multipliers in the theory of maxima and minima.

6.6 A related problem

If in the isoperimetrical problem we interchange the functions F and G, the necessary condition obtained from Euler's rule only changes by replacing λ by $1/\lambda$, and therefore the same curves appear in the solution of both problems. But a curve giving a minimum value to I in the original problem (in the class of curves giving a fixed value to J) will sometimes give to J a maximum value (in the class of curves giving a fixed value to I).

We have met an important example of this phenomenon already in the classical isoperimetrical problem. The closed curve which contains the greatest possible area when the perimeter is prescribed is identical with the curve which gives the least possible value to the perimeter when the area is prescribed. (But the theory developed in §6.4 and §6.5 relates to curves of the form $y = \varphi(x)$, and is not immediately suitable for handling the closed curves in the classical problem and the relative problem. We can meet this difficulty in various ways, for example by the method given below in §6.9, or by treating the problem in parametric form.)

A similar phenomenon is familiar in the ordinary theory of maxima and minima (of functions of several variables) with restrictive conditions.

As a trivial example:

(6.6.1) if $x + y = 1$, the minimum value of $x^2 + y^2$ is $\frac{1}{2}$;

(6.6.2) if $x^2 + y^2 = \frac{1}{2}$, the maximum value of $x + y$ is 1.

6.7 The hanging string

A uniform flexible string, of prescribed length l, is held by the ends at given points A and B. What is the form in which it hangs?

Let the distance AB be denoted by l_0; then $l_0 < l$. The string lies in the vertical plane through A and B, and the form is such that the potential energy is a minimum. Another way of expressing the same principle is to say that the centre of gravity of the string must be as low as possible. Taking Oy vertically upwards, we wish to find a curve minimizing

$$\int_X^{\bar{X}} y\, ds \tag{6.7.1}$$

in the class of curves satisfying the isoperimetrical condition

$$\int_X^{\bar{X}} ds = l. \tag{6.7.2}$$

In this problem

$$F = y\sqrt{(1 + y'^2)}, \qquad G = \sqrt{(1 + y'^2)}. \tag{6.7.3}$$

By Euler's rule the minimizing curve, if there is one, is a minimizing curve for

$$\int_X^{\bar{X}} (y - \lambda)\sqrt{(1 + y'^2)}\, dx, \tag{6.7.4}$$

where λ is a constant to be determined subsequently. We need not repeat the calculation already carried out in §3.9. The extremals are the curves

$$\frac{y - \lambda}{b} = \cosh \frac{x - a}{b}, \tag{6.7.5}$$

with $b > 0$, and the length s of an arc, measured from the lowest point $x = a$, is

$$s = b \sinh \frac{x - a}{b}. \tag{6.7.6}$$

There is precisely one such curve of length l joining A to B, provided of course that $l > l_0$. This we expect on physical grounds; we can prove it in various ways.

(i) *Geometrical proof of uniqueness.* Consider any chosen catenary of the family, and draw the chords PQ parallel to AB. Let us denote the length of the chord PQ by $2p$ and the length of the arc PQ by σ. Then $\sigma/2p$ increases steadily from 1 to ∞ as p increases from 0 to ∞, so $\sigma/2p$ passes just once through the value l/l_0. The uniqueness now follows from the properties of similar figures.

To prove the monotone property of $\sigma/2p$, consider the chords of $y = \cosh x$ making an angle α with Ox. If (ξ, η) is the mid-point of the chord PQ we have

$$\begin{aligned} \eta + p \sin \alpha &= \cosh (\xi + p \cos \alpha), \\ \eta - p \sin \alpha &= \cosh (\xi - p \cos \alpha), \end{aligned} \tag{6.7.7}$$

whence

$$p \sin \alpha = \sinh \xi \sinh (p \cos \alpha). \tag{6.7.8}$$

Moreover, from (6.7.6),

$$\begin{aligned} \sigma &= \sinh (\xi + p \cos \alpha) - \sinh (\xi - p \cos \alpha) \\ &= 2 \cosh \xi \sinh (p \cos \alpha). \end{aligned} \tag{6.7.9}$$

It follows from (6.7.8) and (6.7.9) that

$$\sigma^2 - 4p^2 \sin^2 \alpha = 4 \sinh^2 (p \cos \alpha), \tag{6.7.10}$$

whence

$$\left(\frac{\sigma}{2p}\right)^2 = \sin^2 \alpha + \left\{\frac{\sinh (p \cos \alpha)}{p \cos \alpha}\right\}^2 \cos^2 \alpha, \tag{6.7.11}$$

and the monotone property of $\sigma/2p$ is now evident.

(ii) *Analytic proof of uniqueness.* We wish to show that the prescribed points A, B, and the prescribed length l, determine unique values for the three parameters a, b, λ in (6.7.5). Let us suppose, for definiteness, that $\overline{Y} > Y$ (and as usual $\overline{X} > X$). Then

$$\begin{aligned} l &= b\left(\sinh \frac{\overline{X} - a}{b} - \sinh \frac{X - a}{b}\right) \\ &= 2b \sinh \frac{\overline{X} - X}{2b} \cosh \frac{\overline{X} + X - 2a}{2b}, \end{aligned} \tag{6.7.12}$$

and

$$\begin{aligned} \overline{Y} - Y &= b\left(\cosh \frac{\overline{X} - a}{b} - \cosh \frac{X - a}{b}\right) \\ &= 2b \sinh \frac{\overline{X} - X}{2b} \sinh \frac{\overline{X} + X - 2a}{2b}. \end{aligned} \tag{6.7.13}$$

Hence

$$\tanh \frac{\overline{X} + X - 2a}{2b} = \frac{\overline{Y} - Y}{l}, \tag{6.7.14}$$

and, since $\overline{Y} - Y < l$, the equation (6.7.14) determines a unique value for θ, where

$$\theta = \frac{\overline{X} + X - 2a}{2b}. \tag{6.7.15}$$

Further, from (6.7.12) and (6.7.13),

$$\sqrt{\{l^2 - (\overline{Y} - Y)^2\}} = 2b \sinh \frac{\overline{X} - X}{2b}, \tag{6.7.16}$$

and if we write

$$\varphi = \frac{\overline{X} - X}{2b} \tag{6.7.17}$$

we have

$$\frac{\sinh \varphi}{\varphi} = \frac{\sqrt{\{l^2 - (\overline{Y} - Y)^2\}}}{\overline{X} - X} = k, \text{ say}, \tag{6.7.18}$$

where k is a known constant greater than 1. There is a unique positive value of φ satisfying the equation

$$\sinh \varphi = k\varphi. \tag{6.7.19}$$

Thus θ and φ are determined precisely, and then

$$a = \frac{1}{2}\left\{\overline{X} + X - \frac{\theta}{\varphi}(\overline{X} - X)\right\}, \quad b = \frac{\overline{X} - X}{2\varphi}, \tag{6.7.20}$$

so a and b are uniquely determined. Finally

$$Y - \lambda = b \cosh \frac{X - a}{b} = b \cosh (\theta - \varphi), \tag{6.7.21}$$

and λ also is determined uniquely.

The calculation is simpler if A and B are at the same level. In that case we can take the axis Oy equidistant from A and B, so that $\overline{X} + X = 0$, and then $a = 0$, and b is determined from the equations

$$\varphi = \frac{l_0}{2b}, \qquad \frac{\sinh \varphi}{\varphi} = \frac{l}{l_0}. \tag{6.7.22}$$

Thus the form in which the string hangs is determined uniquely, and we can be sure on physical grounds that it does minimize the potential energy, though no formal proof has been given. But if we are content to assume that a minimizing curve exists, this is it; there is no other competitor.

6.8 The chord-and-arc problem

We consider the following problem. The numbers a, l are given, and $0 < a < l$. It is required to find a curve $y = \varphi(x)$, of length $2l$, lying in the upper half-plane, joining A $(-a, 0)$ to B $(a, 0)$, and enclosing with the chord AB the greatest possible area.

The problem is to find the minimizing curve for

(6.8.1) $$I = \int_{-a}^{a} y\,dx$$

subject to the isoperimetrical condition

(6.8.2) $$J \equiv \int_{-a}^{a} \sqrt{(1 + y'^2)}\,dx = 2l.$$

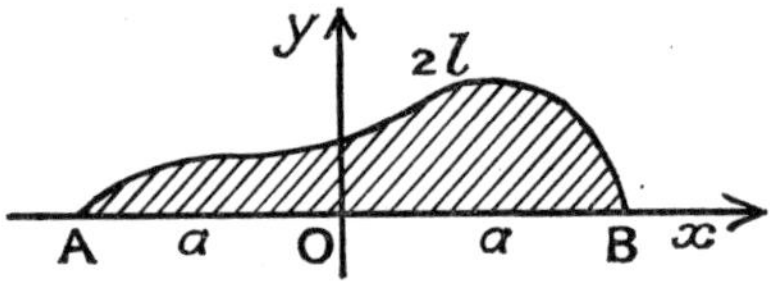

Fig. 6.8*a*

Using Euler's rule, we first seek the extremals for

(6.8.3) $$\int_{-a}^{a} \{y - \lambda\sqrt{(1 + y'^2)}\}\,dx.$$

The integrand does not contain x, so Euler's equation has the first integral

(6.8.4) $$y - \frac{\lambda}{\sqrt{(1 + y'^2)}} = \text{constant}.$$

Writing $y' = \tan\psi$, as usual, we can write (6.8.4) in the form

(6.8.5) $$y - y_0 = \lambda\cos\psi,$$

and then we readily express x also in terms of the parameter ψ, for

(6.8.6) $$dx = \cot\psi\,dy = -\lambda\cos\psi\,d\psi,$$

giving

(6.8.7) $$x - x_0 = -\lambda\sin\psi.$$

It is clear from (6.8.5) and (6.8.7) that the extremals are arcs of circles of radius $|\lambda|$. Moreover, for the integrand in (6.8.3), $V = -\lambda\sin\psi$, and the first corner condition shows that there cannot be a corner on a curve giving a stationary value to the integral (6.8.3).

There are now two cases to consider.

(i) If $a < l < \frac{1}{2}\pi a$ the required curve is the circular arc shown in Fig. 6.8*b*. It is clear that the isoperimetrical condition determines a

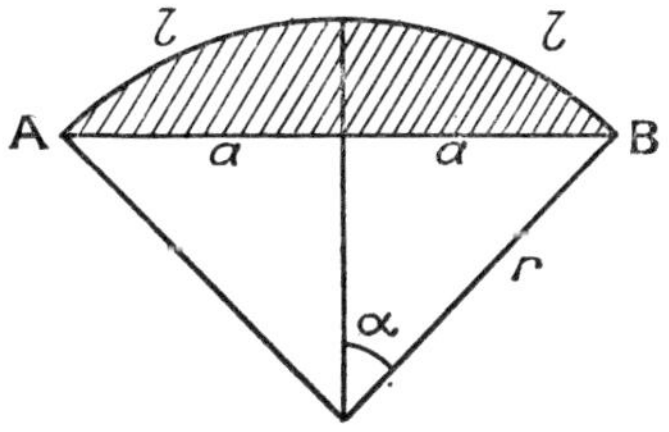

Fig. 6.8*b*

unique solution. To prove this formally, if r is the radius of the circle, and 2α is the angle subtended at the centre by the arc AB (Fig. 6.8*b*) we have

(6.8.8) $$r\alpha = l, \qquad r \sin \alpha = a,$$

and α is determined by the equation

(6.8.9) $$\frac{\sin \alpha}{\alpha} = \frac{a}{l}.$$

Since $\frac{2}{\pi} < \frac{a}{l} < 1$, this equation determines a unique value of α in $(0, \frac{1}{2}\pi)$. When α has been found from (6.8.9) the radius r, and the area Δ bounded by the chord AB and the arc AB, are given by the formulae

(6.8.10) $$r = \frac{a}{\sin \alpha}, \qquad \Delta = a^2 \frac{2\alpha - \sin 2\alpha}{1 - \cos 2\alpha}.$$

In fact Δ is the greatest area attainable, though the formal proof is omitted.

We readily deduce the solution of the classical isoperimetrical problem, already considered in §6.2, if we are content to assume the existence of a maximizing curve. This curve must be a convex curve, as we have noticed already, and if we take two points A, B on the curve, not too far apart, the arc AB must be a circular arc. For otherwise we could increase the area by replacing the arc AB by the circular arc of the same length. Since every small arc is circular, the closed curve must be a circle.

(ii) If $l > \frac{1}{2}\pi a$ the situation is different. We shall find that, if we turn from the *ordinary* to the *parametric* problem (§9.18) the circular arc still gives the maximum area. But this solution is not of the form $y = \varphi(x)$ to which we are restricted in the ordinary problem. For curves of this form the area is bounded, but the supremum is not attained. Its actual value is $2al - \frac{1}{2}\pi a^2$ given by the rectangle and semi-circle shown in Fig. 6.8*c*. Of course the bounding curve in this

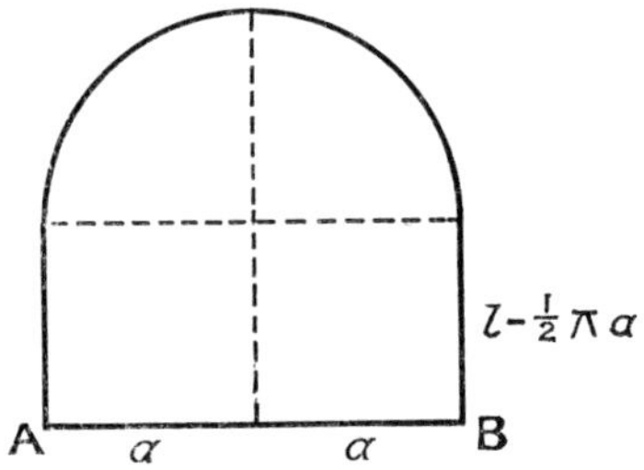

Fig. 6.8*c*

figure is not of the form $y = \varphi(x)$, though we can find curves of this form with an area approximating to the supremum as closely as we wish.

6.9 The classical isoperimetrical problem, Euler's rule

We have already considered this problem by synthetic methods in §6.2; we now consider the solution by Euler's rule. We assume that a maximizing curve of the given length l exists, and that it is a convex curve without corners. We use polar coordinates, taking a point O on the curve as origin, and the tangent at O as initial line. The curve lies wholly on one side of the tangent at O, so we take $0 \leqslant \theta \leqslant \pi$, and in this range r is a uniform function of θ, since a chord through O cuts the curve in only one other point. Thus we have an isoperimetrical problem, of ordinary (not parametric) type, with θ as independent variable (instead of x) and r as dependent variable (instead of y). There are fixed end-points in (θ, r), namely $(0, 0)$ and $(\pi, 0)$.

We wish to find a curve giving the greatest possible value to

$$I = \int_0^\pi \tfrac{1}{2}r^2 \, d\theta \tag{6.9.1}$$

subject to the isoperimetrical condition

$$J = \int_0^\pi \sqrt{(r'^2 + r^2)} \, d\theta = l. \tag{6.9.2}$$

Thus, according to Euler's rule, we need the extremals for

(6.9.3) $$\int_0^{\pi} \{\tfrac{1}{2}r^2 - \lambda\sqrt{(r'^2 + r^2)}\}\, d\theta.$$

The integrand does not contain θ, so Euler's equation has the first integral

(6.9.4) $$\tfrac{1}{2}r^2 - \frac{\lambda r^2}{\sqrt{(r'^2 + r^2)}} = C.$$

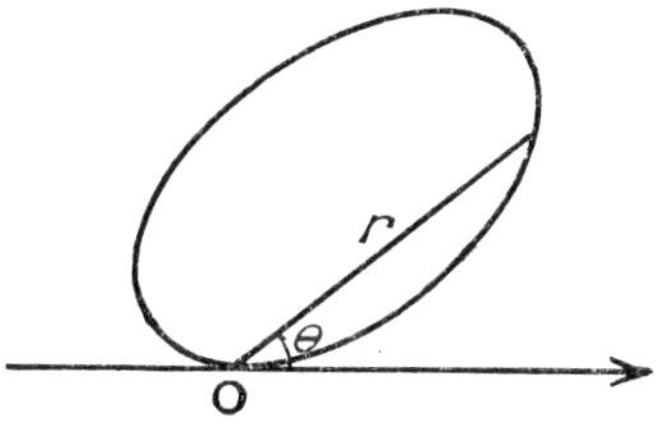

Fig. 6.9

The first member of this equation vanishes when $\theta = 0$, so $C = 0$, and (6.9.4) is equivalent to

(6.9.5) $$r'^2 + r^2 = \text{constant},$$

or say

(6.9.6) $$r'^2 = 4a^2 - r^2, \qquad (a > 0).$$

The solution in which $r \to 0$ as $\theta \to 0$ is

(6.9.7) $$r = 2a \sin \theta,$$

a circle of radius a touching the initial line at O. Finally we choose a to satisfy the isoperimetrical condition, and this makes $a = l/2\pi$. We thus recover the solution previously obtained. The greatest possible area is $l^2/4\pi$, and we recover the isoperimetrical inequality (6.1.1).

6.10 A simple eigenvalue problem

We consider the problem of finding a curve $y = \varphi(x)$ giving a minimum value to

(6.10.1) $$I = \int_0^{\pi} y'^2\, dx$$

subject to

(6.10.2) $$\int_0^{\pi} y^2\, dx = 1,$$

where A is (0, 0) and B is $(\pi, 0)$, i.e. $\varphi(0) = \varphi(\pi) = 0$.

We know the answer already! By Wirtinger's second inequality (§5.11) the minimum value for I is 1, and this is obtained when

(6.10.3) $$y = k \sin x.$$

To satisfy the isoperimetrical condition

(6.10.4) $$k = \pm\sqrt{(2/\pi)}.$$

Let us now consider the formal attack on the problem by means of Euler's rule. We need the extremals for the integrand

(6.10.5) $$y'^2 - \lambda y^2.$$

Euler's equation is

(6.10.6) $$y'' + \lambda y = 0.$$

To make the curve go through A and B we need $\lambda \geqslant 0$. If $\lambda = 0$, the curve is the axis $y = 0$, but this does not satisfy the isoperimetrical condition (6.10.2). If $\lambda > 0$ the possible values of λ are $1^2, 2^2, 3^2, \ldots$. For $\lambda = n^2$ the solution through A and B is

(6.10.7) $$y = k \sin nx,$$

and to satisfy the isoperimetrical condition $k = \pm\sqrt{(2/\pi)}$. The corresponding value of I is n^2. The least value of I, as we have noticed, is 1.

We have here a simple illustration of an important phenomenon. The values of λ giving solutions of (6.10.6) through the prescribed end-points and satisfying (6.10.2) are called *eigenvalues*, and the corresponding functions $\varphi(x)$ are called *eigenfunctions*. For the moment we content ourselves with the remark that there exists an enumerable infinity of eigenvalues, and there is one eigenfunction, unique save for sign, corresponding to each eigenvalue.

6.11 Example of an isoperimetrical problem with a discontinuous solution

Let us consider the problem of minimizing the integral

(6.11.1) $$I = \int_0^1 y'^2\, dx$$

in the family of curves of class D_1 joining $A(0, 0)$ to $B(1, 0)$, and having given length l, where $l > 1$.

Using Euler's rule we seek a minimizing curve for the integral

(6.11.2) $$\int_0^1 \{y'^2 - \lambda\sqrt{(1 + y'^2)}\}\, dx.$$

We have considered this integral already in Example 4 of §3.3. Since the integrand is a function of y', the solution consists of segments of straight lines. The corner conditions are given by the equations (3.3.18) and (3.3.19), where α and β are the values of ψ to left and to right of the corner, and α and β lie in $(-\frac{1}{2}\pi, \frac{1}{2}\pi)$. Since $\alpha \neq \beta$ the equation (3.3.19) proves that λ cannot be zero, and the argument given in §3.3 shows that $\alpha + \beta = 0$. The solution consists of line-segments inclined at angles α and $-\alpha$ to Ox; the isoperimetrical condition shows that $\sec \alpha = l$, and $\lambda = 2 \sec \alpha = 2l$. One solution is shown in Fig. 3.3c. But the solution is not unique, since the reflexion of ACB in AB will serve equally well, or indeed any solution consisting of line-segments inclined at angles α and $-\alpha$ to Ox (cf. Fig. 1.5).

6.12 The isoperimetrical problem with variable end-points

Let us suppose, to fix the ideas, that A is fixed and that B is to lie on a given curve Δ defined by the equations

(6.12.1) $$\overline{X} = p(t),\ \overline{Y} = q(t),$$

where $p(t)$ and $q(t)$ are of class C_1. We will assume also, to simplify the discussion, that the curves joining A to B that are admitted to competition are themselves of class C_1. We shall find necessary conditions for a minimizing curve.

Let us suppose that K_0, $y = \varphi(x)$, is a minimizing curve joining A to a point $B_0(\overline{X}_0, \overline{Y}_0)$ on Δ, and $\varphi(x) \in C_1$. We may suppose, without loss of generality, that $t = 0$ at B_0. Let us, as in §6.5, consider the family

(6.12.2) $$y = \varphi(x) + \alpha\eta(x) + \beta\zeta(x),$$

where $\eta, \zeta \in C_1$. Since A is fixed, $\eta(X) = \zeta(X) = 0$, but $\eta(\overline{X}_0)$, $\zeta(\overline{X}_0)$ do not vanish; in fact, since B lies on Δ,

(6.12.3) $$\mu(t, \alpha, \beta) \equiv \varphi[p(t)] + \alpha\eta[p(t)] + \beta\zeta[p(t)] - q(t) = 0,$$

and this equation defines t as a function of (α, β), say

(6.12.4) $$t = \tau(\alpha, \beta),$$

near $(0, 0)$. Since t vanishes at B_0, $\tau(0, 0) = 0$. In order that (6.12.3) can be solved for t as a function of (α, β) we need the condition

(6.12.5) $$\mu_t(0, 0, 0) \neq 0,$$

and this is the non-tangency condition

(6.12.6) $$\varphi'(\overline{X}_0)p'(0) - q'(0) \neq 0.$$

We assume that this condition is satisfied, i.e. that K_0 is not tangent to Δ at B_0.

We write, as in the fixed end-point problem,

$$\psi(\alpha, \beta) = \int_X^{\overline{X}} F(x, \varphi + \alpha\eta + \beta\zeta, \varphi' + \alpha\eta' + \beta\zeta')\, dx, \tag{6.12.7}$$

and then, by the method used to establish the variable end-point theorem in §4.2,

$$\psi_\alpha(0, 0) = \int_X^{\overline{X}_0} (\eta F_y + \eta' F_{y'})\, dx + \{Up'(0) + Vq'(0)\}\tau_\alpha(0, 0), \tag{6.12.8}$$

where the arguments in F_y and $F_{y'}$ are the elements (x, φ, φ') of K_0, and the arguments in U and V are the elements of K_0 at B_0.

It remains to calculate $\tau_\alpha(0, 0)$. Now from (6.12.3)

(6.12.9)

$$[\{\varphi'[p(t)] + \alpha\eta'[p(t)] + \beta\zeta'[p(t)]\}p'(t) - q'(t)]\tau_\alpha(\alpha, \beta) + \eta[p(t)] = 0,$$

whence

$$\tau_\alpha(0, 0) = \frac{\eta(\overline{X}_0)}{q'(0) - \varphi'(\overline{X}_0)p'(0)}, \tag{6.12.10}$$

and this is a known multiple of η at $\overline{X}_0$, say $M_2\eta(\overline{X}_0)$.

The required modification of the argument previously used for the fixed end-point problem is now clear. We write, as before,

$$\chi(\alpha, \beta) = \int_X^{\overline{X}} G(x, \varphi + \alpha\eta + \beta\zeta, \varphi' + \alpha\eta' + \beta\zeta')\, dx, \tag{6.12.11}$$

and we have

$$\frac{\psi_\alpha(0, 0)}{\chi_\alpha(0, 0)} = \frac{\psi_\beta(0, 0)}{\chi_\beta(0, 0)} \tag{6.12.12}$$

as a necessary condition for K_0 to be a minimizing curve. The first member of this equation involves only η, the second involves only ζ, so (choosing a fixed ζ as before) we have

$$\frac{\psi_\alpha(0, 0)}{\chi_\alpha(0, 0)} = \lambda, \tag{6.12.13}$$

where λ is a constant. Using the formula (6.12.8) for $\psi_\alpha(0, 0)$, with $\tau_\alpha(0, 0) = M_2\eta(\overline{X}_0)$, and using the corresponding formula for

$\chi_\alpha(0, 0)$, (6.12.13) becomes

(6.12.14) $$\int_X^{\overline{X}_0}(\eta F_y{}^* + \eta' F_{y'}{}^*)\,dx + \{U^*p'(0) + V^*q'(0)\}M_2\eta(\overline{X}_0) = 0,$$

where

(6.12.15) $$F^* = F - \lambda G,$$

and U^*, V^* are formed from F^* in the way that U, V are formed from F.

Taking first $\eta(\overline{X}_0) = 0$ we find the first condition as before, namely the equation of du Bois-Reymond for F^*. Then the integral in (6.12.14) vanishes, and, taking now a general variation in which $\eta(\overline{X}_0) \neq 0$, we need also the condition

(6.12.16) $$U^*p'(0) + V^*q'(0) = 0,$$

or

(6.12.17) $$U^*\,d\overline{X} + V^*\,d\overline{Y} = 0,$$

where U^*, V^* belong to K_0 at B_0, and $(d\overline{X}, d\overline{Y})$ is a displacement on Δ.

The upshot is that Euler's rule is extended immediately to the isoperimetrical problem with one variable end-point. We need the function F^* $(= F - \lambda G)$ not only in du Bois-Reymond's equation. but also in the end-condition (6.12.17).

Two simple special cases are worthy of notice. If Δ is a straight line perpendicular to Ox, i.e. if $\overline{X}$ is fixed but $\overline{Y}$ is variable, the end-condition takes the form $V^* = 0$. If Δ is a straight line parallel to Ox, i.e. if $\overline{Y}$ is fixed but $\overline{X}$ is variable, the end-condition takes the form $U^* = 0$.

The extension of the theory to the case in which both end-points are variable is evident; a formal proof will be found in §8.10.

6.13 Applications

We now consider some simple concrete examples of the isoperimetrical problem with variable end-points.

EXAMPLE 1. A uniform flexible string, of length l, has one end A fixed, and the other end B is free to move, without friction, on a curve Δ. To find the form of the string when it hangs in equilibrium.

In this problem

(6.13.1) $$F = \int_X^{\overline{X}} y\sqrt{(1 + y'^2)}\,dx,$$

and

(6.13.2) $$G \equiv \int_X^{\overline{X}} \sqrt{(1 + y'^2)}\,dx = l.$$

The point (X, Y) is fixed, and $(\overline{X}, \overline{Y})$ is constrained to lie on Δ. We write, as in §6.12,

$$F^* = (y - \lambda)\sqrt{(1 + y'^2)}, \tag{6.13.3}$$

where λ is a constant, and

$$U^* = (y - \lambda)\frac{1}{\sqrt{(1 + y'^2)}}, \quad V^* = (y - \lambda)\frac{y'}{\sqrt{(1 + y'^2)}}. \tag{6.13.4}$$

Euler's equation shows that the curve is a catenary, and the end-condition at B is

$$d\overline{X} + y'\,d\overline{Y} = 0, \tag{6.13.5}$$

where y' is the slope of the curve at B_0, and $(d\overline{X}, d\overline{Y})$ is a displacement on Δ. Thus the catenary must be orthogonal to Δ at B_0. Of course in this example the theory merely verifies a result that is evident on physical grounds.

Consider in particular the problem in which Δ is a (not horizontal) straight line. Let p_0 be the perpendicular distance of A from the line Δ. We can prove uniqueness by a geometrical argument as follows.

(i) Suppose that Δ is a vertical straight line. Then the lowest point of the catenary lies on Δ. Take any catenary with axis vertical, say the catenary $y = \cosh x$. Let P be a point on this catenary, p its distance from the axis, σ the arc PV from P to the vertex V (Fig. 6.13a). Then

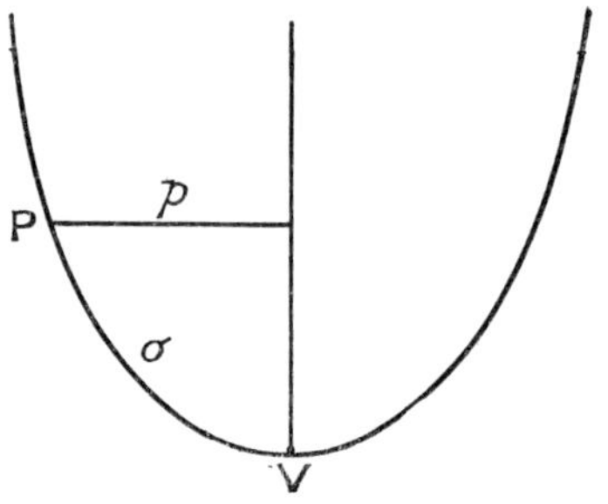

Fig. 6.13a

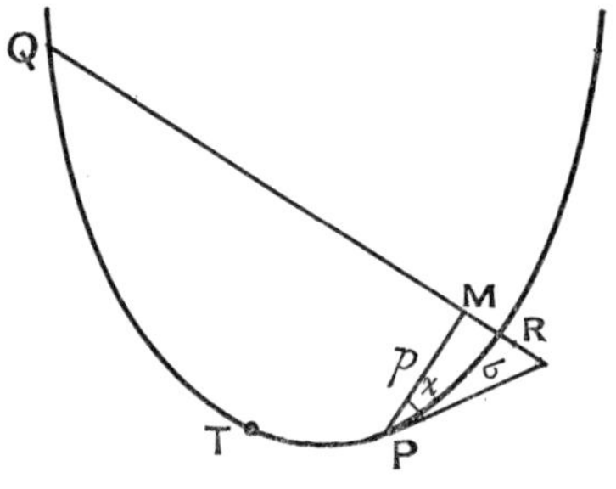

Fig. 6.13b

$p/\sigma = p/\sinh p$, which decreases monotonically from 1 to 0 as p goes from 0 to ∞, and therefore p/σ passes just once through the value p_0/l. The uniqueness of the required catenary through A, with its vertex B_0 on Δ and arc AB_0 of length l, now follows from the properties of similar figures.

(ii) If Δ is not vertical, and P is below Δ, take any catenary with axis vertical, and let R be the (unique) point on this catenary where the normal is parallel to Δ. Let the normal chord at R be QR (Fig. 6.13b), and let P be a point on the arc QR. Let PM be the perpendicular from P on to QR, let the length of PM be p, and the length of the arc PR be σ. Then as P moves from Q to R the ratio p/σ increases steadily from 0 to 1, and passes just once through the value p_0/l. The uniqueness now follows from the properties of similar figures.

To prove that p/σ increases monotonically as P moves from Q to R, we notice first that the result is evident as P moves from Q to T, the point where the tangent is parallel to QR, because in this range p steadily increases and σ steadily decreases. When P lies on the arc TR, $d\sigma/dp = \sec\chi$, where χ is the angle the tangent at P makes with PM. Then

$$\frac{d}{dp}\left(\frac{p}{\sigma}\right) = \frac{\sigma - p\sec\chi}{\sigma^2}, \tag{6.13.6}$$

and this is negative since $p\sec\chi > \sigma$. This completes the proof.

EXAMPLE 2. *Solid of maximum attraction.* The problem is to determine the shape of the solid of prescribed uniform density ρ and prescribed mass M which produces the greatest possible gravitational attraction at some point of space.

We assume on physical grounds that if such a solid exists it is a solid of revolution, and that the maximum field occurs at a pole. Let us take this pole as origin, and the axis of symmetry as the axis Ox. If the surface of the solid (using spherical polar coordinates) is defined by $r = f(\theta)$ the attraction at O is

$$-\int_{\theta=0}^{\pi/2} 2\pi\gamma\rho(1 - \cos\theta)\, d(r\cos\theta), \tag{6.13.7}$$

subject to

$$-\int_{\theta=0}^{\pi/2} \pi\rho r^2 \sin^2\theta\, d(r\cos\theta) = M. \tag{6.13.8}$$

Thus, in virtue of Euler's rule, a necessary condition for a maximum is that the integral

$$\int_{\theta=0}^{\pi/2} (1 - \cos\theta - \lambda r^2\sin^2\theta)\, d(r\cos\theta) \tag{6.13.9}$$

shall be stationary. This is a line-integral of the form $\int R\,dr + T\,d\theta$, and, as in §3.2, Euler's equation is not a differential equation, but reduces to the form

$$\frac{\partial T}{\partial r} - \frac{\partial R}{\partial \theta} = 0, \tag{6.13.10}$$

$$\sin\theta(2\lambda r^2 - \cos\theta) = 0. \tag{6.13.11}$$

The meridian curve has the form

$$r^2 = a^2 \cos \theta \tag{6.13.12}$$

shown in Fig. 6.13c. Since the value a of r at $\theta = 0$ is not prescribed,

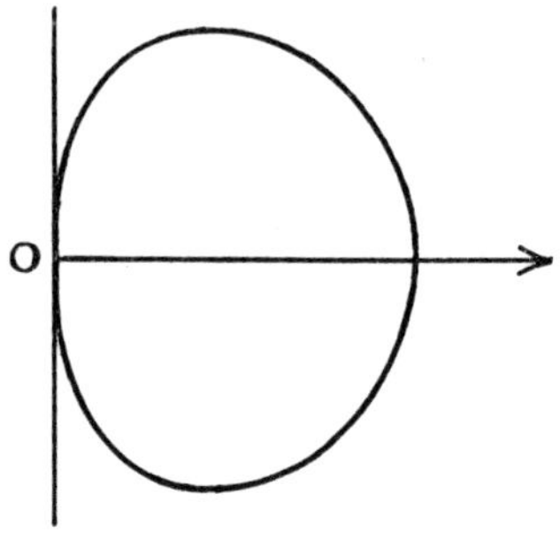

Fig. 6.13*c*

we have a variable end-point problem, and the end-condition at $\theta = 0$ is $R = 0$, which is satisfied. We choose a to give the correct mass,

$$\tfrac{4}{15}\pi\rho a^3 = M, \tag{6.13.13}$$

and then $r^2 = a^2 \cos \theta$ defines the shape of the solid of maximum attraction.

We easily verify the result by physical reasoning, and (assuming always that we may confine attention to solids of revolution) we can prove that the attraction is actually a maximum. The surface is such that a uniform ring of given mass, lying on the surface in a plane normal to the axis, has the same attraction at O wherever it lies on the surface. Moreover if we consider the family of similar surfaces (all with a pole at O and the same axis) for different values of a, the attraction of the ring is larger for a smaller value of a. Thus if we consider another solid of revolution (with a pole at O and the same axis) and having the correct volume, part of it lies outside S and part inside S. The attraction at O of this solid would be increased by moving the part outside S into the vacant part inside S.

EXAMPLE 3. *The chord-and-arc problem with variable end-point.* The problem is to find the curve in the upper half-plane, of given length l, which joins the origin A to a (variable) point B on the positive x-axis, and which is such that the area enclosed by the curve and the x-axis is a maximum.

In this problem, and in some similar problems, it is possible to reduce the isoperimetrical problem with variable end-points to an unrestricted problem with fixed end-points. The method is due to Euler. Let us represent the curve parametrically in the form $(x(s), y(s))$, where s denotes the arc-length measured from A. We have $x'(s) \geqslant 0$, $y(s) \geqslant 0$, $x'^2 + y'^2 = 1$, and the end-conditions are

$$(6.13.14) \qquad x(0) = 0, \quad y(0) = 0, \quad x(l) = \overline{X}, \quad y(l) = 0.$$

The integral we wish to maximize is

$$(6.13.15) \qquad I = \int_0^l yx' \, ds = \int_0^l y\sqrt{(1 - y'^2)} \, ds,$$

where y' now denotes dy/ds. We have thus a fixed end-point problem in the (s, y)-plane, not subject to any isoperimetrical condition. The familiar first integral of Euler's equation leads to $y^2 = c^2(1 - y'^2)$, where $c > 0$, and the solution vanishing at $s = 0$ is

$$(6.13.16) \qquad y = c \sin \frac{s}{c}.$$

The end-condition $y(l) = 0$ gives $c = l/\pi$. This is a maximizing curve. We can prove this, since we now have a fixed end-point problem, from the fundamental sufficiency theorem. We construct a semi-field in the region $0 < y < s < l$ by giving different values to c in (6.13.16), with $s < c\pi$. (All the extremals of the semi-field have the same tangent at A as in (5.14.7)) Now

$$(6.13.17) \qquad \mathscr{W}(s, y, \varpi) = \frac{y}{\sqrt{(1 - p^2)}} [\sqrt{\{(1 - \varpi^2)(1 - p^2)\}} - (1 - \varpi p)],$$

which is negative if $\varpi \neq p$.

Finally, returning to the (x,y)-plane, we have

$$(6.13.18) \qquad y = \frac{l}{\pi} \sin \frac{\pi s}{l}, \qquad x = \frac{l}{\pi}\left(1 - \cos \frac{\pi s}{l}\right),$$

and the maximizing curve in the (x, y)-plane is a semi-circle with its centre on Ox.

EXAMPLE 4. To find the closed surface of revolution which has prescribed area Δ and which encloses the greatest possible volume.

We wish to determine the curve in the upper half-plane, joining the (fixed) point A on the x-axis to the (variable) point B on the x-axis, such that the surface of revolution found by rotating the curve about Ox shall have prescribed area Δ and shall enclose the greatest possible volume. Without loss of generality we can take the point A

as origin. We seek a curve K in the upper half-plane, joining A to B, for which

(6.13.19) $$I = \pi \int_K y^2\, dx$$

has a maximum value, subject to the isoperimetrical condition

(6.13.20) $$J \equiv 2\pi \int_K y\, ds = \Delta.$$

We use the device of Euler introduced in Example 3. We take a new independent variable σ defined by

(6.13.21) $$y\, ds = d\sigma,$$

so σ runs from the lower limit zero to the *fixed* upper limit $\Delta/2\pi$, and y vanishes at both limits. If now we represent the curve parametrically in the form $(x(\sigma), y(\sigma))$, where $x'(\sigma) \geqslant 0$ and $y(\sigma) \geqslant 0$, we have

(6.13.22) $$x'^2 + y'^2 = \frac{1}{y^2},$$

and

(6.13.23) $$I = \pi \int_0^{\bar{X}} y^2\, dx = \pi \int_0^{\Delta/2\pi} y^2 x'\, d\sigma = \pi \int_0^{\Delta/2\pi} y\sqrt{(1 - y^2 y'^2)}\, d\sigma.$$

We now have a problem with fixed end-points. If we change the dependent variable from y to z, where $z = \frac{1}{2}y^2$, we get

(6.13.24) $$I = \pi\sqrt{2} \int_0^{\Delta/2\pi} \sqrt{\{z(1 - z'^2)\}}\, d\sigma,$$

and $z = 0$ at $\sigma = 0$ and at $\sigma = \Delta/2\pi$. This problem has been discussed already in §3.10 and in §5.14. The parabolic extremal

(6.13.25) $$z = \sigma - \frac{\sigma^2}{2a^2},$$

where $a = \sqrt{(\Delta/4\pi)}$, is a maximizing curve. The value of I for the maximizing curve is $\sqrt{(\Delta^3/36\pi)}$.

Let us now return to the original coordinates. Since

(6.13.26) $$x'^2 = \frac{1}{2z}(1 - z'^2) = \frac{1}{a^2},$$

we have $x = \sigma/a$, and the maximizing curve is the semi-circle

(6.13.27) $$(x - a)^2 + y^2 = a^2.$$

The required surface is a sphere. The maximum volume attainable is $\sqrt{(\Delta^3/36\pi)}$, as we have noticed already (cf. (6.2.24)).

Another proof of this result will be given in connexion with the parametric problem in §9.18.

6.14 The Sturm-Liouville problem

We have already considered (§6.10) the problem of minimizing

$$\int_0^1 y'^2\,dx, \qquad y(0) = y(1) = 0, \tag{6.14.1}$$

subject to

$$\int_0^1 y^2\,dx = 1, \tag{6.14.2}$$

and this is equivalent to the problem of minimizing

$$\int_0^1 (y'^2 - ky^2)\,dx, \tag{6.14.3}$$

where k is constant, subject to the same isoperimetrical condition (6.14.2). We now turn to an important generalization of these problems.

We seek a function $y = \varphi(x)$ to minimize

$$I = \int_X^{\overline{X}} (\tau y'^2 - \mu y^2)\,dx + a[\varphi(X)]^2 + b[\varphi(\overline{X})]^2, \tag{6.14.4}$$

subject to the isoperimetrical, or normalizing, condition

$$\int_X^{\overline{X}} \sigma y^2\,dx = 1. \tag{6.14.5}$$

The conditions are as follows. The end-values X and $\overline{X}$ are fixed. The functions τ, μ, and σ are given continuous functions of x; τ and σ are positive for all values of x, and each has a continuous first derivative. The symbols a and b denote prescribed non-negative constants. The end-conditions that occur are of various kinds. In the simplest case $Y = \overline{Y} = 0$; A and B are fixed points on $y = 0$, and the terms $aY^2 + b\overline{Y}^2$ disappear from the problem. In other cases A is free to move on $x = X$ and B on $x = \overline{X}$, so Y and $\overline{Y}$ are variable. Or we may have mixed end-conditions, one end being fixed on $y = 0$, and the other free to move on a given vertical line.

To begin with, it will be convenient to bring the extra terms under the integral sign in the form

(6.14.6) $$\int_X^{\overline{X}} \frac{d}{dx}(\theta y^2)\,dx,$$

where $\theta(x) \in C_1$, $\theta(X) = -a$, $\theta(\overline{X}) = b$. The simplest choice for $\theta(x)$ is the linear function

(6.14.7) $$\{-a(\overline{X} - x) + b(x - X)\}/(\overline{X} - X).$$

Thus the problem takes the form of minimizing

(6.14.8) $$\int_X^{\overline{X}} \{\tau y'^2 - \mu y^2 + \frac{d}{dx}(\theta y^2)\}\,dx$$

subject to the normalizing condition (6.14.5). As we have noticed already (§3.2) the last term in the integrand will make no contribution to Euler's equation; it will only influence the end-conditions.

Using Euler's rule we form Euler's equation for

(6.14.9) $$F^* = \tau y'^2 - \mu y^2 + \frac{d}{dx}(\theta y^2) - \lambda\sigma y^2$$

where λ is a constant to be determined. Euler's equation is

(6.14.10) $$\frac{d}{dx}(\tau y') + (\mu + \lambda\sigma)y = 0.$$

In the fixed end-point problem the end-conditions are

(6.14.11) $$\varphi(X) = \varphi(\overline{X}) = 0.$$

In the variable end-point problem, V^* vanishes at the end-points,

(6.14.12) $$\tau(X)y'(X) - aY = 0, \quad \tau(\overline{X})y'(\overline{X}) + b\overline{Y} = 0.$$

(If a and b are both zero the conditions (6.14.12) reduce to $y'(X) = y'(\overline{X}) = 0$.) In the mixed end-point problem we have one end-condition of each type. The equation (6.14.10) is a *Sturm-Liouville differential equation*, and this equation, with the end-conditions appropriate to the particular problem, is a *Sturm-Liouville system.*

If $y = \varphi(x)$ is a non-zero solution of the differential equation (6.14.10) satisfying the prescribed end-conditions, then $y = k\varphi(x)$ is another such solution, and the normalizing condition (6.14.5) determines a unique value of k^2. A value of λ for which there exists a non-zero solution satisfying the prescribed end-conditions is an *eigenvalue*, and the corresponding solution satisfying the normalizing condition, unique save for sign, is the corresponding *eigenfunction*.

The eigenfunctions possess the important property of *orthogonality*, i.e. if φ_r, φ_s are eigenfunctions corresponding to two different eigenvalues λ_r, λ_s, then

$$\int_X^{\overline{X}} \sigma\varphi_r\varphi_s\,dx = 0. \tag{6.14.13}$$

We can express the normalizing condition (6.14.5) and the orthogonality relation (6.14.13) in the single equation

$$\int_X^{\overline{X}} \sigma\varphi_r\varphi_s\,dx = \delta_r^s. \tag{6.14.14}$$

A set of functions satisfying (6.14.14) is called an *orthonormal set*, and the set is said to be *complete* if there exists no orthonormal set of which it is a proper subset.

To prove the orthogonality relation (6.14.13) we have

$$\frac{d}{dx}(\tau\varphi_r') + (\mu + \lambda_r\sigma)\varphi_r = 0,$$

$$\frac{d}{dx}(\tau\varphi'_s) + (\mu + \lambda_s\sigma)\varphi_s = 0,$$

whence

$$\varphi_s\frac{d}{dx}(\tau\varphi_r') - \varphi_r\frac{d}{dx}(\tau\varphi_s') + (\lambda_r - \lambda_s)\sigma\varphi_r\varphi_s = 0.$$

Therefore

$$(\lambda_r - \lambda_s)\int_X^{\overline{X}} \sigma\varphi_r\varphi_r\,dx = \int_X^{\overline{X}}\left\{\varphi_r\frac{d}{dx}(\tau\varphi_s') - \varphi_s\frac{d}{dx}(\tau\varphi_r')\right\}dx \tag{6.14.15}$$

$$= \int_X^{\overline{X}} \frac{d}{dx}\{\tau(\varphi_r\varphi_s' - \varphi_s\varphi_r')\}\,dx$$

$$= \tau(\varphi_r\psi_s' - \varphi_s\varphi_r')\Big|_X^{\overline{X}}.$$

Now $\tau(\varphi_r\varphi_s' - \varphi_s\varphi_r')$ vanishes both at X and at X. For a fixed end-point, $\varphi_r = \varphi_s = 0$, and the result is obvious. For a free end-point, say A,

$$\tau(X)\varphi_r'(X) = a\varphi_r(X), \quad \tau(X)\varphi_s'(X) = a\varphi_s(X),$$

whence

$$\tau(X)\{\varphi_r(X)\varphi_s'(X) - \varphi_s(X)\varphi_r'(X)\} = 0.$$

Thus, since $\lambda_r - \lambda_s \neq 0$, (6.14.13) is true in all cases.

The general theory of Sturm-Liouville systems is outside the scope of this book, but it may be of interest to mention briefly, without proof, the main line of development. There exists an enumerable infinity of eigenvalues, all positive or zero, and we list them in ascending order of magnitude, $\lambda_1, \lambda_2, \lambda_3, \ldots$. The sequence has the property that $\lambda_n \to \infty$ with n. The eigenfunctions $\varphi_1, \varphi_2, \varphi_3, \ldots$ form a complete orthonormal set.

Consider a function $f(x)$, of class C_2, defined in $(X, \overline{X})$. We can construct the series $\sum_{n=1}^{\infty} c_n\varphi_n(x)$, where the coefficient c_n is given by the equation

$$c_n = \int_X^{\overline{X}} \sigma(x)\varphi_n(x)f(x)\,dx. \tag{6.14.16}$$

The analogy with the determination of the coefficients in a Fourier series is evident, and (remembering that $f(x) \in C_2$) the series converges to $f(x)$ at each point x in $X < x < \overline{X}$. Many of the cases important in physics are *singular*, i.e. either $\sigma(x)$ has a singularity at one end of the range $(X, \overline{X})$, or one of the limits X, $\overline{X}$ is infinite.

We follow the development a little further in the simplest case; X and $\overline{X}$ are finite, $a = b = 0$ (so the terms outside the integral in (6.14.4) are absent), $\mu = 0$, and either σ or τ is constant.

Let us consider the two Sturm-Liouville systems, $\mathscr{A}$:

$$y'' + \lambda\sigma y = 0, \tag{6.14.17}$$

with the end-conditions

$$y(X) = y(\overline{X}) = 0, \tag{6.14.18}$$

and $\mathscr{B}$:

$$\frac{d}{dx}\left(\frac{y'}{\sigma}\right) + \lambda y = 0, \tag{6.14.19}$$

with the end-conditions

$$y'(X) = y'(\overline{X}) = 0. \tag{6.14.20}$$

The same function σ occurs in both systems, and σ is positive, bounded, and of class C_1. We notice that zero is not an eigenvalue for $\mathscr{A}$, but that zero is an eigenvalue for $\mathscr{B}$, the corresponding eigenfunction being constant.

If $\varphi(x)$ satisfies $\mathscr{A}$ (i.e. both the differential equation and the end-conditions) for a certain value of λ, then $\psi(x)$ $(= \varphi'(x))$ satisfies $\mathscr{B}$ (i.e. both the differential equations and the end-conditions) for the same value of λ. Conversely, if $\psi(x)$ satisfies $\mathscr{B}$, $\varphi(x)\left(= \int_X^x \psi(t)\,dt\right)$ satisfies $\mathscr{A}$, *with one exception*: $\varphi(x)$ satisfies (6.14.17) always, but $\varphi(x)$ does not satisfy the boundary conditions (6.14.18) if $\lambda = 0$. The two systems $\mathscr{A}$ and $\mathscr{B}$ have the same eigenvalues, with the exception that $\mathscr{B}$ has the additional eigenvalue zero. If the eigenvalues of $\mathscr{A}$ are $\lambda_1, \lambda_2, \lambda_3, \ldots$, those of $\mathscr{B}$ are $\lambda_0, \lambda_1, \lambda_2, \ldots$, where $\lambda_0 = 0$. (It is convenient to permit here the slight change of notation; in the general theory the smallest eigenvalue for any system was called λ_1.) The eigenfunctions for $\mathscr{B}$ are found (except for the eigenfunction corresponding to λ_0) from those for $\mathscr{A}$ by differentiation.

If the eigenfunction for $\mathscr{A}$ corresponding to the eigenvalue λ_n is $\varphi_n(x)$, the normalizing condition is

$$\int_X^{\overline{X}} \sigma(x)\, \{\varphi_n(x)\}^2\, dx = 1. \tag{6.14.21}$$

The corresponding normalized eigenfunction for $\mathscr{B}$ is $\varphi_n'/\sqrt{\lambda_n}$, for

(6.14.22)

$$\frac{1}{\lambda_n}\int_X^{\overline{X}} \{\varphi_n'(x)\}^2\, dx = -\frac{1}{\lambda_n}\int_X^{\overline{X}} \varphi_n(x)\varphi_n''(x)\, dx = \int_X^{\overline{X}} \sigma(x)\{\varphi_n(x)\}^2\, dx = 1,$$

and $\psi_0(x) = (\overline{X} - X)^{-1/2}$.

If now $f(x)$ is a function of class C_2 defined in $(X, \overline{X})$, and such that $f(X) = f(\overline{X}) = 0$, the eigenfunction expansion of $f(x)$ is $\sum_{n=1}^{\infty} c_n\varphi_n(x)$, where

$$c_n = \int_X^{\overline{X}} f(x)\sigma(x)\varphi_n(x)\, dx. \tag{6.14.23}$$

The corresponding expansion of $f'(x)$ is $d_0\psi_0 + \sum_{n=1}^{\infty} d_n\varphi_n'(x)/\sqrt{\lambda_n}$. But $d_0 = 0$, because

$$\int_X^{\overline{X}} f'(x)\, dx = f(\overline{X}) - f(X) = 0,$$

and, for $n > 0$,

$$d_n = \frac{1}{\sqrt{\lambda_n}}\int_X^{\overline{X}} f'(x)\varphi_n'(x)\, dx = -\frac{1}{\sqrt{\lambda_n}}\int_X^{\overline{X}} f(x)\varphi_n''(x)\, dx$$

$$= \sqrt{\lambda_n}\int_X^{\overline{X}} f(x)\sigma(x)\varphi_n(x)\, dx = \sqrt{\lambda_n}\,c_n.$$

In this case therefore (where $f(x) \in C_2$ and $f(X) = f(\overline{X}) = 0$), if the expansion of $f(x)$ is $\sum_{n=1}^{\infty} c_n\varphi_n(x)$, the expansion of $f'(x)$ is $\sum_{n=1}^{\infty} c_n\varphi_n'(x)$. The expansions converge to $f(x)$ and to $f'(x)$ respectively, so we find $f'(x)$ by term-by-term differentiation of the series for $f(x)$.

CHAPTER VII

Curves in Space

7.1 Necessary conditions for a minimizing curve

We now consider problems involving one independent and two dependent variables; considered geometrically, we now have curves in space instead of curves in a plane. We denote the end-points by $A(X, Y, Z)$ and $B(\overline{X}, \overline{Y}, \overline{Z})$, where $X < \overline{X}$, and the curves to be discussed have the form

(7.1.1) $$y = \varphi(x), \qquad z = \psi(x),$$

where

(7.1.2) $$\varphi(X) = Y, \quad \psi(X) = Z; \quad \varphi(\overline{X}) = \overline{Y}, \quad \psi(\overline{X}) = \overline{Z}.$$

In the problem now to be discussed (the ordinary problem in space of three dimensions, not the parametric problem) our attention is limited to curves lying in the slab $X \leqslant x \leqslant \overline{X}$ and cutting any plane $x = \xi$ in the slab in only one point. Our problem is to find a minimizing curve for

(7.1.3) $$I = \int_X^{\overline{X}} f\{x, \varphi(x), \psi(x), \varphi'(x), \psi'(x)\}\, dx.$$

The function $f(x, y, z, u, v)$ is a given function of the five independent variables x, y, z, u, v, and $f \in C_4$ in an appropriate region R of the five-fold space of (x, y, z, u, v). The curves admitted to competition are of class D_1, i.e. the functions $\varphi(x)$ and $\psi(x)$ are continuous, with derivatives $\varphi'(x)$ and $\psi'(x)$ which are piecewise continuous. Thus the curves have continuously turning tangents except at a finite number of corners. Much of the theory already developed for problems in the plane can be extended in a simple and natural way to problems in space.

We speak of the ordered triple (x, y, z) (or $\{x, \varphi(x), \psi(x)\}$) as a *point* of the curve, of the ordered pair (y', z') (or $\{\varphi'(x), \psi'(x)\}$) as the *slope* of the curve, and of the ordered quintuple (x, y, z, y', z') (or $\{x, \varphi(x), \psi(x), \varphi'(x), \psi'(x)\}$) as an *element* of the curve.

To begin with, let us suppose the end-points A and B to be fixed, and let us suppose that the curve K_0 defined by (7.1.1) is a minimizing curve in the class D_1. We then consider the one-parameter family whose typical member K_α is defined by

(7.1.4) $$y = \varphi(x) + \alpha\eta(x), \quad z = \psi(x) + \alpha\zeta(x),$$

where the functions $\eta(x)$ and $\zeta(x)$ are of class D_1, and vanish at X and at $\overline{X}$. Since K_0 is a minimizing curve in the class D_1 it is *a fortiori* a minimizing curve in the one-parameter family.

Thus if

(7.1.5)
$$\chi(\alpha) = I(K_\alpha) = \int_X^{\overline{X}} f(x, \varphi + \alpha\eta, \psi + \alpha\zeta, \varphi' + \alpha\eta', \psi' + \alpha\zeta')\, dx$$

we have as necessary conditions for a minimizing curve

(7.1.6) $$\chi'(0) = 0, \quad \chi''(0) \geqslant 0.$$

Now

(7.1.7) $$\chi'(0) = \int_X^{\overline{X}} (\eta f_y + \zeta f_z + \eta' f_{y'} + \zeta' f_{z'})\, dx,$$

where the arguments in the derivatives of f in the integrand are the elements x, $\varphi(x)$, $\psi(x)$, $\varphi'(x)$, $\psi'(x)$ of K_0. The integrand in the second member of (7.1.7) is a homogeneous linear form in η, ζ, η', ζ', with coefficients which are known functions of x, and these coefficients are continuous except at the corners of K_0. Further

(7.1.8) $$\chi''(0) = \int_X^{\overline{X}} 2\omega\, dx,$$

where 2ω is a homogeneous quadratic form in η, ζ, η', ζ', the coefficients being known functions of x, namely the elements of the matrix

(7.1.9) $$\begin{pmatrix} f_{yy} & f_{yz} & f_{yy'} & f_{yz'} \\ f_{zy} & f_{zz} & f_{zy'} & f_{zz'} \\ f_{y'y} & f_{y'z} & f_{y'y'} & f_{y'z'} \\ f_{z'y} & f_{z'z} & f_{z'y'} & f_{z'z'} \end{pmatrix},$$

the arguments in the derivatives of f being the elements of K_0.

The equation $\chi'(0) = 0$ holds for an arbitrary choice of η and ζ within the prescribed class, and putting $\zeta(x) = 0$ we have

(7.1.10) $$\int_X^{\overline{X}} (\eta f_y + \eta' f_{y'})\, dx = 0.$$

We now proceed as in §2.3. Writing

(7.1.11) $$\sigma(x) = \int_X^{x} f_y\{t, \varphi(t), \psi(t), \varphi'(t), \psi'(t)\}\, dt,$$

the equation (7.1.10) becomes

$$\int_X^{\overline{X}} (\eta\sigma' + \eta' f_{y'})\, dx = 0 \tag{7.1.12}$$

whence

$$\eta\sigma \Big|_X^{\overline{X}} + \int_X^{\overline{X}} \eta'(f_{y'} - \sigma)\, dx = 0. \tag{7.1.13}$$

But η vanishes at X and $\overline{X}$, so we conclude, in virtue of Lemma 2, §2.1,

(7.1.14)

$$f_{y'}\{x, \varphi(x), \psi(x), \varphi'(x), \psi'(x)\} = \int_X^x f_y\{t, \varphi(t), \psi(t), \varphi'(t), \psi'(t)\}\, dt + C$$

The value of C is of course $f_{y'}(a)$, where a is written for the element of K_0 at A, namely $\{X, \varphi(X), \psi(X), \varphi'(X), \psi'(X)\}$. In a similar way we establish the result

(7.1.15)

$$f_{z'}\{x, \varphi(x), \psi(x), \varphi'(x), \psi'(x)\} = \int_X^x f_z\{t, \varphi(t), \psi(t), \varphi'(t), \psi'(t)\}\, dt + D,$$

where the actual value of the constant D is $f_{z'}(a)$. The equations (7.1.14-15) are the equations of du Bois-Reymond, and they are necessary conditions for a minimizing curve.

On an arc between consecutive corners of K_0 the integrands in the second members of (7.1.14-15) are continuous, so such an arc must satisfy Euler's equations

$$\frac{d}{dx} f_{y'} = f_y, \qquad \frac{d}{dx} f_{z'} = f_z. \tag{7.1.16}$$

These are a pair of simultaneous differential equations of the second order which are satisfied by the functions (7.1.1). The curves of class C_2 defined by Euler's equations (7.1.16) are called *extremals*.

There are some special cases in which the function f has properties which help to simplify the integration. Let us write, by analogy with the notation used in the plane problem,

$$U = f - y' f_{y'} - z' f_{z'}, \quad V = f_{y'}, \quad W = f_{z'}. \tag{7.1.17}$$

Then

$$\frac{dU}{dx} = f_x + y'\left(f_y - \frac{d}{dx} f_{y'}\right) + z'\left(f_z - \frac{d}{dx} f_{z'}\right), \tag{7.1.18}$$

and if now y and z denote functions of x satisfying Euler's equations (7.1.16) we have

$$\frac{dU}{dx} = f_x. \tag{7.1.19}$$

We have therefore,

(i) If f does not contain x explicitly, then U = constant is a first integral of Euler's equations,

(ii) If f does not contain y explicitly, then V = constant is a first integral of Euler's equations,

(iii) If f does not contain z explicitly, then W = constant is a first integral of Euler's equations,

(iv) If f is the sum of a function of (x, y, y') and a function of (x, z, z') the problem is equivalent to two distinct plane problems.

These special cases appear conspicuously in classical dynamics. If x denotes time, and y and z are Lagrangian coordinates for a dynamical system, the Lagrangian equations of motion are the Euler equations derived from the Lagrangian function f. The first integral in (i) is the integral of energy, and the first integrals in (ii) and (iii) are integrals of momentum. In (iv) we have an example of a completely separable system; complete separability occurs for example in the theory of small oscillations if y and z are normal coordinates for the vibrating system.

EXAMPLE 1. To find the extremal joining the origin to the point $B(\bar{X}, \bar{Y}, \bar{Z})$ for the integral

$$\int_0^{\bar{X}} \{\tfrac{1}{2}(y'^2 + z'^2) + k(yz' - zy') - \tfrac{1}{2}n^2(y^2 + z^2)\}\, dx, \tag{7.1.20}$$

where k and n are positive constants.

The Euler equations are

$$y'' - 2kz' + n^2 y = 0, \qquad z'' + 2ky' + n^2 z = 0, \tag{7.1.21}$$

and the integration is elementary,

$$\begin{cases} y = \dfrac{\sin px}{\sin p\bar{X}}\{\bar{Y}\cos k(x - \bar{X}) + \bar{Z}\sin k(x - \bar{X})\} \\[2ex] \quad = \dfrac{R}{\sin p\bar{X}} \sin px.\cos k(x - \bar{X} - \alpha), \\[2ex] z = \dfrac{\sin px}{\sin p\bar{X}}\{-\bar{Y}\sin k(x - \bar{X}) + \bar{Z}\cos k(x - \bar{X})\} \\[2ex] \quad = -\dfrac{R}{\sin p\bar{X}} \sin px.\sin k(x - \bar{X} - \alpha), \end{cases} \tag{7.1.22}$$

where $p = \sqrt{(k^2 + n^2)}$, and, in the formulae on the right, $\bar{Y} = R \cos k\alpha$, $\bar{Z} = R \sin k\alpha$. It is assumed that $p\bar{X}$ is not an integral multiple of π.

EXAMPLE 2. Consider the integral

$$\int_X^{\bar{X}} \{\tfrac{1}{2}(y'^2 + z'^2) + kyz\}\, dx, \tag{7.1.23}$$

where k is a given constant. If we change the dependent variables to u, v, where

$$y = u + v, \qquad z = u - v, \tag{7.1.24}$$

the integral becomes

$$\int_X^{\bar{X}} \{(u'^2 + ku^2) + (v'^2 - kv^2)\}\, dx. \tag{7.1.25}$$

This is an example of (iv) above; the system is completely separable, and the integration is simple.

7.2 The corner conditions

Suppose the minimizing curve has a corner, where $\varphi'(x)$ is discontinuous, or $\psi'(x)$ is discontinuous, or possibly both. At a corner the *integrands* in the second members of (7.1.14) and (7.1.15) are discontinuous, but the *integrals* are continuous functions of x, and therefore the first members are continuous. Thus $V(=f_{y'})$ and $W(=f_{z'})$ are continuous at a corner on a minimizing curve. By an argument precisely similar to that used in §2.6 we see that U $(=f - y'f_{y'} - z'f_{z'})$ is also continuous at a corner.

Consider in particular the problem in which

$$f = \lambda\sqrt{(1 + y'^2 + z'^2)}, \tag{7.2.1}$$

where λ is a function of (x, y, z) which is positive for all values of (x, y, z). In this case

$$U = \lambda \frac{1}{\sqrt{(1 + y'^2 + z'^2)}}, \qquad V = \lambda \frac{y'}{\sqrt{(1 + y'^2 + z'^2)}}, \tag{7.2.2}$$
$$W = \lambda \frac{z'}{\sqrt{(1 + y'^2 + z'^2)}},$$

and no minimizing curve can have a corner.

7.3 Existence and continuity of the second derivatives $\varphi''(x)$, $\psi''(x)$

We consider an element (x, y, z, y', z') of K_0, not at a corner, at which the determinant

$$M \equiv \begin{vmatrix} f_{y'y'} & f_{y'z'} \\ f_{z'y'} & f_{z'z'} \end{vmatrix} \tag{7.3.1}$$

has a value different from zero. Near the value of x for this element the functions $\varphi(x)$, $\psi(x)$ have continuous second derivatives. (The condition $M \neq 0$ is of course the analogue of the condition $N \neq 0$ in the plane problem.)

To prove this statement we extend to the case of two dependent variables the second of the proofs given for the case of one dependent variable in §2.7.

Consider the functions $m(x)$, $n(x)$ defined implicitly by the equations

$$\lambda(x, m, n) = 0, \quad \mu(x, m, n) = 0, \tag{7.3.2}$$

where

$$\begin{cases} \lambda(x, m, n) \equiv f_{y'}\{x, \varphi(x), \psi(x), m, n\} \\ \qquad\qquad - \int_X^x f_y\{t, \varphi(t), \psi(t), \varphi'(t), \psi'(t)\}\, dt - C, \\ \mu(x, m, n) \equiv f_{z'}\{x, \varphi(x), \psi(x), m, n\} \\ \qquad\qquad - \int_X^x f_z\{t, \varphi(t), \psi(t), \varphi'(t), \psi'(t)\}\, dt - D, \end{cases} \tag{7.3.3}$$

In virtue of the *implicit function theorem* we know that if (x_0, m_0, n_0) is a particular solution of (7.3.2), and if

$$\frac{\partial(\lambda, \mu)}{\partial(m, n)} \tag{7.3.4}$$

has a value different from zero at (x_0, m_0, n_0), then the equations (7.3.2) define unique solutions $m(x)$, $n(x)$ in the neighbourhood of x_0, and these functions take the values m_0, n_0 at x_0. Moreover, if λ and μ are of class C_n, the solutions $m(x)$, $n(x)$ are also of class C_n.

Now the equations (7.3.2) have the solutions

$$m(x) = \varphi'(x), \quad n(x) = \psi'(x), \tag{7.3.5}$$

in virtue of (7.1.14–15). Moreover λ and μ have continuous first derivatives with respect to x, m, n near each solution $(x, m, n) = \{x, \varphi'(x), \psi'(x)\}$ which is not a corner of K_0 (since $f \in C_2$, and $\varphi'(x)$, $\psi'(x)$ are continuous), and (7.3.4) is not zero because (7.3.1) is not zero. Hence $m(x), n(x) \in C_1$, so $\varphi''(x)$, $\psi''(x)$ exist and are continuous.

An arc of a minimizing curve which contains no corner and whose elements are such that (M) nowhere vanishes (and therefore such that (M) has the same sign throughout) is called *regular*.

We have seen that, on a regular arc, the second derivatives $\varphi''(x)$, $\psi''(x)$ exist and are continuous. The argument can be extended, exactly as for the plane case in §2.7, to show that the third and fourth derivatives also exist and are continuous.

All of this refers to a point of K_0 which is not a corner. If there is a corner at $x = x_0$, and we consider the arc to the right (left) of the corner, the derivatives $\varphi''(x)$, $\psi''(x)$ tend to unique limits as $x \to x_0$ from above (below), and these limits are the (one-sided) derivatives of $\varphi'(x)$ and of $\psi'(x)$ at $x_0 + 0$ (or at $x_0 - 0$). The proof is, with only trivial modification, the same as that given in §2.7, and need not be repeated here.

7.4 The extremals

Near the elements of a regular extremal arc K_0 the equations (7.1.16) are linear in y'' and z'',

$$(7.4.1)\qquad \begin{cases} f_{y'y'}y'' + f_{y'z'}z'' = f_y - f_{y'x} - f_{y'y}y' - f_{y'z}z', \\ f_{z'y'}y'' + f_{z'z'}z'' = f_z - f_{z'x} - f_{z'y}y' - f_{z'z}z', \end{cases}$$

and (since (7.3.1) is non-zero in the neighbourhood of an element of K_0) these equations can be solved for y'' and z'',

$$(7.4.2)\qquad y'' = A(x, y, z, y', z'), \quad z'' = B(x, y, z, y', z'),$$

where A and B are of class C_2. The existence theorem for a system of differential equations assures us that these equations have a unique system of solutions $\varphi(x)$, $\psi(x)$ through each initial element $(x, y, z, y', z') = (\xi, \eta, \zeta, \eta', \zeta')$ in a sufficiently small neighbourhood of the elements of K_0. The solutions have the form

$$(7.4.3)\qquad y = \varphi(x;\ \xi, \eta, \zeta, \eta', \zeta'), \quad z = \psi(x;\ \xi, \eta, \zeta, \eta', \zeta'),$$

and $\varphi, \psi, \varphi', \psi' \in C_2$ in a neighbourhood of the sets $(x, \xi, \eta, \zeta, \eta', \zeta')$ belonging to K_0. The equations (7.4.3) represent a four-parameter family of extremals. For example we may think of ξ as fixed, and then $(\eta, \zeta, \eta', \zeta')$ represent the prescribed values of (y, z, y', z') —assumed sufficiently near to the values for K_0—at $x = \xi$.

In general the solutions of Euler's equations will be found in a form

$$(7.4.4)\qquad y = \varphi(x;\ a, b, c, d) \qquad z = \psi(x;\ a, b, c, d),$$

and the parameters a, b, c, d will not in general be those appearing in (7.4.3). The extremal arc K_0 is given by a particular set $(a, b, c, d) = (a_0, b_0, c_0, d_0)$, and the equations (7.4.4) represent extremal arcs when (a, b, c, d) lies in a sufficiently small neighbourhood of (a_0, b_0, c_0, d_0). The extremal arc K_0 is embedded in the four-parameter family.

The determinant Δ, the analogue of the determinant appearing in (2.8.5),

$$(7.4.5) \qquad \Delta = \begin{vmatrix} \varphi_a & \varphi_b & \varphi_c & \varphi_d \\ \psi_a & \psi_b & \psi_c & \psi_d \\ \varphi_a' & \varphi_b' & \varphi_c' & \varphi_d' \\ \psi_a' & \psi_b' & \psi_c' & \psi_d' \end{vmatrix}$$

does not vanish on a regular extremal arc.

We notice first that if we take the parameters (a, b, c, d) to be $(\eta, \zeta, \eta', \zeta')$, as in (7.4.3), the value of Δ at $x = \xi$ is $+1$. This follows easily from the identities

$$(7.4.6) \quad \begin{cases} \eta = \varphi(\xi; \xi, \eta, \zeta, \eta', \zeta'), & \zeta = \psi(\xi; \xi, \eta, \zeta, \eta', \zeta'), \\ \eta' = \varphi'(\xi; \xi, \eta, \zeta, \eta', \zeta'), & \zeta' = \psi'(\xi; \xi, \eta, \zeta, \eta', \zeta'). \end{cases}$$

Thus, by continuity, Δ does not vanish near $x = \xi$ if we make this particular choice of parameters.

To prove the general result we prove the result analogous to (2.8.7) for the plane case, namely

$$(7.4.7) \qquad M\,\Delta = \text{constant}$$

along an extremal. We have

$$(7.4.8) \quad \frac{d\Delta}{dx} = \begin{vmatrix} \varphi_a & \varphi_b & \varphi_c & \varphi_d \\ \psi_a & \psi_b & \psi_c & \psi_d \\ \varphi_a'' & \varphi_b'' & \varphi_c'' & \varphi_d'' \\ \psi_a' & \psi_b' & \psi_c' & \psi_d' \end{vmatrix} + \begin{vmatrix} \varphi_a & \varphi_b & \varphi_c & \varphi_d \\ \psi_a & \psi_b & \psi_c & \psi_d \\ \varphi_a' & \varphi_b' & \varphi_c' & \varphi_d' \\ \psi_a'' & \psi_b'' & \psi_c'' & \psi_d'' \end{vmatrix}$$

But, from (7.4.2),

$$(7.4.9) \qquad \varphi'' = A(x, \varphi, \psi, \varphi', \psi'),$$

$$(7.4.10) \qquad \varphi_a'' = A_\varphi \varphi_a + A_\psi \psi_a + A_{\varphi'} \varphi_a' + A_{\psi'} \psi_a',$$

and using this, and the three similar formulae in the first determinant in the second member of (7.4.8), we see that this determinant is equal to

$A_{\varphi'}\,\Delta$. Then, using the similar result for the second determinant, we have

$$\frac{d\Delta}{dx} = (A_{\varphi'} + B_{\psi'})\,\Delta. \tag{7.4.11}$$

Next, if we solve (7.4.1) for y'' and z'' we get the identities defining the functions A and B,

$$MA = f_{z'z'}P - f_{y'z'}Q, \tag{7.4.12}$$

$$MB = f_{y'y'}Q - f_{z'y'}P, \tag{7.4.13}$$

where for the moment we write, for compactness, P and Q for the second members of the equations (7.4.1),

$$P = f_y - f_{y'x} - f_{y'y}y' - f_{y'z}z', \tag{7.4.14}$$

$$Q = f_z - f_{z'x} - f_{z'y}y' - f_{z'z}z'. \tag{7.4.15}$$

We differentiate (7.4.12) partially with respect to y', (7.4.13) partially with respect to z', and differentiate M totally with respect to x, and we have, on adding the three equations,

$$\begin{aligned} M(A_{y'} + B_{z'}) + M_{y'}A + M_{z'}B + \frac{dM}{dx} &= f_{z'z'}P_{y'} - f_{y'z'}Q_{y'} + f_{y'y'}Q_{z'} - f_{z'y'}P_{z'} + M_x + M_y y' \\ &\quad + M_z z' + M_{y'}y'' + M_{z'}z''. \end{aligned} \tag{7.4.16}$$

Now on an extremal arc $y'' = A$ and $z'' = B$, so the terms with $M_{y'}$ and $M_{z'}$ cancel out, and we are left with

$$\begin{aligned} M(A_{y'} + B_{z'}) + \frac{dM}{dx} &= f_{z'z'}P_{y'} - f_{y'z'}Q_{y'} + f_{y'y'}Q_{z'} \\ &\quad - f_{z'y'}P_{z'} + M_x + M_y y' + M_z z'. \end{aligned} \tag{7.4.17}$$

But the second member of (7.4.17) is identically zero, giving

$$\frac{dM}{dx} = -(A_{y'} + B_{z'})M, \tag{7.4.18}$$

or, reverting to the notation of (7.4.11)

$$\frac{dM}{dx} = -(A_{\varphi'} + B_{\psi'})M. \tag{7.4.19}$$

From (7.4.11) and (7.4.19) we have

$$M\frac{d\Delta}{dx} + \Delta\frac{dM}{dx} = 0, \tag{7.4.20}$$

and this implies the required result (7.4.7).

7.5 Variable end-points

We now turn to the problem analogous to that discussed in §4.1. We consider the variation in the value of the integral, taken along a curve from A to B,

$$I = \int_X^{\bar{X}} f(x, y, z, y', z')\, dx \tag{7.5.1}$$

when we change the path of integration to a neighbouring path. We suppose that the equations of du Bois-Reymond (7.1.14–15) are satisfied on the original path K_0 joining A_0 to B_0. We consider a one-parameter family of curves, of which the typical member K_α is

$$y = \varphi(x, \alpha), \qquad z = \psi(x, \alpha), \tag{7.5.2}$$

the original curve K_0 being given by $\alpha = 0$. The end-points are variable, and we assume that we can use the same parameter α to define the end-points, and that $X(\alpha)$, $\bar{X}(\alpha)$ are of class C_1 in a neighbourhood of $\alpha = 0$. We shall suppose that $\varphi(x, \alpha)$ and $\psi(x, \alpha)$ are of class C_1 in a neighbourhood of the segment

$$X(0) \leqslant x \leqslant \bar{X}(0), \qquad \alpha = 0, \tag{7.5.3}$$

and further that $\varphi_\alpha'(x, \alpha)$ and $\psi_\alpha'(x, \alpha)$ are continuous in the same domain. It will be noticed that, for the moment, we deal with an arc without corners. We write $\eta(x)$ for $\varphi_\alpha(x, 0)$ and $\zeta(x)$ for $\psi_\alpha(x, 0)$, and $\eta(x)$, $\zeta(x) \in C_1$. We notice that $\eta(x)\, d\alpha$ and $\zeta(x)\, d\alpha$ are the contemporaneous variations in the values of y and z from a point on the original to a point on the varied curve. It may be necessary, as in §4.1, to extend the original curve K_0 to the left of X and to the right of $\bar{X}$ in order to obtain the varied curve by contemporaneous variations.

We denote the integral along K_α by $\chi(\alpha)$,

$$\chi(\alpha) = \int_{X(\alpha)}^{\bar{X}(\alpha)} f\{x, \varphi(x, \alpha), \psi(x, \alpha), \varphi'(x, \alpha), \psi'(x, \alpha)\}\, dx, \tag{7.5.4}$$

and therefore, remembering that the limits of integration now depend upon α, we have

$$\chi'(0) = f(b)\bar{X}'(0) - f(a)X'(0) + \int_{X(0)}^{\bar{X}(0)} (\eta f_y + \zeta f_z + \eta' f_{y'} + \zeta' f_{z'})\, dx, \tag{7.5.5}$$

where a denotes the element of K_0 at A_0, namely

$$\{X(0), \varphi(X, 0), \psi(X, 0), \varphi'(X, 0), \psi'(X, 0)\},$$

and b denotes the element of K_0 at B_0. The arguments in the derivatives of f in the integrand are the elements of K_0, so the coefficients of η, ζ, η', ζ' are known continuous functions of x.

Now K_0 satisfies the equations of du Bois-Reymond, so

$$(7.5.6)\quad f_{y'}\{x, \varphi(x, 0), \psi(x, 0), \varphi'(x, 0), \psi'(x, 0)\} = \sigma(x) + C,$$

where

$$(7.5.7)\quad \sigma(x) = \int_X^x f_y\{t, \varphi(t, 0), \psi(t, 0), \varphi'(t, 0), \psi'(t, 0)\}\, dt,$$

and similarly

$$(7.5.8)\quad f_{z'}\{x, \varphi(x, 0), \psi(x, 0), \varphi'(x, 0), \psi'(x, 0)\} = \tau(x) + D,$$

where

$$(7.5.9)\quad \tau(x) = \int_X^x f_z\{t, \varphi(t, 0), \psi(t, 0), \varphi'(t, 0), \psi'(t, 0)\}\, dt\,.$$

Thus the integral in the second member of (7.5.5) can be written in the form

$$(7.5.10)\quad \int_{X(0)}^{\overline{X}(0)} \{\eta\sigma' + \eta'(\sigma + C) + \zeta\tau' + \zeta'(\tau + D)\}\, dx$$
$$= \eta(\sigma + C) + \zeta(\tau + D)\Big|_{X(0)}^{\overline{X}(0)}$$
$$= \eta f_{y'} + \zeta f_{z'}\Big|_{A_0}^{B_0},$$

where the arguments in $f_{y'}$ and $f_{z'}$ are the elements of K_0 at A_0 and B_0. Thus the formula (7.5.5) for $\chi'(0)$ takes the form

$$(7.5.11)\quad \chi'(0) = f(b)\overline{X}'(0) + \eta\{\overline{X}(0)\}f_{y'}(b) + \zeta\{\overline{X}(0)\}f_{z'}(b)$$
$$- f(a)X'(0) - \eta\{X(0)\}f_{y'}(a) - \zeta\{X(0)\}f_{z'}(a).$$

The final step is the expression of the result in terms of the actual displacements of the end-points, so we must suppress the contemporaneous displacements appearing in (7.5.11). Now

$$(7.5.12)\quad Y(\alpha) = \varphi(X, \alpha),$$

and therefore

$$(7.5.13)\quad dY = \varphi_\alpha(X, 0)\, d\alpha + \varphi'(X, 0)\, dX$$
$$= \eta\{X(0)\}\, d\alpha + \varphi'(X, 0)\, dX,$$

with similar results for dZ, and for $d\overline{Y}$ and $d\overline{Z}$. These are of course already familiar (cf. (4.2.10)). If now we substitute for

$$(7.5.14)\quad \eta\{X(0)\},\ \zeta\{X(0)\},\ \eta\{\overline{X}(0)\} \text{ and } \zeta\{\overline{X}(0)\}$$

in (7.5.11) we find

$$dI = \chi'(0)\, d\alpha = U(b)\, d\overline{X} + V(b)\, d\overline{Y} + W(b)\, d\overline{Z}$$
$$- U(a)\, dX - V(a)\, dY - W(a)\, dZ,$$

or, compactly,

$$dI = U\,dx + V\,dy + W\,dz\Big|_{A_0}^{B_0}. \tag{7.5.15}$$

This is the fundamental result.

The result has been established on the assumption that K_0 is an arc of class C_1, i.e. without a corner; but the result is still valid if K_0 has a finite number of corners. This follows, as in Corollary 4 of §4.2, from the corner conditions (§7.2).

7.6 The problem of the minimizing curve with variable end-points

Let us suppose that the end-points are subject to the conditions

$$\psi^\mu(X, Y, Z, \overline{X}, \overline{Y}, \overline{Z}) = 0, \qquad \mu = 1, 2, \ldots, p \leqslant 6, \tag{7.6.1}$$

where $\psi^\mu \in C_3$ in an appropriate domain of the 6-fold, and the p conditions are independent. The minimizing curve consists of an arc, or of arcs, satisfying Euler's equations and also satisfying the end-conditions. These conditions are conveniently expressed by the statement that there exist constants $e^1, e^2, \ldots, e^p$, such that

$$(U\,dx + V\,dy + W\,dz)\Big|_A^B + \sum_{\mu=1}^{p} e^\mu\,d\psi^\mu = 0 \tag{7.6.2}$$

for arbitrary values of the displacements $dX, dY, dZ, d\overline{X}, d\overline{Y}, d\overline{Z}$ of the end-points.

The problem with fixed end-points is the trivial case $p = 6$. In this case the end-conditions give no useful information, as we expect; they merely determine the values of the constant e^μ.

In most problems the end-conditions separate out into two distinct sets, one set involving (X, Y, Z) and one involving $(\overline{X}, \overline{Y}, \overline{Z})$. Such problems are said to have separated end-conditions.

EXAMPLE. To find a minimizing curve for $\int \lambda\,ds$, where $\lambda = \lambda(x, y, z) > 0$ for all (x, y, z), when the end-point A is constrained to lie on the surface defined by $F(X, Y, Z) = 0$, and the end-point B is constrained to lie on the curve defined by the equation

$$G(\overline{X}, \overline{Y}, \overline{Z}) = H(\overline{X}, \overline{Y}, \overline{Z}) = 0.$$

The curve satisfies the equations of du Bois-Reymond, and the end-conditions are given by

$$(U\,dx + V\,dy + W\,dz)\Big|_A^B + e^1\,dF + e^2\,dG + e^3\,dH = 0, \tag{7.6.3}$$

the equation holding for arbitrary values of $dX, dY, dZ, d\overline{X}, d\overline{Y}, d\overline{Z}$.

Now, as in (7.2.2),

$$U = \lambda l,\ V = \lambda m,\ W = \lambda n, \tag{7.6.4}$$

where l, m, n are the direction cosines of the tangent to the curve. Equating to zero the coefficients of dX, dY, dZ, $d\overline{X}$, $d\overline{Y}$, $d\overline{Z}$ in (7.6.3) we find

$$\left\{\begin{aligned} &\lambda l_1 = e^1\frac{\partial F}{\partial X},\quad \lambda m_1 = e^1\frac{\partial F}{\partial Y},\quad \lambda n_1 = e^1\frac{\partial F}{\partial Z},\\ &\lambda l_2 = -e^2\frac{\partial G}{\partial \overline{X}} - e^3\frac{\partial H}{\partial \overline{X}},\quad \lambda m_2 = -e^2\frac{\partial G}{\partial \overline{Y}} - e^3\frac{\partial H}{\partial \overline{Y}},\\ &\lambda n_2 = -e^2\frac{\partial G}{\partial \overline{Z}} - e^3\frac{\partial H}{\partial \overline{Z}}\end{aligned}\right. \tag{7.6.5}$$

where (l_1, m_1, n_1) are the direction cosines of the tangent to the curve at A, and (l_2, m_2, n_2) at B. The curve is normal to the given surface at A and perpendicular to the given curve at B.

7.7 Weierstrass's necessary condition and Legendre's necessary condition

The argument given in §4.4 for the plane problem can be extended in a simple and natural way to problems in space.

Let P (x_0, y_0, z_0) be a point on an arc without corners of a minimizing curve $y = \varphi(x)$, $z = \psi(x)$, and let $Q(\xi, \eta, \zeta)$ be a point of the arc with $\xi > x_0$. We denote the segment PQ of the arc by K. Let Γ, defined by $y = \lambda(x)$, $z = \mu(x)$, be an arbitrary admissible arc through P, and let R be the point on Γ whose x-coordinate is α, where $\alpha \geqslant x_0$. Let us now construct a one-parameter family of arcs Δ_α joining the points R of Γ to Q, the family being so chosen that Δ_α coincides with K when R is at P. For example we can define such a family by the equations

$$\begin{aligned} y &= \varphi(x) + \left\{\frac{\lambda(\alpha) - \varphi(\alpha)}{\xi - \alpha}\right\}(\xi - x),\\ z &= \psi(x) + \left\{\frac{\mu(\alpha) - \psi(\alpha)}{\xi - \alpha}\right\}(\xi - x). \end{aligned} \tag{7.7.1}$$

If now $\chi(\alpha)$ is the value of I along the path consisting of the segment PR of Γ and the arc Δ_α, a necessary condition for a minimizing curve is $\chi'(x_0) \geqslant 0$. Now

$$\chi(\alpha) = I(\Gamma_{PR}) + I(\Delta_\alpha), \tag{7.7.2}$$

and therefore, using the variable end-point theorem (7.5.15), we have

$$(7.7.3)\quad \chi'(x_0) = f(x_0, y_0, z_0, \varpi, \rho) - U(x_0, y_0, z_0, p, q) - \varpi V(x_0, y_0, z_0, p, q) - \rho W(x_0, y_0, z_0, p, q),$$

where

$$(7.7.4)\quad \varpi = \lambda'(x_0), \quad \rho = \mu'(x_0), \quad p = \varphi'(x_0), \quad q = \psi'(x_0).$$

Hence we have, as a necessary condition for a minimizing curve, that at any element (x, y, z, y', z') of an arc of the curve

$$(7.7.5)\quad f(x, y, z, \varpi, \rho) - f(x, y, z, y', z') - (\varpi - y')f_{y'}(x, y, z, y', z') - (\rho - z')f_{z'}(x, y, z, y', z') \geqslant 0$$

for arbitrary values of ϖ and ρ. The function on the left in (7.7.5) is Weierstrass's excess function for the problem in space. We denote it by $E(x, y, z, y', z', \varpi, \rho)$, and the condition

$$(7.7.6)\quad E(x, y, z, y', z', \varpi, \rho) \geqslant 0$$

is Weierstrass's necessary condition. If (x, y, z, y', z') is any element of a minimizing curve, (7.7.6) must hold for all real values of ϖ and ρ.

Now, by Taylor's theorem,

$$(7.7.7)\quad 2E(x, y, z, y', z', \varpi, \rho) = (\varpi - y')^2 f_{y'y'} + 2(\varpi - y')(\rho - z')f_{y'z'} + (\rho - z')^2 f_{z'z'},$$

the arguments in the second derivatives of f being

$$(7.7.8)\quad x, y, z, \bar{\varpi}, \bar{\rho}$$

where $\bar{\varpi}$ lies between y' and ϖ, and $\bar{\rho}$ lies between z' and ρ. In (7.7.6) let us substitute for ϖ and ρ, which are arbitrary, the values $y' + \varepsilon\eta$, $z' + \varepsilon\zeta$, where η, ζ are arbitrary real constants. Then (7.7.6) holds for all values of ε, and letting $\varepsilon \to 0$ we find

$$(7.7.9)\quad \eta^2 f_{y'y'} + 2\eta\zeta f_{y'z'} + \zeta^2 f_{z'z'} \geqslant 0,$$

where the arguments in the second derivatives of f are now the components x, y, z, y', z' of an element of the minimizing curve.

The equation (7.7.9) is Legendre's necessary condition. For every element of the minimizing curve the quadratic form on the left in (7.7.9) is a positive semi-definite form. An equivalent statement is that

$$(7.7.10)\quad f_{y'y'} \geqslant 0, \qquad M \geqslant 0,$$

(where M is the determinant (7.3.1)) for every element of the minimizing curve.

Legendre's condition is necessary even for a weak relative minimum; this can be proved by a modification of the method used for the case of one dependent variable in §2.11.

7.8 Fields of extremals

So far the theory for curves in space has followed fairly closely the theory for plane curves, but when we come to the notion of a field of extremals a new phenomenon appears.

Let us, to begin with, follow a line of argument similar to that used for the plane problem in §5.2. Consider a two-parameter family of extremals K defined by the equations

$$y = \varphi(x, \alpha, \beta), \qquad z = \psi(x, \alpha, \beta). \tag{7.8.1}$$

The parameters α, β belong to a domain $\mathscr{A}$ of (α, β), and the functions $\varphi, \varphi', \psi, \psi'$ have continuous second derivatives in the domain $\mathscr{R}$ of (x, α, β) defined by

$$(\alpha, \beta) \in \mathscr{A}, \qquad X(\alpha, \beta) < x < \overline{X}(\alpha, \beta). \tag{7.8.2}$$

The Jacobian $\dfrac{\partial(\varphi, \psi)}{\partial(\alpha, \beta)}$ does not vanish in $\mathscr{R}$, and we can solve the equations (7.8.1) for α and β as functions of (x, y, z)

$$\alpha = \lambda(x, y, z), \qquad \beta = \mu(x, y, z), \tag{7.8.3}$$

and the functions $\lambda(x, y, z)$, $\mu(x, y, z)$ are of class C_2 in the domain Φ of (x, y, z) defined by (7.8.1) and (7.8.2). There is one and only one extremal of the family through each point of Φ.

We now introduce the slope functions p and q, defined in a similar way to the slope function for the plane problem in §5.1,

$$\begin{aligned} p(x, y, z) &= \varphi'\{x, \lambda(x, y, z), \mu(x, y, z)\}, \\ q(x, y, z) &= \psi'\{x, \lambda(x, y, z), \mu(x, y, z)\}, \end{aligned} \tag{7.8.4}$$

so that p and q are uniform functions of position in Φ, each of class C_2. We then introduce the functions $u(x, y, z)$, $v(x, y, z)$, $w(x, y, z)$, defined (by analogy with (5.1.7)) as follows,

$$u = U(x, y, z, p, q), \quad v = V(x, y, z, p, q), \quad w = W(x, y, z, p, q), \tag{7.8.5}$$

and u, v, w are uniform functions of position in Φ of class C_2.

The crucial point at which the theory diverges from the corresponding theory in the plane is that the Pfaffian form

(7.8.6) $$\omega \equiv u\,dx + v\,dy + w\,dz$$

is not in general a perfect differential. The Hilbert line-integral $\int\omega$ is not invariant, i.e. it does not have the same value for all curves joining the same two end-points. We shall restrict the term *field* to the case where the Hilbert integral *is* invariant. This requires that ω is a perfect differential of a uniform function, and this implies a restriction on the two-parameter family which has no analogue for the one-parameter family in the plane problem.

Let $\Gamma (= \Gamma_{A_1A_2})$ be a curve (not an extremal) of class D_1 in Φ joining A_1 to A_2, and let us consider the extremals of the family through the points of Γ. One of these extremals passes through each point of Γ, and they build up a surface Σ on which Γ lies. Let $\Delta (= \Delta_{B_1B_2})$ be another curve lying on Σ, i.e. a curve cutting the extremals through the points of Γ; the point B_1 on Δ lies on the extremal through A_1, and the point B_2 on Δ lies on the extremal through A_2 (Fig. 5.1). Then, as in §5.1, we have the equation analogous to (5.1.9),

(7.8.7) $$I(K_{A_2B_2}) - I(K_{A_1B_1}) = H(\Delta_{B_1B_2}) - H(\Gamma_{A_1A_2}),$$

where H is the line-integral $\int\omega$. It is clear from (7.8.7) that if $\Delta'_{B_1B_2}$ is another curve joining B_1 to B_2, *and lying on* Σ, then

(7.8.8) $$H(\Delta_{B_1B_2}) = H(\Delta'_{B_1B_2}).$$

But this is not enough for our purpose. For the two-parameter family to constitute a field we need (7.8.8) to hold for all curves $\Delta_{B_1B_2}$ in Φ, not only for curves lying on Σ.

One simple special case in which (7.8.8) holds for all curves $\Delta'_{B_1B_2}$ is that in which all the extremals of the family pass through a point Q. In general Q must lie outside Φ (since only one extremal of the family passes through any point of Φ); alternatively we may work with the semi-field through Q.

As an illustration, suppose the integrand is $f(y', z')$, a function only of y' and z', so that the extremals are straight lines. We can take for our two-parameter family the straight lines through O, Φ being the region $x > 0$, or some part of that region. The slope functions are

(7.8.9) $$p = y/x, \qquad q = z/x,$$

so that

$$(7.8.10)\qquad \begin{aligned} u &= f\left(\frac{y}{x}, \frac{z}{x}\right) - \frac{y}{x} f_{y'}\left(\frac{y}{x}, \frac{z}{x}\right) - \frac{z}{x} f_{z'}\left(\frac{y}{x}, \frac{z}{x}\right), \\ v &= f_{y'}\left(\frac{y}{x}, \frac{z}{x}\right), \qquad w = f_{z'}\left(\frac{y}{x}, \frac{z}{x}\right). \end{aligned}$$

The fact that ω is a complete differential is easily verified; in fact

$$(7.8.11)\qquad \omega = d\left\{x f\left(\frac{y}{x}, \frac{z}{x}\right)\right\}.$$

Let us now turn from this special case and consider a general two-parameter family of extremals (7.8.1). Let $\xi(\alpha, \beta)$ be a function, of class C_1, in $\mathscr{A}$. Then the coordinates

$$(7.8.12)\qquad \begin{aligned} \xi(\alpha, \beta), \qquad \eta(\alpha, \beta) &= \varphi\{\xi(\alpha, \beta), \alpha, \beta\}, \\ \zeta(\alpha, \beta) &= \psi\{\xi(\alpha, \beta), \alpha, \beta\}, \end{aligned}$$

define a surface S, which is met by the extremal (7.8.1) at $x = \xi$. Then, *if the integral H taken along a curve lying on S is invariant* (i.e. it has a value depending only on the end-points A_1 and A_2, not on the path) *the family* (7.8.1) *constitutes a field.* The proof is immediate. Let B_1 and B_2 be two points of Φ, and let the extremals through B_1 and B_2 meet S in A_1 and A_2. Let Δ be any curve (of class D_1) lying in Φ and joining B_1 to B_2, and let Γ be the corresponding curve on S joining A_1 to A_2 (i.e. Γ is the curve traced out by the intersections with S of the extremals through points of Δ). Now from (7.8.7)

$$(7.8.13)\qquad H(\Delta_{B_1B_2}) = I(K_{A_2B_2}) - I(K_{A_1B_1}) + H(\Gamma_{A_1A_2}),$$

and the invariance of $H(\Delta_{B_1B_2})$ follows, since each term in the second member of (7.8.13) is invariant.

7.9 Another approach to the theory of fields in space

Let Φ be a simply-connected region of (x, y, z)-space, and let $p(x, y, z)$ and $q(x, y, z)$ be two functions of class C_2 in Φ, such that the elements (x, y, z, p, q) are admissible, i.e. they lie in the region R. Let us construct the functions u, v, w as follows:

$$(7.9.1)\qquad u = f - p f_{y'} - q f_{z'}, \qquad v = f_{y'}, \qquad w = f_{z'},$$

the arguments in f and its derivatives being $\{x, y, z, p(x, y, z), q(x, y, z)\}$.

Then we easily verify, by straightforward differentiation, the following results:

(7.9.2)
$$\begin{cases} \left(\dfrac{\partial v}{\partial x} - \dfrac{\partial u}{\partial y}\right) - q\left(\dfrac{\partial w}{\partial y} - \dfrac{\partial v}{\partial z}\right) = f_{y'x} + f_{y'y}p + f_{y'z}q \\ \quad + f_{y'y'}\left(\dfrac{\partial p}{\partial x} + p\dfrac{\partial p}{\partial y} + q\dfrac{\partial p}{\partial z}\right) + f_{y'z'}\left(\dfrac{\partial q}{\partial x} + p\dfrac{\partial q}{\partial y} + q\dfrac{\partial q}{\partial z}\right) - f_y, \\ -\left(\dfrac{\partial u}{\partial z} - \dfrac{\partial w}{\partial x}\right) + p\left(\dfrac{\partial w}{\partial y} - \dfrac{\partial v}{\partial z}\right) = f_{z'x} + f_{z'y}p + f_{z'z}q \\ \quad + f_{z'y'}\left(\dfrac{\partial p}{\partial x} + p\dfrac{\partial p}{\partial y} + q\dfrac{\partial p}{\partial z}\right) + f_{z'z'}\left(\dfrac{\partial q}{\partial x} + p\dfrac{\partial q}{\partial y} + q\dfrac{\partial q}{\partial z}\right) - f_z. \end{cases}$$

Suppose now that the functions $p(x, y, z)$ and $q(x, y, z)$ are chosen in such a way that the Pfaffian form

(7.9.3)
$$\omega \equiv u\,dx + v\,dy + w\,dz$$

is a perfect differential; in this case the Hilbert integral $\int\omega$ is invariant. Then the first members of (7.9.2) vanish identically in Φ, and therefore the second members also vanish identically in Φ. If now we consider the curves defined by the differential equations

(7.9.4)
$$\frac{dy}{dx} = p(x, y, z), \qquad \frac{dz}{dx} = q(x, y, z),$$

one and only one of these curves passes through each point of Φ. Moreover, for these curves $\{y(x), z(x)\}$

(7.9.5)
$$y' = p, \quad y'' = \frac{\partial p}{\partial x} + p\frac{\partial p}{\partial y} + q\frac{\partial p}{\partial z}; \quad z' = q, \quad z'' = \frac{\partial q}{\partial x} + p\frac{\partial q}{\partial y} + q\frac{\partial q}{\partial z},$$

(cf. equation (5.3.1)), and the vanishing of the second members of (7.9.2) implies

(7.9.6)
$$\frac{d}{dx}f_{y'} - f_y = 0, \qquad \frac{d}{dx}f_{z'} - f_z = 0,$$

so the curves are extremals. Since the Hilbert integral is invariant, the curves are the extremals of a field.

7.10 Jacobi's necessary condition

It is easy to extend the theory of Jacobi's necessary condition for a minimizing curve, expounded for the plane problem in §5.4, to curves in space.

Consider the case in which a one-parameter family of extremals through a point A has an envelope D. Let K be one of the extremals of this family, and let B be another point on K. Then the arc K_{AB} cannot be a minimizing arc if it contains a point of contact with the envelope D. To prove this we have only to modify the argument of §5.4, confining our attention to curves in the surface S built up by the one-parameter family. We construct a semi-field in S by deleting the parts of the extremals beyond the points of contact with D. We have seen that the Hilbert integral is invariant for the semi-field, so the proof is almost the same as that for the plane problem in §5.4. (Fig. 5.4 must now be interpreted as representing curves in the surface S, not curves in a plane.)

7.11 The fundamental sufficiency theorem

We suppose that K is an extremal arc joining A to B, and that this arc is embedded in a field Φ. In what circumstances can we be sure that K is a minimizing arc?

Let Γ be any curve $\{\varphi(x), \psi(x)\}$ lying in Φ and joining the same two end-points. The functions $\varphi(x)$ and $\psi(x)$ are of class D_1. The argument is now very similar to that used in §5.5. We have

$$(7.11.1) \qquad I(\Gamma) - I(K) = I(\Gamma) - H(K) = I(\Gamma) - H(\Gamma),$$

and the difference $I(\Gamma) - I(K)$ is expressed as an integral along Γ, namely

(7.11.2)

$$\int_X^{\overline{X}} \{f(x, y, z, \varpi, \rho) - [f(x, y, z, p, q) - pf_{y'}(x, y, z, p, q) \\ - qf_{z'}(x, y, z, p, q)] - \varpi f_{y'}(x, y, z, p, q) - \rho f_{z'}(x, y, z, p, q)\}\, dx,$$

where ϖ, ρ are the values of y', z' on Γ, and p, q are the slope functions of the field.

The integrand in (7.11.2) is

$$(7.11.3) \quad f(x, y, z, \varpi, \rho) - f(x, y, z, p, q) \\ - (\varpi - p)f_{y'}(x, y, z, p, q) - (\rho - q)f_{z'}(x, y, z, p, q).$$

Now the excess function of Weierstrass is the function (of seven independent variables)

(7.11.4)

$$E(x, y, z, y', z', Y', Z') = f(x, y, z, Y', Z') - f(x, y, z, y', z') \\ - (Y' - y')f_{y'}(x, y, z, y', z') - (Z' - z')f_{z'}(x, y, z, y', z').$$

The integrand (7.11.3) is the function $E(x, y, z, p, q, \varpi, \rho)$, and, since the slope functions p and q are known functions of (x, y, z), this is a function of the five independent variables (x, y, z, ϖ, ρ), say

$$E(x, y, z, p, q, \varpi, \rho) = \mathscr{W}(x, y, z, \varpi, \rho). \tag{7.11.5}$$

Thus, combining the results just found, we have

$$I(\Gamma) - I(K) = \int_X^{\bar{X}} \mathscr{W}(x, y, z, \varpi, \rho)\, dx. \tag{7.11.6}$$

If then

$$\mathscr{W}(x, y, z, \varpi, \rho) \geqslant 0 \tag{7.11.7}$$

for all points (x, y, z) of Φ, and for arbitrary values of ϖ and ρ, we have

$$I(\Gamma) \geqslant I(K), \tag{7.11.8}$$

and K is a genuinely minimizing curve. This is the fundamental sufficiency theorem for curves in space.

7.12 Some concrete illustrations

We consider some simple concrete illustrations of the preceding theory.

EXAMPLE 1. *Line-integral.* We consider the integral

$$I = \int P\, dx + Q\, dy + R\, dz = \int (P + Qy' + Rz')\, dx, \tag{7.12.1}$$

where P, Q, R are functions of position in space, of class C_1. If $P\, dx + Q\, dy + R\, dz$ is a perfect differential, the value of the integral depends only on the end-points, not on the path, and no problem of a minimizing curve arises. In this case curl $(P, Q, R) = \mathbf{0}$.

Suppose now that curl $(P, Q, R) \neq \mathbf{0}$. The Euler equations for the integrand $P + Qy' + Rz'$ are easily seen to be equivalent to the equations

$$\frac{dx}{R_y - Q_z} = \frac{dy}{P_z - R_x} = \frac{dz}{Q_x - P_y}, \tag{7.12.2}$$

which represent a family of curves, which we can call "lines of force", one through each point. If the points A and B do not lie on the same line of force there is no solution of Euler's equations through them.

Even if A and B lie on the same line of force this is not in general a minimizing curve. A simple way of seeing this is to notice that, if the Pfaffian form $P\, dx + Q\, dy + R\, dz$ is not a perfect differential, it can be transformed (in virtue of Pfaff's theorem) by an appropriate change of variables, to the form $dx + y\,dz$. For the integral

$$I = \int dx + y\,dz = \int (1 + yz')\,dx \tag{7.12.3}$$

the lines of force are the straight lines parallel to Ox. If $A(X, Y, Z)$ and $B(\overline{X}, Y, Z)$ lie on the same line of force, the line is not minimizing. For if this line, from A to B, is denoted by K, and any other curve joining A to B is denoted by Γ, we see that

$$I(\Gamma) - I(K) = \int y\,dz, \tag{7.12.4}$$

where the integral on the right is taken round the closed curve which is the projection of Γ on the plane $x = 0$, and this integral can have either sign.

EXAMPLE 2. Consider the integral

$$\int \{\tfrac{1}{2}(y'^2 + z'^2) + cz\}\,dx, \tag{7.12.5}$$

where c is a prescribed positive number.

The excess function (7.11.4) is easily seen to be

$$E = \tfrac{1}{2}(Y' - y')^2 + \tfrac{1}{2}(Z' - z')^2, \tag{7.12.6}$$

and therefore, if we can construct a field,

$$\mathscr{W} = \tfrac{1}{2}(\varpi - p)^2 + \tfrac{1}{2}(\rho - q)^2. \tag{7.12.7}$$

In this case therefore an extremal arc of the field is certainly minimizing in comparison with other curves in the field.

The extremals are the parabolas

$$y = a + bx, \qquad z = a' + b'x + \tfrac{1}{2}cx^2, \tag{7.12.8}$$

and there is a unique extremal through the points $A(X, Y, Z)$ and $B(\overline{X}, \overline{Y}, \overline{Z})$ if $\overline{X} > X$. To prove that this extremal is a minimizing curve we have to construct a field in which it is embedded. Let the constants a, b, a', b' in (7.12.8) be given the special values required to make the extremal pass through A and B. Then a simple field meeting our requirements is given by the two-parameter family

$$y = \alpha + a + bx, \qquad z = \beta + a' + b'x + \tfrac{1}{2}cx^2. \tag{7.12.9}$$

One member of this family goes through each point of space, and the Hilbert integral is invariant. For

(7.12.10) $U = -\frac{1}{2}(y'^2 + z'^2) + cz, \quad V = y', \quad W = z',$

and for the two-parameter family (7.12.9)

(7.12.11) $$p = b, \quad q = b' + cx$$

giving

(7.12.12) $u = -\frac{1}{2}\{b^2 + (b' + cx)^2\} + cz, \quad v = b, \quad w = b' + cx,$

and it is clear that $u\,dx + v\,dy + w\,dz$ is a perfect differential. Even more simply it suffices (cf. §7.8) to prove that the Hilbert integral is invariant for curves in the plane $x = 0$, and this is immediately obvious.

EXAMPLE 3. The integral is

(7.12.13) $$I = \int \lambda\,ds = \int \lambda\sqrt{(1 + y'^2 + z'^2)}\,dx,$$

where λ is a given function of (x, y, z), assumed positive for all points of the region considered.

In this case, as we have noticed already in §7.2,

(7.12.14) $$U = \frac{\lambda}{\sqrt{(1 + y'^2 + z'^2)}}, \qquad V = \frac{\lambda y'}{\sqrt{(1 + y'^2 + z'^2)}}, \qquad W = \frac{\lambda z'}{\sqrt{(1 + y'^2 + z'^2)}},$$

and

(7.12.15)
$$\begin{aligned}\mathscr{W}(x, y, z, \varpi, \rho) &= E(x, y, z, p, q, \varpi, \rho)\\ &= \frac{\lambda}{\sqrt{(1 + p^2 + q^2)}}\{\sqrt{[(1 + p^2 + q^2)(1 + \varpi^2 + \rho^2)]}\\ &\quad - (1 + p\varpi + q\rho)\} > 0.\end{aligned}$$

We see therefore that if we can construct a field, the conditions for the fundamental sufficiency theorem are fulfilled; an extremal arc, embedded in the field, is a genuinely minimizing curve.

The Hilbert integral is

(7.12.16) $$\begin{aligned}H &= \int \frac{\lambda}{\sqrt{(1 + p^2 + q^2)}}(dx + p\,dy + q\,dz)\\ &= \int \lambda(l\,dx + m\,dy + n\,dz),\end{aligned}$$

where (l, m, n) are direction cosines of the tangent to the extremal of the field at (x, y, z). This suggests at once a simple way of constructing a field. If we take a surface S, as in §7.8, and construct the extremals meeting S normally, then the Hilbert integral taken along any curve lying on S is zero. Therefore we can construct a field Φ (with these extremals cutting S normally) if we arrange (for example, by truncating each extremal at a suitable point) that one and only one extremal passes through each point of Φ. Let us consider two particular examples of this type.

(i) $\lambda = 1/z$. Here

(7.12.17) $$I = \int \frac{1}{z} \sqrt{(1 + y'^2 + z'^2)}\, dx,$$

and we confine our attention to the region $z > 0$. We suppose that Oz is drawn vertically upwards. The extremals are semi-circles in vertical planes, with their centres on the plane $z = 0$, and there is a unique extremal arc joining any two points A and B in the region $z > 0$. If the vertical plane through A and B is the plane

(7.12.18) $$x \sin \alpha - y \cos \alpha + h = 0$$

the extremal can be represented in terms of a parameter θ by the equations

(7.12.19) $$\begin{cases} x = (a - b \sin \theta) \cos \alpha - h \sin \alpha, \\ y = (a - b \sin \theta) \sin \alpha + h \cos \alpha, \\ z = b \cos \theta. \end{cases}$$

A simple way to construct a field in which this extremal is embedded is to use the same formulae (7.12.19), now allowing the symbols b and h to represent variable parameters defining the extremals of the field. This will achieve our objective, since precisely one member of this two-parameter family passes through each point of the region $z > 0$, and all the extremals of the family cut the plane

(7.12.20) $$x \cos \alpha + y \sin \alpha = a$$

orthogonally. The slope functions of the field are easily found to be

(7.12.21) $$p = \tan \alpha, \quad q = \frac{a - x \cos \alpha - y \sin \alpha}{z \cos \alpha},$$

and

(7.12.22)

$$u\,dx + v\,dy + w\,dz = \frac{1}{\sqrt{\{z^2 + (a - x\cos\alpha - y\sin\alpha)^2\}}}$$

$$\times \left(\cos\alpha\,dx + \sin\alpha\,dy + \frac{a - x\cos\alpha - y\sin\alpha}{z}\,dz\right),$$

and this is a complete differential $d\psi$, where

(7.12.23) $$\psi = -\sinh^{-1}\left(\frac{a - x\cos\alpha - y\sin\alpha}{z}\right).$$

Thus all the required conditions are satisfied, and therefore the extremal arc gives a smaller value to I than any other curve of class D_1 joining A to B and lying in the region $z > 0$.

(ii) $\lambda = \sqrt{z}$. Here

(7.12.24) $$I = \int \sqrt{\{z(1 + y'^2 + z'^2)\}}\,dx,$$

and we confine attention to the region $z > 0$, and $\sqrt{z}$ means the positive square root. The extremals are the parabolas

(7.12.25) $$x = a + r\cos\alpha,\ y = b + r\sin\alpha,\ z = c + \frac{1}{4c}r^2,\quad (c > 0).$$

We give two methods of constructing a field for this problem.

(*a*) Let us take the extremals meeting the plane $x = 0$ normally,

(7.12.26) $$y = \text{constant},\qquad z = c + \frac{x^2}{4c},\qquad (c > 0).$$

These parabolas all touch the planes $z = \pm x$, and we construct a field in the trough $z > |x|$ by deleting the parts of the parabolas beyond the points of contact with the planes $z = \pm x$.

It may be of interest to find the explicit form of the Hilbert integral and to verify the invariance. For a given point (x, y, z) in the trough

(7.12.27) $$c = \tfrac{1}{2}\{z + \sqrt{(z^2 - x^2)}\},$$

where we need the positive sign before the radical. The formula for c can also be written in the forms

(7.12.28) $$c = \tfrac{1}{4}\{\sqrt{(z + x)} + \sqrt{(z - x)}\}^2$$

$$= \frac{x^2}{\{\sqrt{(z + x)} - \sqrt{(z - x)}\}^2}.$$

For the slope functions of the field

$$(7.12.29)\quad p = 0, \quad q = \frac{x}{2c} = \frac{1}{2x}\{\sqrt{(z+x)} - \sqrt{(z-x)}\}^2,$$

so that

$$(7.12.30)\quad 1 + p^2 + q^2 = \frac{z}{c} = \frac{z}{x^2}\{\sqrt{(z+x)} - \sqrt{(z-x)}\}^2$$
$$= \frac{4z}{\{\sqrt{(z+x)} + \sqrt{(z-x)}\}^2}.$$

Thus

$$(7.12.31)\quad \frac{1}{\sqrt{(1+p^2+q^2)}} = \frac{1}{2\sqrt{z}}\{\sqrt{(z+x)} + \sqrt{(z-x)}\}$$

and

$$(7.12.32)\quad \frac{q}{\sqrt{(1+p^2+q^2)}} = \frac{1}{2\sqrt{z}}\{\sqrt{(z+x)} - \sqrt{(z-x)}\},$$

giving

(7.12.33)

$$\omega = \frac{\sqrt{z}}{\sqrt{(1+p^2+q^2)}}(dx + q\,dz)$$
$$= \tfrac{1}{2}\{\sqrt{(z+x)} + \sqrt{(z-x)}\}\,dx + \tfrac{1}{2}\{\sqrt{(z+x)} - \sqrt{(z-x)}\}\,dz$$
$$= \tfrac{1}{3}d\{(z+x)^{3/2} - (z-x)^{3/2}\},$$

and the invariance of the Hilbert integral is verified.

The extremal of the type (7.12.25) joining two points A and B of the region $z > |x|$ gives a smaller value to I than any other curve of class D_1 joining A to B and lying in this region.

(*b*) Another way of constructing a field is to take a two-parameter family of extremals meeting a given line. For example the extremals

$$(7.12.34)\quad x = r\cos\alpha, \quad y = r\sin\alpha, \quad z = c + \frac{1}{4c}(\beta - r)^2,$$

all meet the line Oz. The symbol c here represents a positive constant, fixed once for all, the two parameters are α and β, and if we delete the parts of the parabolas beyond the points of contact with the plane $z = c$ (so that $\beta > r$ always) we have a field in a region lying above the plane $z = c$ and not containing any part of Oz. The parameters α and β, for the extremal through a given point (x, y, z), are given by

$$(7.12.35)\quad \tan\alpha = y/x, \quad \beta = r + \sqrt{\{4c(z-c)\}}, \quad (r = \sqrt{(x^2+y^2)}),$$

and the slope functions are

(7.12.36)
$$p = \tan\alpha = \frac{y}{x}, \quad q = -\frac{1}{2c}(\beta - r)\sec\alpha = -\frac{r}{x}\sqrt{\left(\frac{z-c}{c}\right)}.$$

Thus

$$1 + p^2 + q^2 = \frac{zr^2}{cx^2} \tag{7.12.37}$$

and

$$\begin{aligned} \omega &= \frac{\sqrt{cx}}{r}\left(dx + \frac{y}{x}\,dy - \frac{r}{x}\sqrt{\left(\frac{z-c}{c}\right)}\,dz\right) \\ &= \sqrt{c}\,\frac{x\,dx + y\,dy}{r} - \sqrt{(z-c)}\,dz \\ &= d\{r\sqrt{c} - \tfrac{2}{3}(z-c)^{3/2}\}. \end{aligned} \tag{7.12.38}$$

Since ω is a perfect differential the invariance of the Hilbert integral is verified.

7.13 Problems in $(n + 1)$ dimensions

Much of the theory developed in this Chapter for curves in ordinary space can be extended to space of $(n + 1)$ dimensions. There is one independent variable x, and n dependent variables $y_1, y_2, \ldots, y_n$. In this section we give a brief summary of these results. The proofs are in general essentially the same as those for three dimensions, and the reader will easily supply the appropriate modifications of wording and notation.

The integrand is

$$f(x, y_1, y_2, \ldots, y_n, y_1', y_2', \ldots, y_n'), \tag{7.13.1}$$

and the fundamental problem is to find a curve

$$y_r = \varphi_r(x), \qquad (r = 1, 2, \ldots, n), \tag{7.13.2}$$

joining the fixed end-points

$$(X, Y_1, Y_2, \ldots, Y_n), \quad (\overline{X}, \overline{Y}_1, \overline{Y}_2, \ldots, \overline{Y}_n), \tag{7.13.3}$$

and minimizing the integral

$$I = \int_X^{\overline{X}} f(x, y_1, y_2, \ldots, y_n, y_1', y_2', \ldots, y_n')\,dx. \tag{7.13.4}$$

The integrand f is assumed to be of class C_4 in an appropriate region

R of the $(2n + 1)$-fold space of $(x, y_1, y_2, \ldots, y_n, y_1', y_2', \ldots, y_n')$, and the functions $\varphi_r(x)$ are of class D_1.

We shall sometimes use the condensed notation, already introduced in (1.10.8), writing

$$f(x, y, y') \tag{7.13.5}$$

instead of (7.13.1); here y stands for the n-term row $y_1, y_2, \ldots, y_n$, and y' for the row $y_1', y_2', \ldots, y_n'$. Similarly $\varphi(x)$ will denote the row $\varphi_1(x), \varphi_2(x), \ldots, \varphi_n(x)$, and so on.

Let us suppose that the curve K_0, defined by (7.13.2), is a minimizing curve. We then consider the one-parameter family whose typical member K_α is given by

$$y_r = \varphi_r(x) + \alpha\eta_r(x), \qquad r = 1, 2, \ldots, n, \tag{7.13.6}$$

where the functions $\eta_r(x)$ are of class D_1, and vanish at X and at $\overline{X}$. Since K_0 is a minimizing curve in the class D_1, it is certainly a minimizing curve in the one-parameter family (7.13.6). Then if

$$\chi(\alpha) = I(K_\alpha) = \int_X^{\overline{X}} f(x, \varphi + \alpha\eta, \varphi' + \alpha\eta')\, dx \tag{7.13.7}$$

a necessary condition for a minimum at $\alpha = 0$ is

$$\chi'(0) = 0. \tag{7.13.8}$$

This leads, as in §7.1, to the equations of du Bois-Reymond

$$f_{y_r'}\{x, \varphi(x), \varphi'(x)\} = \int_X^x f_{y_r}\{t, \varphi(t), \varphi'(t)\}\, dt + C_r, \tag{7.13.9}$$

where the value of the constant C_r is $f_{y_r'}\{X, \varphi(X), \varphi'(X)\}$.

On an arc between corners the functions $\varphi_r(x)$ must satisfy Euler's equations

$$\frac{d}{dx} f_{y_r'} = f_{y_r}, \qquad r = 1, 2, \ldots, n. \tag{7.13.10}$$

These are a set of n simultaneous equations of the second order to determine the functions $\varphi_r(x)$.

We write, extending the notation of (7.1.17),

$$U(x, y, y') = f - \Sigma y_r' f_{y_r'}, \quad V_r(x, y, y') = f_{y_r'}. \tag{7.13.11}$$

If f does not contain x explicitly, $U =$ constant is an integral of Euler's equations; and if f does not contain y_r explicitly, $V_r =$ constant is an integral. At a corner on a minimizing curve U is continuous, and so are $V_1, V_2, \ldots, V_n$.

Let us now consider the variation of I when we vary the original curve to a neighbouring one; the variation now involves a displacement of the end-points. The original curve itself is assumed to satisfy the equations of du Bois-Reymond. The procedure is similar to that given for $n = 2$ in §7.5. We consider a one-parameter family of curves of which the typical member K_α is given by

$$y_r = \varphi_r(x, \alpha), \qquad X(\alpha) \leqslant x \leqslant \overline{X}(\alpha), \tag{7.13.12}$$

the original curve K_0 being the particular member of this family given by $\alpha = 0$. We suppose in the first instance that $\varphi_r(x, \alpha) \in C_1$ in a neighbourhood of the segment

$$X(0) \leqslant x \leqslant \overline{X}(0), \qquad \alpha = 0, \tag{7.13.13}$$

and that $\varphi_{r_\alpha}'(x, \alpha)$ $\left(\text{i.e. } \dfrac{\partial^2 \varphi_r}{\partial x\, \partial \alpha}\right)$ is continuous in the same domain. If $\chi(\alpha) = I(K_\alpha)$ the fundamental result, expressing the variation in terms of the contemporaneous variations of the end-points, is the analogue of (7.5.5), namely

(7.13.14)

$$\chi'(0) = f(b)\overline{X}'(0) - f(a)X'(0) + \int_{X(0)}^{\overline{X}(0)} (\Sigma f_{y_r}\eta_r + \Sigma f_{y_r'}\eta_r')\, dx.$$

Here $\eta_r(x)\, d\alpha$ is the contemporaneous variation of y_r,

$$\eta_r(x) = \left[\frac{\partial}{\partial \alpha}\varphi_r(x, \alpha)\right]_{\alpha=0}, \tag{7.13.15}$$

a represents the element of the original curve at A,

$$X(0),\ \varphi_r\{X(0), 0\},\ \varphi_r'\{X(0), 0\}, \tag{7.13.16}$$

and b the element of the original curve at B.

The integral in the second member of (7.13.14) is equal to

$$\Sigma \eta_r f_{y_r'} \Big|_{A_0}^{B_0} \tag{7.13.17}$$

as in (7.5.10), and the contemporaneous displacements of the end-points appearing in (7.13.14) are related to the actual displacements by formulae analogous to (4.2.10) and to (7.5.13)

$$dY_r = \eta_r\{X(0)\}\, d\alpha + \varphi_r'\{X(0), 0\}\, dX. \tag{7.13.18}$$

Substituting these results in (7.13.14) we arrive at the variable end-point theorem for $(n + 1)$ dimensions

(7.13.19) $$dI = (U\,dX + \Sigma V_r\,dY_r)\Big|_A^B.$$

As before, the result has been established on the assumption that K_0 is a curve without corners; but the result is still valid if K_0 has a finite number of corners.

Consider now the problem of finding a minimizing curve when the end-points are not fixed, but subject to the conditions

(7.13.20) $$\psi^\mu(X, Y, \overline{X}, \overline{Y}) = 0, \qquad \mu = 1, 2, \ldots, p < 2n + 2.$$

(Here we use the condensed notation, Y standing for the n components $Y_1, Y_2, \ldots, Y_n$, and $\overline{Y}$ for $\overline{Y}_1, \overline{Y}_2, \ldots, \overline{Y}_n$.) The necessary condition, analogous to (7.6.2), is that there exist constants $e^1, e^2, \ldots, e^p$ such that

(7.13.21) $$(U\,dX + \Sigma V_r\,dY_r)\Big|_A^B + \sum_{\mu=1}^{p} e^\mu\,d\psi^\mu = 0$$

for arbitrary values of $dX, dY, d\overline{X}, d\overline{Y}$.

Weierstrass's necessary condition and Legendre's necessary condition can be established for curves in $(n + 1)$-space by an argument similar to that given in §7.7. The excess function $E(x, y, y', \varpi)$, a function of the $(3n + 1)$ variables

(7.13.22) $$x, y_1, y_2, \ldots, y_n, y_1', y_2', \ldots, y_n', \varpi_1, \varpi_2, \ldots, \varpi_n,$$

is defined by the formula

(7.13.23)

$$E(x, y, y', \varpi) = f(x, y, \varpi) - f(x, y, y') - \Sigma(\varpi_r - y_r')f_{y_r'}(x, y, y'),$$

and Weierstrass's necessary condition is that for every element (x, y, y') of a minimizing curve

(7.13.24) $$E(x, y, y', \varpi) \geqslant 0$$

for all real values of $\varpi_1, \varpi_2, \ldots, \varpi_n$. Legendre's necessary condition (a weaker condition than that of Weierstrass) is that, for any element of a minimizing curve, the quadratic form whose matrix is $f_{y_r'y_s'}$ is a positive semi-definite form.

A field is a region Φ of the $(n + 1)$-space with a family of trexemals such that one and only one of these extremals passes through each point of Φ, and such that the Hilbert integral

(7.13.25) $$\int u\,dx + \Sigma v_r\,dy_r$$

is invariant. Here, as before, u and v_r are the functions formed from U and V_r by substituting for each y_r' the corresponding slope function p_r of the field,

(7.13.26) $$u = U(x, y, p) \qquad v_r = V_r(x, y, p).$$

The fundamental sufficiency theorem asserts that if an extremal arc K_{AB} is embedded in a field, and if at each point of the field the function

(7.13.27) $$\mathscr{W}(x, y, \varpi) = E(x, y, p, \varpi)$$

is positive, then K_{AB} gives a smaller value to I than any other curve (of class D_1) lying in Φ and joining the same end-points A and B.

7.14 Lagrange's equations deduced from Hamilton's principle

One of the most important applications of the theory presented in the preceding section occurs in the classical dynamics. We consider a holonomic system with n degrees of freedom. Let us change to the notation which is usual in dynamics, denoting the independent variable, the time, by t (instead of x), and the dependent variables by $q_1, q_2, \ldots, q_n$ (instead of $y_1, y_2, \ldots, y_n$). The q's are the Lagrangian coordinates for the dynamical system, functions of t to be determined, and their values at time t describe the configuration of the dynamical system. We may assume that each $q_r(t)$ is of class C_2.

The Lagrangian function L,

(7.14.1) $$L = T - V,$$

plays a fundamental role in the theory. Here T denotes the kinetic energy function for the dynamical system, and V the potential energy function. In the simplest case, that of the so-called *natural system*, T is a homogeneous quadratic form in $\dot{q}_1, \dot{q}_2, \ldots, \dot{q}_n$, with coefficients a_{rs} which are functions of the q's,

(7.14.2) $$T = \tfrac{1}{2}\Sigma\Sigma a_{rs}\dot{q}_r\dot{q}_s,$$

and V is a given function of the q's. But in more complicated cases T may contain a quadratic form T_2, a linear form T_1, and a term T_0 which is a function of the q's,

(7.14.3) $$T = T_2 + T_1 + T_0.$$

And further, in exceptional cases, the coefficients in T_2 and T_1, and the functions T_0 and V, may involve t as well as the q's. In the most general case, therefore,

$$L = L(t, q_1, q_2, \ldots, q_n, \dot{q}_1, \dot{q}_2, \ldots, \dot{q}_n) \tag{7.14.4}$$

or, in the condensed notation,

$$L = L(t, q, \dot{q}). \tag{7.14.5}$$

We may assume that $L \in C_2$ in an appropriate region of the $(2n + 1)$-fold space of $(t, q, \dot{q})$.

Let us suppose that during the motion the system passes through the configuration $Q_1, Q_2, \ldots, Q_n$ at $t = \theta$ and through the configuration $\bar{Q}_1, \bar{Q}_2, \ldots, \bar{Q}_n$ at $t = \bar{\theta}$, where $\bar{\theta} > \theta$. Hamilton's principle, the simplest of the *variation principles* of dynamics, asserts that the integral,

$$\int_{\theta}^{\bar{\theta}} L\, dt \tag{7.14.6}$$

taken along the actual motion, is stationary compared with neighbouring motions joining the same terminal points and occupying the same interval of time. Since the time-interval for the varied motion is the same as for the actual motion, we can deal throughout with contemporaneous variations.

The terminal points in the $(n + 1)$-fold space of (t, q) are fixed, and we have therefore a fixed end-point problem in the Calculus of Variations. The Euler equations, expressing necessary conditions for a stationary value of the integral (7.14.6), are

$$\frac{d}{dt}\frac{\partial L}{\partial \dot{q}_r} = \frac{\partial L}{\partial q_r}, \qquad r = 1, 2, \ldots, n, \tag{7.14.7}$$

and these are Lagrange's equations of motion for the dynamical system.

If L does not contain t, $U =$ constant is a first integral of the equations (7.14.7), and we have therefore

$$\Sigma \dot{q}_r \frac{\partial L}{\partial \dot{q}_r} - L = C, \tag{7.14.8}$$

a result usually referred to as *Jacobi's integral*. Since

$$\Sigma \dot{q}_r \frac{\partial L}{\partial \dot{q}_r} = 2T_2 + T_1 \tag{7.14.9}$$

the result (7.14.8) is equivalent to

$$T_2 + V - T_0 = C. \tag{7.14.10}$$

For a natural system this takes the familiar form

$$T + V = C, \tag{7.14.11}$$

the so-called *integral of energy*.

If L does not contain one of the coordinates, say q_1 (though it must of course contain $\dot{q}_1$), the coordinate q_1 is said to be *ignorable*, and we have at once the first integral

$$\frac{\partial L}{\partial \dot{q}_1} = \text{constant}. \tag{7.14.12}$$

Such an integral is called an *integral of momentum*.

The integrals of energy and of momentum have already been noticed, in the case of a dynamical system with only one freedom in §2.9, and in the case of a system with two freedoms in §7.1.

We have already considered, in §§5.9–5.13, for some simple special cases, the question whether the integral (7.14.6) is or is not a genuine minimum when the motion of the system is the motion actually occurring in nature.

CHAPTER VIII

The Problem of Lagrange

8.1 The problem of Lagrange

There is one independent variable x, and there are n dependent variables $y_1, y_2, \ldots, y_n$. We consider curves

$$(8.1.1)\quad y_1 = \varphi_1(x), y_2 = \varphi_2(x), \ldots, y_n = \varphi_n(x), \quad (X \leqslant x \leqslant \overline{X}),$$

connecting the (variable) end-points $A(X, Y_1, Y_2, \ldots, Y_n)$ and $B(\overline{X}, \overline{Y}_1, \overline{Y}_2, \ldots, \overline{Y}_n)$, satisfying the differential equations

$$(8.1.2)\quad g^{\beta}(x, y_1, y_2, \ldots, y_n, y_1', y_2', \ldots, y_n') = 0,$$
$$(\beta = 1, 2, \ldots, m;\ m < n),$$

and the end-conditions

$$(8.1.3)\quad \psi^{\mu}(X, Y_1, Y_2, \ldots, Y_n, \overline{X}, \overline{Y}_1, \overline{Y}_2, \ldots, \overline{Y}_n) = 0,$$
$$(\mu = 1, 2, \ldots, p;\ p \leqslant 2n + 2),$$

where

$$(8.1.4)\quad Y_r = \varphi_r(X), \quad \overline{Y}_r = \varphi_r(\overline{X}).$$

We wish to find among these curves one which minimizes the integral

$$(8.1.5)\quad I = \int_X^{\overline{X}} f(x, \varphi_1, \varphi_2, \ldots, \varphi_n, \varphi_1', \varphi_2', \ldots, \varphi_n')\, dx.$$

A problem of a more general type, the problem of Bolza, requires a minimizing curve for

$$(8.1.6)\quad \chi(X, Y_1, Y_2, \ldots, Y_n, \overline{X}, \overline{Y}_1, \overline{Y}_2, \ldots, \overline{Y}_n)$$
$$+ \int_X^{\overline{X}} f(x, \varphi_1, \varphi_2, \ldots, \varphi_n, \varphi_1', \varphi_2', \ldots, \varphi_n')\, dx,$$

and a third problem of the same class, the problem of Mayer, is like the problem of Bolza, but with the integral absent and only the function χ of the end-points surviving. The problem of Bolza clearly contains the problems of Lagrange and of Mayer as special cases. But in fact it is easy to see that the problem of Bolza is equivalent to a problem of Lagrange with one additional variable, and in this discussion we shall confine our attention in the first instance to the problem of Lagrange.

We shall sometimes write the single symbol y as a condensed notation for the row $y_1, y_2, \ldots, y_n$; similarly we write y' for $y_1', y_2', \ldots, y_n'$: φ for $\varphi_1, \varphi_2, \ldots, \varphi_n$: and so on. Thus we can state our problem as the problem of minimizing

$$I = \int_X^{\overline{X}} f(x, \varphi, \varphi')\, dx \tag{8.1.7}$$

in the class of curves satisfying the m differential equations

$$g^\beta(x, y, y') = 0 \tag{8.1.8}$$

and the p end-conditions

$$\psi^\mu(X, Y, \overline{X}, \overline{Y}) = 0. \tag{8.1.9}$$

The conditions assumed are as follows. We suppose in the first instance that the functions $\varphi_1(x), \varphi_2(x), \ldots, \varphi_n(x)$ are of class C_1, so at this stage we exclude curves with corners. The functions f and g^β are assumed to be of class C_3 in an appropriate domain R_1 of the $(2n + 1)$-fold space of (x, y, y'), and the equations (8.1.2) must be independent, so the m-rowed matrix whose β-th row is

$$g^\beta_{y_1'} \quad g^\beta_{y_2'} \quad \cdots \quad g^\beta_{y_n'}$$

is everywhere of rank m in R_1. The functions ψ^μ appearing in the end-conditions are of class C_3 in a domain R_2 of the $(2n + 2)$-fold space of $(X, Y, \overline{X}, \overline{Y})$, and the p-rowed matrix whose μ-th row is

$$\psi^\mu_X \, \psi^\mu_{Y_1} \psi^\mu_{Y_2} \cdots \psi^\mu_{Y_n} \, \psi^\mu_{\overline{X}} \, \psi^\mu_{\overline{Y}_1} \, \psi^\mu_{\overline{Y}_2} \cdots \psi^\mu_{\overline{Y}_n}$$

has rank p in R_2.

In practice the end-conditions (8.1.3) will usually separate into one set involving only the coordinates of A and another set involving only the coordinates of B. In that case the problem is said to have *separated* end-conditions. For the fixed end-point problem p has its greatest possible value $(2n + 2)$; in that case we can write the equations (8.1.3) in the form

$$X - a = 0,\ Y_r - b_r = 0,\ \overline{X} - \overline{a} = 0,\ \overline{Y}_r - \overline{b}_r = 0. \tag{8.1.10}$$

In the problems discussed previously we have usually begun with the fixed end-point problem, but in the problem of Lagrange we shall find it expedient to deal with the general problem of variable end-points (including that of fixed end-points as a special case) right from the start.

We call a curve $y = \varphi(x)$ *admissible* if all the functions φ_r are of class C_1, if the elements (x, φ, φ') lie in R_1 and satisfy the differential equations $g^\beta = 0$, and the end-points $(X, Y, \overline{X}, \overline{Y})$ lie in R_2 and satisfy the end-conditions $\psi^\mu = 0$. We denote the class of admissible curves by κ'. The problem is to find among the curves K of κ' a curve K_0 for which $I(K)$ is a minimum. To establish necessary conditions we set out from the assumption that the curve K_0 joining A_0 to B_0 is a minimizing curve, and the final step in the argument is one that is now familiar; we select from κ' a one-parameter family κ'' of which K_0 is a member, and we express the condition that K_0 is minimizing in this one-parameter family. We shall find, as a necessary condition, that K_0 satisfies the conditions for a minimizing curve for the integrand

(8.1.11) $$F = l^0 f + \sum_{\beta=1}^{m} l^\beta g^\beta,$$

where l^0 is a non-zero constant, and $l^1, l^2, \ldots, l^m$ are functions of x to be determined. In the variable end-point problem there are also the p end-conditions $\psi^\mu = 0$, and further the condition

(8.1.12) $$(U\,dx + V\,dy)\Big|_{A_0}^{B_0} + \sum_{\mu=1}^{p} e^\mu d\psi^\mu = 0$$

must be satisfied for arbitrary values of the differentials dX, dY, $d\overline{X}$, $d\overline{Y}$, where the coefficients e^μ are constants to be determined. (The functions U and V_r are formed from F in the usual way, and $V\,dy$ stands for $\Sigma V_r\,dy_r$.)

8.2 Normality

A difficulty arises if the arc K_0 is such that it satisfies the equations of du Bois-Reymond derived from an integrand F *in which* $l^0 = 0$. If there exist multipliers $l^1, l^2, \ldots, l^m$, which are continuous functions of x, such that K_0 satisfies the equations of du Bois-Reymond derived from

(8.2.1) $$l^1 g^1 + l^2 g^2 + \ldots + l^m g^m,$$

the arc K_0 is said to be *abnormal.* The notion of abnormality relates solely to the functions g^β: a curve which is abnormal is abnormal whatever the original integrand f. A minimizing arc which is not abnormal is said to be *normal.* For a normal minimizing arc we can put $l^0 = 1$, and then the remaining multipliers $l^1, l^2, \ldots, l^m$ are unique; for otherwise the difference between two sets of multipliers (each with $l^0 = 1$) would give a set of multipliers with $l^0 = 0$.

There are various degrees of abnormality. An arc K_0 is said to have abnormality of order q if there are q, and only q, linearly independent sets of multipliers (each with $l^0 = 0$) such that K_0 satisfies the equations of du Bois-Reymond derived from (8.2.1). For a normal arc, $q = 0$.

Some simple concrete examples, in three-dimensional space (x, y, z), may help to clarify the ideas. Here $m = 1$, and there is just one equation of the type (8.1.2),

$$g^1(x, y, z, y', z') = 0.$$

(i) If

$$g^1 \equiv \frac{d}{dx}\,\varphi(x, y, z) = \varphi_x + \varphi_y y' + \varphi_z z', \tag{8.2.2}$$

where $\varphi \in C_4$, the admissible curves lie on the surfaces $\varphi =$ constant. There is no admissible curve joining A to B unless $\varphi(\bar{X}, \bar{Y}, \bar{Z}) = \varphi(X, Y, Z)$. In this trivial case *all* admissible arcs are abnormal, because the Euler equations derived from $l^1 g^1$ (where l^1 is a constant) disappear (§3.2).

(ii) If

$$g^1 \equiv \varphi(y', z'), \tag{8.2.3}$$

any straight line of the form

$$y = ax + b, \qquad z = cx + d, \tag{8.2.4}$$

with $\varphi(a, c) = 0$, is abnormal, since (8.2.4) satisfies the equations of du Bois-Reymond derived from $\varphi(y', z')$.

(iii) Suppose that

$$g^1 \equiv z' - \sqrt{(1 + y'^2)}, \tag{8.2.5}$$

and that the end-points A and B are fixed. We take the axis Oz vertically upwards, and assume that $\bar{Z} > Z$, i.e. that the height of B is greater than that of A. Let K be a curve joining A to B, and let Γ be the plane curve which is the projection of K on $z = 0$; the end-points of Γ are M and N, which are the projections of A and B on $z = 0$. If $d\sigma$ is the element of length of Γ, $g^1 = 0$ is equivalent to

$$dz = d\sigma. \tag{8.2.6}$$

Then the length of Γ from M to N must be equal to $\bar{Z} - Z$. If $\bar{Z} - Z > \lambda_0$, where λ_0 is the distance MN, the curves Γ are the curves of length $\bar{Z} - Z$ joining M to N. The corresponding curves K belonging to the class κ' lie on the cylinders with vertical generators through the points of Γ, and the tangent to K at any point makes an angle $\frac{1}{4}\pi$ with the vertical.

If $\bar{Z} - Z = \lambda_0$ there is only one curve Γ joining M to N, namely the line-segment MN, and there is only one curve K of class κ' joining A to B, namely K_0 the line-segment AB. In this case the arc K_0 is abnormal; it satisfies the equations of du Bois-Reymond for the integrand (8.2.5). We notice that K_0 cannot be varied to a neighbouring curve in the class κ', because κ' contains only the one member K_0.

If $\bar{Z} - Z < \lambda_0$ there is no arc joining A to B and satisfying (8.2.5); the class κ' is empty. This phenomenon has been noticed earlier in connexion with the isoperimetrical problem, §6.4.

In this book we shall not consider the abnormal cases; we shall assume that the curve K_0, postulated to be a minimizing curve, is normal. We shall find that in that case it can be embedded in a family of arcs belonging to κ'; the minimizing curve is not isolated, and the minimizing problem is not trivial.

8.3 The equations of variation

Let us consider a one-parameter family of curves K_α,

(8.3.1) $$y_r = \varphi_r(x, \alpha),$$

containing K_0 for $\alpha = 0$. We assume that the functions $\varphi_r(x, \alpha)$ and $\varphi_r'(x, \alpha)$ are continuous, and possess derivatives with respect to α which are continuous in a domain of (x, α) containing the closed region

(8.3.2) $$X(\alpha) \leqslant x \leqslant \bar{X}(\alpha), \qquad |\alpha| \leqslant \varepsilon.$$

We assume also that the functions $X(\alpha)$, $\bar{X}(\alpha)$ defining the end-points have continuous derivatives $X'(\alpha)$, $\bar{X}'(\alpha)$ in the domain $|\alpha| < \varepsilon$. We write

(8.3.3) $$\xi = X'(0), \quad \bar{\xi} = \bar{X}'(0),$$

so the variations of the end-points in the x-direction are $\xi\, d\alpha$ and $\bar{\xi}\, d\alpha$. We write

(8.3.4) $$\eta_r(x) = \left[\frac{\partial}{\partial\alpha}\varphi_r(x, \alpha)\right]_{\alpha=0},$$

so that $\eta(x)\, d\alpha$ is the contemporaneous variation from K_0. Also it will be convenient to have a notation for the values of $\eta_r(x)$ at A_0 and B_0, and we write

(8.3.5) $$\zeta_r = \eta_r\{X(0)\}, \qquad \bar{\zeta}_r = \eta_r\{\bar{X}(0)\}.$$

Each of the variations $\eta_r(x)$ has a continuous first derivative $\eta_r'(x)$.

The *set of variations* of the family along K_0 is the set

(8.3.6) $$\xi, \bar{\xi}, \eta_1(x), \eta_2(x), \ldots, \eta_n(x),$$

or say, concisely,

(8.3.7) $$\xi, \bar{\xi}, \eta(x).$$

Now if the curves K_α satisfy the differential equations (8.1.2) for all sufficiently small values of α, we have

(8.3.8) $$g^\beta\{x, \varphi(x, \alpha), \varphi'(x, \alpha)\} = 0,$$

and then, differentiating with respect to α (and putting $\alpha = 0$ after differentiating) we see that the variations $\eta_r(x)$ satisfy the m linear differential equations

(8.3.9) $$G^\beta \equiv g^\beta_{y_r}\eta_r + g^\beta_{y_r'}\eta_r' = 0.$$

In these equations the arguments in the derivatives of g^β are the elements of K_0, and the repeated suffix r implies summation from 1 to n. The equations (8.3.9) are spoken of as the *equations of variation along* K_0. It is important to observe that the coefficients of η_r and of η_r' in the equations of variation are known functions of x, completely determined when K_0 is given, and independent of any family in which K_0 is embedded. A set of variations ξ, $\bar{\xi}$, η is said to be *admissible* if the η's satisfy (8.3.9).

We next consider the end-points. If the coordinates of the end-points satisfy the equations $\psi^\mu = 0$ for all sufficiently small values of α, the displacements of the end-points satisfy the p equations

(8.3.10) $$\psi^\mu_X\, dX + \psi^\mu_{Y_r}\, dY_r + \psi^\mu_{\bar{X}}\, d\bar{X} + \psi^\mu_{\bar{Y}_r}\, d\bar{Y}_r = 0,$$

where again the repeated suffix r implies summation from 1 to n.

It will be convenient to express the equations (8.3.10) in a form involving the contemporaneous displacements $\zeta_r\, d\alpha$ instead of the actual displacements dY_r. Now

(8.3.11) $$dX = \xi\, d\alpha,$$

and, by a now-familiar argument,

(8.3.12) $$dY_r = [d\varphi_r\{X(\alpha), \alpha\}]_{\alpha=0} = (\zeta_r + p_r\xi)\, d\alpha,$$

where $p_1, p_2, \ldots, p_n$ refer to the slope of K_0 at A_0,

(8.3.13) $$p_r = \varphi_r'\{X(0), 0\}.$$

Thus, supplying the corresponding formulae for the end B_0, we see that (8.3.10) leads to

(8.3.14)

$$\Psi^{\mu} \equiv (\psi^{\mu}_{X} + \psi^{\mu}_{Y_r} p_r)\xi + \psi^{\mu}_{Y_r}\zeta_r + (\psi^{\mu}_{\bar{X}} + \psi^{\mu}_{\bar{Y}_r}\bar{p}_r)\bar{\xi} + \psi^{\mu}_{\bar{Y}_r}\bar{\zeta}_r = 0.$$

The p equations (8.3.14) are the *equations of variation of the end-conditions*. We notice that Ψ^{μ} is a linear form in the $(2n + 2)$ variables $(\xi, \zeta, \bar{\xi}, \bar{\zeta})$ with known constant coefficients. (We recall that when we derive the varied curve by contemporaneous variations it may be necessary to extend its range of definition in the way described in §1.2.)

The proof of the multiplier rule depends upon two lemmas which we now establish.

8.4 Lemma 1

Let K_0 be a curve satisfying the differential equations $g^{\beta} = 0$, and let $\eta_1(x), \eta_2(x), \ldots, \eta_n(x)$ be n given functions of x, of class C_1, satisfying the m equations of variation $G^{\beta} = 0$. Then there is a one-parameter family of curves K_{α}, $y_r = \varphi_r(x, \alpha)$, all satisfying $g^{\beta} = 0$, containing K_0 for $\alpha = 0$, and having the prescribed functions $\eta_r(x)$ as the variations of the family along K_0.

The curve K_0 satisfies the differential equations (8.1.2), $g^{\beta} = 0$, but it is not obvious *a priori* that there are also neighbouring curves with the same property. The lemma shows not only that such curves do exist, but also that we can prescribe in advance the variations from K_0, provided of course that these prescribed variations are admissible.

To establish the lemma we make use of the following device. We introduce $(n - m)$ new functions

(8.4.1) $$g^{\gamma}(x, y_1, y_2, \ldots, y_n, y'_1, y'_2, \ldots, y'_n)$$

of class C_3 in R_1, and forming with the functions g^{β} a set of n independent functions of $y'_1, y'_2, \ldots, y'_n$. If we substitute the elements of K_0 in g^{γ} we get a continuous function of x, say z^{γ}, and we then have a set of n differential equations

(8.4.2) $$g^{\beta} = 0, \quad g^{\gamma} = z^{\gamma},$$

$$(\beta = 1, 2, \ldots, m;\ \gamma = (m + 1), (m + 2), \ldots, n),$$

satisfied by K_0.

Next, if we substitute in g^γ the one-parameter family $y_r = \varphi_r(x, \alpha)$, then the variation of g^γ along K_0 is (as in (8.3.9))

$$G^\gamma(x, \eta, \eta') \equiv g^\gamma_{y_r}\eta_r + g^\gamma_{y_r'}\eta_r'. \tag{8.4.3}$$

Thus G^γ has a known value Z^γ, a continuous function of x, when K_0 and the variations $\eta_r(x)$ are prescribed.

We now consider the set of n differential equations

$$g^\beta = 0, \quad g^\gamma = z^\gamma + \alpha Z^\gamma. \tag{8.4.4}$$

For $\alpha = 0$ they have solutions which are the equations defining K_0. More generally they have solutions

$$y_r = \mathscr{Y}_r(x, x^0, y^0, \alpha), \tag{8.4.5}$$

with initial point (x^0, y^0) $(= (x^0, y_1^0, y_2^0, \ldots, y_n^0))$, for which the functions $\mathscr{Y}_r$, $\mathscr{Y}_r'$ are continuous and have continuous partial derivatives of at least the third order with respect to the parameters x^0, y^0, α in a neighbourhood of the set $(x, X(0), Y(0), 0)$ belonging to K_0. In particular the functions

$$y_r = \mathscr{Y}_r(x, X(0), Y(0) + \alpha\zeta, \alpha) = \varphi_r(x, \alpha) \tag{8.4.6}$$

say, then define a one-parameter family satisfying $g^\beta = 0$ on an interval containing $(X(0), \overline{X}(0))$. These functions φ_r have at $X(0)$ the initial values

$$Y_r(0) + \alpha\zeta_r, \tag{8.4.7}$$

so the variations of the family along K_0 have at $X(0)$ the correct initial values ζ_r. But also these variations satisfy

$$G^\beta = 0, \quad G^\gamma = Z^\gamma, \tag{8.4.8}$$

so they must be identical with the prescribed variations $\eta_r(x)$, since these functions are the unique solutions of the linear differential equations (8.4.8) with the correct initial values at $X(0)$. This completes the proof of the lemma.

If the set of variations $\xi, \bar{\xi}, \eta$ of the family along K_0 is prescribed, not merely the functions η, we have only to choose the functions $X(\alpha)$, $\overline{X}(\alpha)$ so that

$$X'(0) = \xi, \quad \overline{X}'(0) = \bar{\xi}. \tag{8.4.9}$$

The simplest choice would be the linear functions

$$X(\alpha) = X(0) + \xi\alpha, \quad \overline{X}(\alpha) = \overline{X}(0) + \bar{\xi}\alpha. \tag{8.4.10}$$

16

Of course when ξ, $\bar{\xi}$, η are prescribed the values of ζ, $\bar{\zeta}$ are determined, and the resulting values of ξ, ζ, $\bar{\xi}$, $\bar{\zeta}$ will not in general satisfy (8.3.14).

COROLLARY 1. We can extend the lemma to N-parameter families of curves. Consider N sets of functions $\eta_r^\sigma(x)$, for $\sigma = 1, 2, \ldots, N$, each set satisfying the equations of variation (8.3.9). Then there exists an N-parameter family of curves

$$y_r = \varphi_r(x, \alpha_1, \alpha_2, \ldots, \alpha_N) = \varphi_r(x, \alpha) \tag{8.4.11}$$

say, containing K_0 for $\alpha = 0$ (i.e. for $\alpha_1 = \alpha_2 = \ldots = \alpha_N = 0$), and having $\eta^\sigma(x)$ as its variation with respect to α_σ along K_0. The proof follows the same lines as the proof of the lemma, the equations (8.4.4) being replaced by

$$g^\beta = 0, g^\gamma = z^\gamma + \alpha_1 Z_1^\gamma + \alpha_2 Z_2^\gamma + \ldots + \alpha_N Z_N^\gamma. \tag{8.4.12}$$

If further, for each of these sets, the values of ξ and $\bar{\xi}$ are prescribed, we must replace (8.4.10) by the equations

$$\begin{aligned} X(\alpha) &= X(0) + \xi^1\alpha_1 + \xi^2\alpha_2 + \ldots + \xi^N\alpha_N, \\ \bar{X}(\alpha) &= \bar{X}(0) + \bar{\xi}^1\alpha_1 + \bar{\xi}^2\alpha_2 + \ldots + \bar{\xi}^N\alpha_N. \end{aligned} \tag{8.4.13}$$

COROLLARY 2. In the lemma the functions $\eta_1(x), \eta_2(x), \ldots, \eta_n(x)$ are prescribed functions of class C_1. But if we change our point of view, and suppose the $(n - m)$ functions Z^γ to be prescribed continuous functions (the functions g^γ having been prescribed once for all) then the equations (8.4.8) constitute a set of n linear differential equations of the first order satisfied by $\eta_1, \eta_2, \ldots, \eta_n$, and there are unique solutions for the η's if their values at one point (say the values $\bar{\zeta}_r$ at $\bar{X}(0)$) are prescribed.

COROLLARY 3. If N sets of variations $\eta_r^\sigma(x)$, for $\sigma = 1, 2, \ldots, N$, are given, each set satisfying (8.3.9), we can find a set of variations linearly independent of them. For each set of variations determines a corresponding set of Z^γ's, and we have only to take a set of Z^γ's linearly independent of these sets, and determine the corresponding η's as in Corollary 2.

8.5 Lemma 2

Let $l^0, c^1, c^2, \ldots, c^n$ be prescribed arbitrary constants, and let

$$F = l^0 f + l^s g^s, \tag{8.5.1}$$

where s is summed from 1 to n, and the multipliers $l^1, l^2, \ldots, l^n$ are functions of x to be determined. Then a unique set of multipliers $l^1, l^2, \ldots, l^n$, continuous in $(X(0), \bar{X}(0))$, is determined by the requirement that the elements of K_0 satisfy the n equations of du Bois-Reymond,

$$F_{y_r'}\{x, \varphi(x), \varphi'(x)\} = \int_{X(0)}^{x} F_{y_r}\{t, \varphi(t), \varphi'(t)\}\, dt + c^r. \tag{8.5.2}$$

To prove the lemma, we write for the moment

$$v^r = F_{y_r'} = l^0 f_{y_r'} + l^s g^s_{y_r'}, \tag{8.5.3}$$

so that each v^r is a linear function of $l^1, l^2, \ldots, l^n$, with coefficients which are known continuous functions of x. Conversely, l^r is a linear function of $v^1, v^2, \ldots, v^n$, with coefficients which are known continuous functions of x. Now

$$\frac{dv^r}{dx} = F_{y_r} = l^0 f_{y_r} + l^s g^s_{y_r}, \tag{8.5.4}$$

and the second members of the n equations (8.5.4) can be expressed as linear functions of $v^1, v^2, \ldots, v^n$, with coefficients which are known continuous functions of x. We have thus a set of linear differential equations satisfied by the v's, and these differential equations, with the prescribed initial values

$$v^r\{X(0)\} = c^r \tag{8.5.5}$$

determine uniquely the functions v^r. Hence the multipliers l^r (which are known linear functions of the v's) are also uniquely determined. This completes the proof of the lemma.

COROLLARY. Since the solutions of (8.5.4), for prescribed initial values, are unique, we see that l^0, $v^r(x)$ do not vanish simultaneously unless they are identically zero, and the same is true of the multipliers l^0, $l^r(x)$.

8.6 The first variation of I

Let us consider to begin with a one-parameter family (8.3.1), $y_r = \varphi_r(x, \alpha)$, containing K_0 for $\alpha = 0$, and let

$$\Omega(\alpha) = I(K_\alpha) = \int_{X(\alpha)}^{\bar{X}(\alpha)} f(x, \varphi, \varphi')\, dx. \tag{8.6.1}$$

Then, as in (7.13.14), we have

$$\Omega'(0) = f\xi \Big|_{A_0}^{B_0} + \int_{X(0)}^{\bar{X}(0)} (f_{y_r}\eta_r + f_{y_r'}\eta_r')\, dx = \Theta(\xi, \bar{\xi}, \eta) \tag{8.6.2}$$

say, where ξ, $\bar{\xi}$, $\eta(x)$ are the variations of the family along K_0, and the arguments in f_{y_r} and $f_{y_r'}$ are the elements of K_0. The value of $\Theta(\xi, \bar{\xi}, \eta)$ is completely defined by (8.6.2) when the functions $\varphi_r(x, 0)$ defining K_0 and the variations ξ, $\bar{\xi}$, $\eta(x)$ are prescribed. The curve K_0, $y_r = \varphi_r(x, 0)$, satisfies (8.4.2), and the variations are chosen to be admissible variations, so that $\eta_1(x), \eta_2(x), \dots, \eta_n(x)$ satisfy (8.4.8).

We write, as in (8.5.1),

(8.6.3) $$F = l^0 f + l^s g^s,$$

where s is summed from 1 to n, and the multipliers l^s are functions of x to be determined. Since the variations $\eta_r(x)$ satisfy (8.4.8) the value of $l^0\Theta(\xi, \bar{\xi}, \eta)$ found from (8.6.2) is not altered if we add to the integrand the terms

$$l^\beta G^\beta + l^\gamma(G^\gamma - Z^\gamma),$$

where β is summed from 1 to m and γ from $(m + 1)$ to n. Thus

(8.6.4)
$$l^0\Theta(\xi, \bar{\xi}, \eta) = l^0 f\xi \Big|_{A_0}^{B_0} + \int_{X(0)}^{\bar{X}(0)} \{l^0(f_{y_r}\eta_r + f_{y_r'}\eta_r')$$
$$+ l^\beta(g^\beta_{y_r}\eta_r + g^\beta_{y_r'}\eta_r') + l^\gamma(g^\gamma_{y_r}\eta_r + g^\gamma_{y_r'}\eta_r' - Z^\gamma)\}\, dx$$
$$= l^0 f\xi \Big|_{A_0}^{B_0} + \int_{X(0)}^{\bar{X}(0)} (F_{y_r}\eta_r + F_{y_r'}\eta_r' - l^\gamma Z^\gamma)\, dx.$$

We now appeal to Lemma 2. We choose the constants $l^0, c^1, c^2, \dots, c^n$, and then we determine the multipliers $l^1, l^2, \dots, l^n$ from du Bois-Reymond's equations (8.5.2). Then, on integrating by parts, we have

(8.6.5) $$l^0\Theta(\xi, \bar{\xi}, \eta) = (l^0 f\xi + F_{y_r'}\eta_r)\Big|_{A_0}^{B_0} - \int_{X(0)}^{\bar{X}(0)} l^\gamma Z^\gamma\, dx.$$

8.7 Necessary conditions for a minimizing curve

We start from the assumption that K_0 is a minimizing curve in the class κ' (i.e. in the class of curves satisfying the differential equations (8.1.2) and the end-conditions (8.1.3)) and we deduce necessary conditions which must be satisfied by K_0. The first step is the construction of a one-parameter family κ'' which is a sub-class of κ'.

We proceed as in Corollary 1 of Lemma 1, with $N = p + 1$. We take $(p + 1)$ independent sets of variations ξ^σ, $\bar{\xi}^\sigma$, $\eta^\sigma(x)$, each satisfying the equations of variation (8.3.9). We then construct a $(p + 1)$-parameter family of curves

$$y_r = \varphi_r(x, \alpha_1, \alpha_2, \ldots, \alpha_{p+1}) = \varphi_r(x, \alpha) \tag{8.7.1}$$

say, containing K_0 for $\alpha = 0$ (i.e. for $\alpha_1 = \alpha_2 = \ldots = \alpha_{p+1} = 0$), and having the set ξ^σ, $\bar{\xi}^\sigma$, $\eta^\sigma(x)$ as the variations with respect to α_σ along K_0. If now we suppose the α's to be not independent, but to be so related that the p end-conditions (8.1.3) are satisfied by the family (8.7.1), then the family is reduced to a one-parameter family κ'' which is a sub-class of κ'; for example we can in general think of the p end-conditions as defining $\alpha_1, \alpha_2, \ldots, \alpha_p$ as functions of the single parameter α_{p+1}.

When the values (8.7.1) are substituted, I becomes a function of the α's,

$$I = \psi(\alpha_1, \alpha_2, \ldots, \alpha_{p+1}) \tag{8.7.2}$$

and the end-conditions (8.1.3) become p equations of condition

$$\chi^\mu(\alpha_1, \alpha_2, \ldots, \alpha_{p+1}) = 0, \qquad (\mu = 1, 2, \ldots, p), \tag{8.7.3}$$

and we now have a problem in the ordinary theory of maxima and minima; the function $\psi(\alpha_1, \alpha_2, \ldots, \alpha_{p+1})$, where the α's are subject to the p conditions (8.7.3), is a minimum when all the α's are zero. A first-order necessary condition is that the Jacobian Δ of the $(p + 1)$ functions ψ, χ^μ with respect to the $(p + 1)$ parameters α should vanish for $\alpha_1 = \alpha_2 = \ldots = \alpha_{p+1} = 0$. Now the σ-th column of Δ, for $\sigma = 1, 2, \ldots, p + 1$, is

$$\begin{array}{c} \Theta(\xi^\sigma, \bar{\xi}^\sigma, \eta^\sigma) \\ \Psi^1(\xi^\sigma, \bar{\xi}^\sigma, \eta^\sigma) \\ \cdot \quad \cdot \quad \cdot \\ \Psi^p(\xi^\sigma, \bar{\xi}^\sigma, \eta^\sigma). \end{array} \tag{8.7.4}$$

Each element in this column contains a linear form, with known coefficients, in

$$\xi^\sigma, \zeta_1^\sigma, \zeta_2^\sigma, \ldots, \zeta_n^\sigma, \bar{\xi}^\sigma, \bar{\zeta}_1^\sigma, \bar{\zeta}_2^\sigma, \ldots, \bar{\zeta}_n^\sigma, \tag{8.7.5}$$

and the first element contains, in addition, the integral involving the $(n - m)$ functions Z^γ formed for $\eta^\sigma(x)$. The rank of the determinant is not greater than p, and we shall see that we can choose the $(p + 1)$ variations in such a way that its rank is in fact p. Let us choose the variations in this way. Then there exist constants $l^0, e^1, e^2, \ldots, e^p$, not all zero, and uniquely determined save for a constant factor, such that

$$(8.7.6) \qquad l^0\Theta(\xi^\sigma, \bar{\xi}^\sigma, \eta^\sigma) + e^\mu\Psi^\mu(\xi^\sigma, \bar{\xi}^\sigma, \eta^\sigma) = 0$$

for each value of σ from 1 to $(p + 1)$. (In (8.7.6) the repeated affix μ is summed from 1 to p.)

But this is not the complete picture. In fact (8.7.5) must hold for every admissible set of variations ξ, $\bar{\xi}$, η, not merely for the $(p + 1)$ sets originally chosen. If this were not so, a column of the form (8.7.4) not satisfying (8.7.6), and substituted for one of the original columns of Δ, would give a determinant of rank $(p + 1)$. This is impossible because the vanishing of Δ comes from the fact that K_0 is minimizing in the class κ'. Thus

$$(8.7.7) \qquad l^0\Theta(\xi, \bar{\xi}, \eta) + e^\mu\Psi^\mu(\xi, \bar{\xi}, \eta) = 0$$

holds *for an arbitrary admissible variation* ξ, $\bar{\xi}$, η. If we substitute the value of Θ as found in (8.6.5) we have

$$(8.7.8) \qquad (l^0f\xi + F_{y_r'}\eta_r)\Big|_{A_0}^{B_0} - \int_{X(0)}^{\bar{X}(0)} l^\gamma Z^\gamma\,dx + e^\mu\Psi^\mu = 0.$$

The first member of (8.7.7) is the sum of a linear form in the variables

$$(8.7.9) \qquad \xi, \zeta_1, \zeta_2, \ldots, \zeta_n, \bar{\xi}, \bar{\zeta}_1, \bar{\zeta}_2, \ldots, \bar{\zeta}_n,$$

and the integral.

The coefficient of ζ_r in the first member of (8.7.8) is

$$(8.7.10) \qquad (-F_{y_r'})_{A_0} + e^\mu\left(\frac{\partial\psi^\mu}{\partial Y_r}\right)_{A_0} = -c^r + e^\mu\left(\frac{\partial\psi^\mu}{\partial Y_r}\right)_{A_0},$$

and this can be made to vanish for all values of r by an appropriate choice of the constants c^r. And when this choice has been made the multipliers $l^1, l^2, \ldots, l^n$ are uniquely determined (Lemma 2). The remainder of the first member of (8.7.8)—i.e. the terms other than those in $\zeta_1, \zeta_2, \ldots, \zeta_n$—must vanish for any arbitrarily selected set ξ, $\bar{\xi}$, $\bar{\zeta}_r$, Z^γ (with Z^γ continuous) since any chosen set of functions Z^γ and values $\bar{\zeta}_r$ determine an admissible variation (Lemma 1, Corollary 2). Taking $\xi = \bar{\xi} = \bar{\zeta}_r = 0$ it follows that the last $(n - m)$ multipliers $l^{m+1}, l^{m+2}, \ldots, l^n$ vanish identically, since the Z's can be chosen arbitrarily. The result does not surprise us!—indeed any value of the last $(n - m)$ multipliers other than zero would appear unlikely in view of the wide choice open to us for the g^γ's.

It is now easy to see that the coefficient of each of the surviving $(n+2)$ variables $\xi, \bar{\xi}, \bar{\zeta}_1, \bar{\zeta}_2, \ldots, \bar{\zeta}_n$ in (8.7.7) is zero. To prove this we have only to consider an admissible variation in which one and only one of these is not zero.

Thus, for any admissible variation, the coefficient of each of the variables (8.7.9) in

$$(8.7.11) \qquad (F\xi \mid F_{y_r'}\eta_r)\Big|_{A_0}^{B_0} + e^{\mu}\Gamma^{\mu}$$

is zero, where now

$$(8.7.12) \qquad F = l^0 f + \sum_{\beta=1}^{m} l^{\beta} g^{\beta},$$

and we have used the fact that $l^0 f = F$ on K_0, since the elements of K_0 make $g^{\beta} = 0$.

Finally we suppress the contemporaneous variations ζ_r, $\bar{\zeta}_r$ of the end-points in favour of the actual displacements, i.e. we express the result in terms of the variables

$$(8.7.13) \quad dX, dY_1, dY_2, \ldots, dY_n, d\bar{X}, d\bar{Y}_1, d\bar{Y}_2, \ldots, d\bar{Y}_n,$$

instead of the variables (8.7.8). Now, as in (8.3.12),

$$(8.7.14) \qquad \zeta_r \, d\alpha = dY_r - p_r \xi \, d\alpha,$$

and there is a similar formula for $\bar{\zeta}_r \, d\alpha$, while Ψ^{μ}, expressed in terms of the displacements (8.7.13), is merely $d\psi^{\mu}$. We thus express our result in the more familiar form

$$(8.7.15) \qquad (U\,dx + V\,dy)\Big|_{A_0}^{B_0} + e^{\mu}\, d\psi^{\mu} = 0,$$

where $V\,dy$ means $\sum_{r=1}^{n} V_r\, dy_r$, and this equation (8.7.15) is true *for arbitrary values* of the displacements $dX, dY, d\bar{X}, d\bar{Y}$. The functions U and V are defined as usual by the equations

$$(8.7.16) \qquad U = F - y_r' F_{y_r'}, \qquad V_r = F_{y_r'}.$$

Another way of stating the end-conditions (8.7.15) is that

$$(8.7.17) \qquad (U\,dx + V\,dy)\Big|_{A_0}^{B_0}$$

must vanish for any permissible variation of the end-points, that is for any variation satisfying the p conditions $d\psi^{\mu} = 0$.

8.8 The multiplier rule

An admissible arc K_0 is said to satisfy the multiplier rule if there exist constants $l^0, e^1, e^2, \ldots, e^p$, not all zero, and a function

$$F = l^0 f + \sum_{\beta=1}^{m} l^\beta g^\beta, \tag{8.8.1}$$

with multipliers $l^\beta(x)$ continuous in $(X(0), \overline{X}(0))$, such that the equations

$$F_{y_r'} = \int_{X(0)}^{x} F_{y_r}\, dx + c^r, \qquad g^\beta = 0, \tag{8.8.2}$$

are satisfied along K_0, and such that the equations

$$(U\, dx + V\, dy)\Big|_{A_0}^{B_0} + \sum_{\mu=1}^{p} e^\mu\, d\psi^\mu = 0, \qquad \psi^\mu = 0, \tag{8.8.3}$$

hold at the ends A_0 and B_0 of K_0 for every choice of the differentials $dX, dY, d\overline{X}, d\overline{Y}$. For an arc satisfying the multiplier rule the multipliers $l^0, l^\beta(x)$ do not vanish simultaneously at any point of the interval $(X(0), \overline{X}(0))$.

The theorem we have proved is this: *Every minimizing arc for the problem of Lagrange must satisfy the multiplier rule.*

COROLLARY 1. The theorem is valid if we admit curves with a finite number of corners, but in that case the multipliers are in general discontinuous at the corners of K_0. To prove this the proof already given needs only slight modification.

COROLLARY 2. For the problem of Bolza, where the functional to be minimized has the form (8.1.6), we must add the term $l^0\, d\chi$ in the first member of the first equation (8.8.3).

COROLLARY 3. Since K_0 is normal, l^0 cannot be zero, and we can take $l^0 = 1$ by merely dividing the set l^0, l^β by a suitable constant. The multipliers in the form $1, l^\beta$ are unique (as we have noticed already in §8.2) since if there were two such sets their difference would be an abnormal set, and for our problem, with K_0 assumed to be normal, no abnormal set of multipliers exists.

COROLLARY 4. If the end-points are fixed, the end-conditions give no information, as indeed we should expect. Thus, for example, if we write the $(2n + 2)$ equations $\psi^\mu = 0$ in the form (8.1.10), the constants e^μ are merely the values of U and of V_r at A_0, and the values of $-U$ and of $-V_r$ at B_0.

Some special cases are worthy of notice. If A is fixed at A_0, and B is free to move in the direction Ox (so that $\overline{Y}_1, \overline{Y}_2, \ldots, \overline{Y}_n$

are fixed), the end-conditions give $U = 0$ at B_0. If A is fixed at A_0, and $\bar{X}$ is fixed, and if some of $\bar{Y}_1, \bar{Y}_2, \ldots, \bar{Y}_n$ are fixed and some are not, the end-conditions give $V_r = 0$ at B_0 for the values of r corresponding to the free $\bar{Y}_r$'s.

8.9 The matrix D

Consider the matrix **D**, with $(p + 1)$ rows and $(p + 1)$ columns, whose σ-th column is given by (8.7.4). We have assumed already that the $(p + 1)$ sets of variations ξ^σ, $\bar{\xi}^\sigma$, $\eta^\sigma(x)$, can be so chosen that this matrix has rank p. We now turn to the proof of this fact. If the maximum rank attainable by the matrix formed by the last p rows of **D** were less than p, there would be a set of constants $l^0, e^1, e^2, \ldots, e^p$ for which (8.7.7) holds *and for which* $l^0 = 0$. But in that case there would exist a set of multipliers $l^0, l^1, l^2, \ldots, l^p$, with $l^0 = 0$, and this is impossible since K_0 is normal. Thus our assumption that the $(p + 1)$ sets of variations can be so chosen that **D** has rank p is justified.

Let us then choose the variations used in §8.7 in such a way that the determinant of the last p rows of the first p columns of **D** does not vanish. Then the p equations (8.7.3) can be solved for $\alpha_1, \alpha_2, \ldots, \alpha_p$ as functions of α_{p+1},

$$\text{(8.9.1)} \qquad \alpha_\mu = A_\mu(\alpha_{p+1}), \qquad (\mu = 1, 2, \ldots, p),$$

and the functions $A_\mu(\alpha_{p+1})$ vanish at $\alpha_{p+1} = 0$, and have continuous derivatives near $\alpha_{p+1} = 0$. We have thus an explicit representation of the one-parameter family κ'', satisfying both (8.1.2) and (8.1.3) for sufficiently small values of α_{p+1}, and containing K_0 for $\alpha_{p+1} = 0$.

Let us consider this one-parameter family, obtained from (8.7.1) by substituting $\alpha_\mu = A_\mu(\alpha)$ for $\mu = 1, 2, \ldots, p$, where we now write α in place of α_{p+1}. The variations of the family along K_0 are

$$\text{(8.9.2)} \quad \xi + \xi^\mu A_\mu'(0), \quad \bar{\xi} + \bar{\xi}^\mu A_\mu'(0), \quad \eta_s(x) + \eta_s^\mu(x) A_\mu'(0),$$

where μ is summed from 1 to p, and s runs from 1 to n. If the last n of these are not identically zero the family will surely contain arcs not identical with K_0. But when the first p sets of functions $\eta_s^\mu(x)$ have been chosen in the way described, to give rank p to the matrix **D**, the $(p + 1)$-th set of variations $\eta_s(x)$ can always be selected linearly independent of them (Lemma 1, Corollary 3). Thus the last n variations in (8.9.2) are not identically zero, and the family contains arcs of κ' not identical with K_0.

We can go further. If ξ, $\bar{\xi}$, $\eta(x)$ is a set of variations along K_0 *satisfying both* (8.3.9) *and* (8.3.14), then we can choose the one-parameter family κ'' so that it has this set ξ, $\bar{\xi}$, $\eta(x)$ as its variations along K_0. Now the one-parameter family will have the desired variations if the symbols ξ, $\bar{\xi}$, $\eta(x)$ in (8.9.2) represent these variations, and if $A'_\mu(0) = 0$ for all values of μ. The equations (8.7.3) are identically satisfied if we substitute $A_\mu(\alpha)$ for α_μ, and differentiating with respect to α, for $\alpha = 0$, we find

$$\Psi^{\mu}(\xi^\sigma, \bar{\xi}^\sigma, \eta^\sigma)A'_\sigma(0) + \Psi^\mu(\xi, \bar{\xi}, \eta) = 0 \qquad \mu = 1, 2, \ldots, p. \tag{8.9.3}$$

Now the last term in each of these equations vanishes, because the set ξ, $\bar{\xi}$, η satisfies (8.3.14), and the determinant $|\Psi^\mu(\xi^\sigma, \bar{\xi}^\sigma, \eta^\sigma)|$, with p rows and p columns, is different from zero. Hence all the values $A'_\mu(0)$ vanish, and the result follows. The upshot is that, if K_0 is normal, it is never isolated, and we can embed it in a family κ'' belonging to κ'. And moreover, if we have a prescribed set of variations satisfying both the equations of variation along K_0 and the equations of variation of the end-conditions, then we can choose κ'' so that the variations of the family along K_0 have these prescribed values.

8.10 The isoperimetrical problem

The multiplier rule is not altogether easy to establish, but on the other hand the theorem, once established, is quite simple to use. We have noticed already that the problem of Lagrange embraces as special cases all the problems previously discussed. In this section we consider again the isoperimetrical problem in the plane, of which an *ad hoc* solution has already been given (at least so far as necessary conditions are concerned) in Chapter VI. In subsequent sections we will consider some further applications illustrating the power and versatility of the theorem.

For the isoperimetrical problem we wish to find a minimizing curve for

$$\int_X^{\bar{X}} F(x, y, y')\, dx \tag{8.10.1}$$

in the class of curves joining the (fixed or variable) end-points A and B, and satisfying the isoperimetrical condition

$$\int_X^{\bar{X}} G(x, y, y')\, dx = l. \tag{8.10.2}$$

We take two dependent variables y and z, and we have one equation of condition

$$g^1 \equiv z' - G(x, y, y') = 0. \tag{8.10.3}$$

In the notation of §8.1, $n = 2$ and $m = 1$. A minimizing curve, if it exists, must consist of arcs satisfying Euler's equations for

$$F(x, y, y') + \mu\{z' - G(x, y, y')\}, \tag{8.10.4}$$

where $\mu = \mu(x)$ is a multiplier to be determined. Euler's equations are

$$\frac{d}{dx}(F_{y'} - \mu G_{y'}) = F_y - \mu G_y, \qquad \frac{d\mu}{dx} = 0, \tag{8.10.5}$$

so $\mu(x)$ is a constant, $\mu(x) = \lambda$, and thus (since the term $\lambda z'$ contributes nothing in Euler's equations, as in (3.2.6)) we recover Euler's rule.

Now consider the end-conditions; the end-points are $(X, Y, 0)$ and $(\overline{X}, \overline{Y}, l)$. If the original plane problem has fixed end-points we now have a fixed end-point problem in three dimensions, l being prescribed, and the end-conditions give no useful information. Next, let us consider the variable end-point problem, where A can move on a curve Γ, and B on a curve Δ in the (x, y)-plane. If, by way of illustration, we express the end-conditions in the form (8.1.3) we have

$$\psi^1(X, Y) = 0, \quad \psi^2(\overline{X}, \overline{Y}) = 0, \quad Z = 0, \quad \overline{Z} - l = 0, \tag{8.10.6}$$

and $p = 4$. The end-conditions give, as in (8.7.15),

$$(U^*\,dx + V^*\,dy + \mu\,dz)\Big|_A^B + e^1\left(\frac{\partial\psi^1}{\partial X}dX + \frac{\partial\psi^1}{\partial Y}dY\right) + e^2\left(\frac{\partial\psi^2}{\partial \overline{X}}d\overline{X} + \frac{\partial\psi^2}{\partial \overline{Y}}d\overline{Y}\right) + e^3\,dZ + e^4\,d\overline{Z} = 0, \tag{8.10.7}$$

where U^*, V^* belong to

$$F^* = F - \mu G. \tag{8.10.8}$$

(The term $\mu z'$ in (8.10.4) contributes nothing to the coefficients of dX and $d\overline{X}$ in (8.10.7).) The equation (8.10.7) holds for arbitrary values of dX, dY, dZ, $d\overline{X}$, $d\overline{Y}$, $d\overline{Z}$. The coefficients of dZ and of $d\overline{Z}$ are irrelevant (they only prove $e^3 = -e^4 = \lambda$), and the others merely prove that

(8.10.9) $$U^* \, dx + V^* \, dy = 0$$

for the permissible variations of A on Γ and of B on Δ. This is, of course, precisely the result previously found in §6.12.

EXAMPLE. Hanging string of given length. We have already discussed this problem, both for fixed end-points (§6.7) and for variable end-points (§6.13) by the method of Euler's rule, which we established in §6.5 and which we have now recovered by the multiplier rule. It may be of interest, however, to exhibit the solution of the problem considered *ab initio* as a Lagrange problem. Taking t as the arc-length, measured from A, we wish to minimize

(8.10.10) $$\int_0^l y \, dt$$

subject to the condition

(8.10.11) $$g^1 \equiv \dot{x}^2 + \dot{y}^2 - 1 = 0.$$

Here t is the independent variable, and the end-points are $(0, X, Y)$ and $(l, \overline{X}, \overline{Y})$. Thus we need Euler's equations for

(8.10.12) $$F \equiv y + \tfrac{1}{2}\mu(\dot{x}^2 + \dot{y}^2 - 1),$$

where μ $(= \mu(t))$ is a multiplier to be determined. The equations are

(8.10.13) $$\frac{d}{dt}(\mu\dot{x}) = 0, \qquad \frac{d}{dt}(\mu\dot{y}) = 1,$$

so

(8.10.14) $$\mu\dot{x} = b, \qquad \mu\dot{y} = t - t_0,$$

where b and t_0 are constants; t_0 is in fact the value of t at the lowest point of the string. We have at once

(8.10.15) $$\mu^2 = b^2 + (t - t_0)^2.$$

We introduce a new variable θ in place of t,

(8.10.16) $$t - t_0 = b \sinh \theta, \qquad \mu = b \cosh \theta,$$

and the equations (8.10.14) become

(8.10.17) $$\frac{dx}{d\theta} = \frac{dx}{dt}\frac{dt}{d\theta} = b, \qquad \frac{dy}{d\theta} = \frac{dy}{dt}\frac{dt}{d\theta} = t - t_0 = b \sinh \theta,$$

whence

$$x - a = b\theta, \qquad y - y_0 = b\cosh\theta, \tag{8.10.18}$$

and the form in which the string hangs is given by

$$y - y_0 = b\cosh\frac{x - a}{b}. \tag{8.10.19}$$

Now consider the end-conditions. In the fixed end-point problem the end-conditions merely re-affirm that the length of the string is l. (The length of the string, measured from the lowest point, is $t - t_0 = b\sinh\dfrac{x-a}{b}$.) In the variable end-point problem the end-conditions give, in addition,

$$\dot{x}\,dx + \dot{y}\,dy = 0 \tag{8.10.20}$$

at each end, and this is of course the condition already found in §6.13.

8.11 Brachistochrone in a resisting medium

A bead slides on a wire in the form of a curve in a vertical plane joining A to B, and the bead starts from A with prescribed velocity W. When the speed is w the motion is resisted by a force $R(w)$ per unit mass, but there is no other frictional force. The problem is to find the form of the curve so that the bead reaches B in the shortest possible time. The problem is of great interest historically, because it was solved, in the sense of reduction to quadratures, by Euler.

The equation of motion for the bead is

$$w\frac{dw}{ds} = g\frac{dy}{ds} - R, \tag{8.11.1}$$

where s is the arc-length of the curve, and the axis Oy is taken vertically downwards. If we express the curve in parametric form $x(\tau)$, $y(\tau)$, where these functions are assumed to be of class C_1, the equation takes the form

$$g^1 \equiv ww' - gy' + R\sqrt{(x'^2 + y'^2)} = 0. \tag{8.11.2}$$

The integral to be minimized is

$$I = \int_\theta^{\bar{\theta}} \frac{\sqrt{(x'^2 + y'^2)}}{w}\,d\tau. \tag{8.11.3}$$

We have a Lagrange problem, with three dependent variables x, y, w, and one equation of condition $g^1 = 0$. The end-points are (θXYW) and $(\bar{\theta}\bar{X}\bar{Y}\bar{W})$, where $(X, Y, \bar{X}, \bar{Y}, W)$ are prescribed; but θ, $\bar{\theta}$, $\bar{W}$ are not prescribed. We need Euler's equation for

$$F = \sqrt{(x'^2 + y'^2)}\left(\frac{1}{w} + \mu R\right) + \mu w w' - \mu g y', \tag{8.11.4}$$

where $\mu = \mu(\tau)$. We write

$$H = H(\tau, w) = \frac{1}{w} + \mu R, \tag{8.11.5}$$

and then

$$F = H\sqrt{(x'^2 + y'^2)} + \mu w w' - \mu g y'. \tag{8.11.6}$$

Writing the first integrals $F_{x'} =$ constant, $F_{y'} =$ constant, and the Euler equation for w, we have

$$H\frac{dx}{ds} = a, \tag{8.11.7}$$

$$H\frac{dy}{ds} = b + \mu g, \tag{8.11.8}$$

$$w\frac{d\mu}{ds} = H_w, \tag{8.11.9}$$

where a and b are constants to be determined. The end-condition $F_{w'} = 0$ at B gives $\mu w = 0$ at B; we may assume that $\bar{W} \neq 0$, so $\mu = 0$ at B.

Now from (8.11.7) and (8.11.8)

$$H^2 = a^2 + (b + \mu g)^2, \tag{8.11.10}$$

and this equation serves to express μ as a function of w. The fact that $\mu = 0$ at B gives

$$\bar{W}^2 = \frac{1}{a^2 + b^2}. \tag{8.11.11}$$

Let us assume, for definiteness, that during the motion the resistance is never as large as the weight, so that $R < g$ for all relevant values of w. Then (8.11.10) gives

$$(g^2 - R^2)\mu + \left(bg - \frac{R}{w}\right) = \pm\sqrt{f(w)} \tag{8.11.12}$$

where

(8.11.13)

$$(a^2 + b^2)f(w) = \left\{(a^2 + b^2)R - \frac{bg}{w}\right\}^2 + a^2g^2\left\{\frac{1}{w^2} - (a^2 + b^2)\right\}.$$

Further, dividing (8.11.7) and (8.11.8) by (8.11.9) we have

$$(8.11.14) \qquad dx = \frac{aw\,d\mu}{HH_w}, \qquad dy = \frac{(b + \mu g)w\,d\mu}{HH_w},$$

and from these equations we can express x and y in terms of the parameter w. Now, from (8.11.5) and (8.11.10),

$$(8.11.15) \qquad H(H_w\,dw + R\,d\mu) = g(b + \mu g)\,d\mu,$$

giving

$$(8.11.16) \qquad HH_w\,dw = \left\{\mu(g^2 - R^2) + \left(bg - \frac{R}{w}\right)\right\} d\mu,$$

so the equations (8.11.14) become

$$(8.11.17) \qquad dx = \frac{aw\,dw}{\sqrt{f(w)}}, \qquad dy = \frac{(b + \mu g)w\,dw}{\sqrt{f(w)}}.$$

If then we consider for definiteness a problem in which $W > 0$, and in which w steadily increases from W to $\overline{W}$ during the motion, we have

$$(8.11.18) \qquad x - X = \int_W^w \frac{a\xi\,d\xi}{\sqrt{f(\xi)}}, \qquad y - Y = \int_W^w \frac{(b + g\lambda(\xi))\xi\,d\xi}{\sqrt{f(\xi)}},$$

where $\lambda(w)$ is the value of μ given by (8.11.12), and the positive square root is taken. Thus x and y are expressed parametrically in terms of w,

$$(8.11.19) \qquad x - X = \varphi(w;\ a, b), \qquad y - Y = \psi(w;\ a, b),$$

and the constants a and b are determined from the equations

(8.11.20)

$$\overline{X} - X = \varphi\left(\frac{1}{\sqrt{(a^2 + b^2)}};\ a, b\right), \qquad \overline{Y} - Y = \psi\left(\frac{1}{\sqrt{(a^2 + b^2)}};\ a, b\right).$$

8.12 Integrand containing y''

We seek a minimizing curve for

$$(8.12.1) \qquad I = \int_X^{\overline{X}} f(x, y, y', y'')\,dx,$$

where $f \in C_3$, and we consider curves $y = \varphi(x)$, where $\varphi(x) \in C_4$.

A variety of end-conditions are possible. For example, at an end-point, (i) both position and slope may be prescribed, i.e. x, y, y' are all prescribed, or (ii) x, y may be prescribed, with y' unrestricted, or (iii) x, y' may be prescribed, with y unrestricted, or (iv) x may be prescribed, with both y and y' unrestricted. The end-conditions will not always be of the same type at both ends.

We treat the problem as a Lagrange problem in three dimensions; $n = 2$, $m = 1$. We seek a minimizing curve for

(8.12.2) $$\int_X^{\overline{X}} f(x, y, z, z')\, dx$$

in the class of curves satisfying

(8.12.3) $$g \equiv y' - z = 0.$$

(Or we could use the integrand $f(x, y, y', z')$.) For the integrand

(8.12.4) $$F \equiv f(x, y, z, z') + \mu(y' - z),$$

where the multiplier μ is a function of x to be determined, the Euler equations are

(8.12.5) $$\frac{d\mu}{dx} = f_y, \quad \frac{d}{dx} f_{z'} = f_z - \mu.$$

The end-conditions in the four cases mentioned are as follows. In (i) the end-conditions give no information (and of course this is exactly what we expect, since the conditions suffice to determine the curve completely). In (ii) $f_{z'} = 0$ at the end-point, in (iii) $\mu = 0$ at the end-point, and in (iv) both $f_{z'}$ and μ vanish at the end-point.

Let us now revert to the original notation, using f to denote $f(x, y, y', y'')$. We easily interpret the results that we have found. We see from (8.12.5) that the minimizing curve must satisfy the differential equation

(8.12.6) $$f_y - \frac{d}{dx} f_{y'} + \frac{d^2}{dx^2} f_{y''} = 0.$$

For the end-conditions, in (ii) $f_{y''} = 0$ at the end-point, in (iii) $f_{y'} - \dfrac{d}{dx} f_{y''} = 0$ at the end-point, and in (iv) both these conditions are fulfilled.

EXAMPLE 1. As a concrete example let us consider the integral

$$I = \int_0^1 y''^2\, dx, \tag{8.12.7}$$

where A is the origin and B is the point (1, 1). The differential equation (8.12.6) is $y^{\text{iv}} = 0$, and the solution is a cubic polynomial

$$y = a + bx + cx^2 + dx^3. \tag{8.12.8}$$

(i) If $y'(x)$ has the prescribed value zero at A and at B the curve is

$$y = 3x^2 - 2x^3. \tag{8.12.9}$$

It is easy to see that this cubic does in fact minimize the integral in the class C_4. If we consider the curve

$$y = 3x^2 - 2x^3 + \zeta, \tag{8.12.10}$$

where $\zeta \in C_4$, and ζ, ζ' both vanish when $x = 0$ and also when $x = 1$, we have for this curve

(8.12.11)

$$I = \int_0^1 (6 - 12x + \zeta'')^2\, dx = I_0 + 12\int_0^1 (1 - 2x)\zeta''\, dx + \int_0^1 \zeta''^2\, dx,$$

and

$$\int_0^1 (1 - 2x)\zeta''\, dx = ((1 - 2x)\zeta' + 2\zeta)\Big|_0^1 = 0. \tag{8.12.12}$$

Hence $I > I_0$ unless $\zeta'' = 0$ for all x in (0, 1), and this would imply $\zeta = 0$.

(ii) If the slopes are not prescribed at A and B the end-conditions give $y'' = 0$ at A and B, and the solution is the linear segment $y = x$. This again is clearly minimizing, since for the linear segment, $I = 0$, whereas, for any other curve joining the given end-points, $I > 0$.

EXAMPLE 2. *The bending of beams.* We consider a beam which is nearly horizontal, occupying a position slightly displaced from the stretch $x = 0$ to $x = l$ on the x-axis. The beam is heavy, or is loaded, so that the weight per unit length is $w(x)$, where $w(x)$ is a given continuous function of x. Taking the axis Oy vertically downwards, the potential energy is

(8.12.13) $$I = \int_0^l (\tfrac{1}{2}\kappa y''^2 - wy)\, dx,$$

where $\kappa = \kappa(x)$ is a given function of x of class C_2. In the position of equilibrium I is a minimum.

The differential equation is

(8.12.14) $$\frac{d^2}{dx^2}(\kappa y'') - w = 0.$$

The end-conditions are, in (ii) $y'' = 0$, and in (iii) $\dfrac{d}{dx}(\kappa y'') = 0$.

Let us be content to discuss more particularly the simple case of a uniform beam, in which both κ and w are positive constants. The differential equation is

(8.12.15) $$y^{\text{iv}} = w/\kappa,$$

and the solution has the form

(8.12.16) $$y = A + Bx + Cx^2 + Dx^3 + \frac{w}{\kappa}\frac{x^4}{4!}.$$

We consider four simple special cases as follows.

(*a*) The beam is clamped horizontally at both ends. Here y and y' vanish both at $x = 0$ and at $x = l$, and the solution is easily seen to be

(8.12.17) $$y = \frac{w}{24\kappa} x^2(l - x)^2.$$

(*b*) The beam is supported at the same level at both ends. Here $y = 0$ at $x = 0$ and at $x = l$, and $y'' = 0$ at both ends in virtue of the end-conditions. The solution is easily seen to be

(8.12.18) $$y = \frac{w}{24\kappa}(l^3x - 2lx^3 + x^4).$$

This can also be written in the form

(8.12.19) $$y = \frac{w}{24\kappa}(5a^4 - 6a^2\xi^2 + \xi^4),$$

where a is written for $\tfrac{1}{2}l$, and ξ is written for $x - \tfrac{1}{2}l$.

(*c*) The beam is clamped horizontally at $x = 0$ and is free at $x = l$.

In this case $y = y' = 0$ at $x = 0$, while $y'' = y''' = 0$ at $x = l$. The solution is

$$y = \frac{w}{24\kappa} x^2(6l^2 - 4lx + x^2). \tag{8.12.20}$$

The "sag" at the free end $x = l$ is $wl^4/8\kappa$.

(*d*) The beam is clamped horizontally at $x = 0$, and a weight W is hung from the other end. The functional to be minimized is

$$-W\overline{Y} + \int_0^l (\tfrac{1}{2}\kappa y''^2 - wy)\, dx, \tag{8.12.21}$$

where $\overline{Y}$ denotes as usual the value of y at $x = l$. We have here a problem of Bolza, and the end-conditions at $x = l$ (§8.8, Corollary 2) are $y'' = 0$ and $\kappa y''' = -W$. The solution is

$$y = \frac{w}{24\kappa} x^2(6l^2 - 4lx + x^2) + \frac{W}{6\kappa} x^2(3l - x). \tag{8.12.22}$$

8.13 Geodesics

We consider the problem of finding the curve of shortest length lying on a given surface and joining two given points of the surface. The subject is too large to pursue in detail here, but we can establish the fundamental property.

We suppose the surface to be represented by the equation $\varphi(x, y, z) = 0$, where $\varphi \in C_2$, and express the curve parametrically in the form $\{x(t), y(t), z(t)\}$, where these functions are assumed to be of class C_2. Thus our problem is that of finding a minimizing curve for

$$I = \int_T^{\overline{T}} \sqrt{(\dot{x}^2 + \dot{y}^2 + \dot{z}^2)}\, dt \tag{8.13.1}$$

in the class of curves satisfying the condition

$$g^1 \equiv \varphi(x, y, z) = 0. \tag{8.13.2}$$

Here $n = 3$ and $m = 1$.

We have here a problem in which the equation of condition does not contain the derivatives $\dot{x}, \dot{y}, \dot{z}$. It may be mentioned in passing that the proof of the multiplier rule for problems of this type is simpler than it is for the general case.

Using the multiplier rule we need Euler's equations for

$$F = \sqrt{(\dot{x}^2 + \dot{y}^2 + \dot{z}^2)} + \mu\varphi, \tag{8.13.3}$$

where $\mu = \mu(t)$. The typical Euler equation is

$$\frac{d}{dt}\frac{\dot{x}}{\sqrt{(\dot{x}^2 + \dot{y}^2 + \dot{z}^2)}} = \mu\frac{\partial\varphi}{\partial x}, \tag{8.13.4}$$

which we can write in the form

$$\frac{d}{dt}\frac{dx}{ds} = \mu\frac{\partial\varphi}{\partial x}, \tag{8.13.5}$$

where s is the arc-length of the curve. Hence

$$\frac{d^2x}{ds^2} = \frac{\mu}{\dot{s}}\frac{\partial\varphi}{\partial x}, \tag{8.13.6}$$

and the three equations of this type exhibit the fundamental property of a geodesic, namely that the principal normal to the curve at a point P coincides with the normal to the surface at P. The end-points are (T, X, Y, Z) and $(\overline{T}, \overline{X}, \overline{Y}, \overline{Z})$, and (X, Y, Z) and $(\overline{X}, \overline{Y}, \overline{Z})$ are fixed points on the surface $\varphi = 0$. The end-conditions give no information.

We can attack the problem in another way which well illustrates the usefulness and versatility of the multiplier rule. Let us take t to be the arc-length of the geodesic. Then our problem is to minimize

$$I = \int_T^{\overline{T}} dt, \tag{8.13.7}$$

subject to the two conditions

$$g^1 \equiv \varphi(x, y, z) = 0, \tag{8.13.8}$$

$$g^2 \equiv \dot{x}^2 + \dot{y}^2 + \dot{z}^2 - 1 = 0. \tag{8.13.9}$$

Here $n = 3$, $m = 2$. The problem is a problem of Mayer (§8.1) since the functional to be minimized can be expressed as a function of the end-values, namely $\chi = \overline{T} - T$.

We write

$$F = 1 + \lambda\varphi + \tfrac{1}{2}\mu(\dot{x}^2 + \dot{y}^2 + \dot{z}^2 - 1), \tag{8.13.10}$$

where the multipliers λ and μ are functions of t to be determined. The typical Euler equation is

$$\frac{d}{dt}(\mu\dot{x}) = \lambda\frac{\partial\varphi}{\partial x}. \tag{8.13.11}$$

We see easily that μ is constant; if we multiply the equation (8.13.11) by $\mu\dot{x}$, and add together the three equations of this type, we get

$$(8.13.12)\quad \frac{d}{dt}\{\tfrac{1}{2}\mu^2(\dot{x}^2+\dot{y}^2+\dot{z}^2)\} = \lambda\mu\left(\dot{x}\frac{\partial\varphi}{\partial x}+\dot{y}\frac{\partial\varphi}{\partial y}+\dot{z}\frac{\partial\varphi}{\partial z}\right) = 0,$$

giving

$$(8.13.13)\quad \frac{d}{dt}(\tfrac{1}{2}\mu^2) = 0,$$

and therefore μ is constant. Thus

$$(8.13.14)\quad \ddot{x} = \frac{\lambda}{\mu}\frac{\partial\varphi}{\partial x}$$

and there are two similar equations. We see again that the principal normal to the curve coincides with the principal normal to the surface.

Actually $\mu = 1$; for, since T, $\overline{T}$ are not prescribed, the end-conditions give $U = 0$ at A and B, and

$$(8.13.15)\quad U = 1 + \lambda\varphi + \tfrac{1}{2}\mu(\dot{x}^2+\dot{y}^2+\dot{z}^2-1) - \mu(\dot{x}^2+\dot{y}^2+\dot{z}^2)$$
$$= 1 - \mu.$$

8.14 Lagrange's equations deduced from the principle of Least Action

As we know, the deduction of Lagrange's equations of motion in the classical dynamics from Hamilton's principle is simple (§7.14). The deduction from the principle of Least Action, though less simple, is an interesting and important dialectical exercise.

There is one independent variable t, and n dependent variables $q_1, q_2, \ldots, q_n$, and we assume that the functions $q_r(t)$ are of class C_2 in the relevant range of values of t. We consider the integral

$$(8.14.1)\quad I = \int_\theta^{\bar{\theta}} 2T\,dt,$$

where $2T$ is a homogeneous quadratic form in $\dot{q}_1, \dot{q}_2, \ldots, \dot{q}_n$,

$$(8.14.2)\quad 2T = \Sigma\Sigma a_{rs}\dot{q}_r\dot{q}_s,$$

the coefficients a_{rs} being functions of $(q_1, q_2, \ldots, q_n)$ of class C_1. The principle of Least Action asserts that I is stationary for the actual motion in the class of curves satisfying the equation

$$(8.14.3)\quad g^1 \equiv T + V - C = 0,$$

where V is a given function of $(q_1, q_2, \ldots, q_n)$ of class C_1, and C is a constant (the constant of energy). The end-conditions are that A is fixed, i.e. $\theta, Q_1, Q_2, \ldots, Q_n$ are all prescribed, but B is not fixed, though the upper terminal point in the q-space is fixed, i.e. $\bar{Q}_1, \bar{Q}_2, \ldots \bar{Q}_n$ are all prescribed, but $\bar{\theta}$ is variable.

In this problem $m = 1, p = 2n + 1$. The multiplier rule implies that the orbit is an extremal for the integrand

$$F \equiv 2T + \mu(T + V - C) \tag{8.14.4}$$

where the multiplier μ is a function of t to be determined. The only information provided by the end-conditions is that U, formed for F, vanishes at $\bar{\theta}$. Now

$$\begin{aligned} U = F - \dot{q}_r F_{\dot{q}_r} &= 2T + \mu(T + V - C) - 2(2 + \mu)T \\ &= -2(\mu + 1)T, \end{aligned} \tag{8.14.5}$$

where we have used (8.14.3) and the relation $\dot{q}_r \dfrac{\partial T}{\partial \dot{q}_r} = 2T$. Thus the information provided by the end-conditions is simply

$$\mu(\bar{\theta}) = -1. \tag{8.14.6}$$

The typical Euler equation for the integrand F is

$$\frac{d}{dt}\left\{(2 + \mu)\frac{\partial T}{\partial \dot{q}_r}\right\} = (2 + \mu)\frac{\partial T}{\partial q_r} + \mu\frac{\partial V}{\partial q_r}, \tag{8.14.7}$$

which can also be written in the form

$$(2 + \mu)\left\{\frac{d}{dt}\left(\frac{\partial T}{\partial \dot{q}_r}\right) - \frac{\partial T}{\partial q_r}\right\} = \mu\frac{\partial V}{\partial q_r} - \frac{d\mu}{dt}\frac{\partial T}{\partial \dot{q}_r}. \tag{8.14.8}$$

If we multiply the equation (8.14.8) by $\dot{q}_r$, and sum for $r = 1$ to $r = n$, we get

$$(2 + \mu)\left\{\dot{q}_r\frac{d}{dt}\left(\frac{\partial T}{\partial \dot{q}_r}\right) - \dot{q}_r\frac{\partial T}{\partial q_r}\right\} = \mu\frac{\partial V}{\partial q_r}\dot{q}_r - \frac{d\mu}{dt}\dot{q}_r\frac{\partial T}{\partial \dot{q}_r} \tag{8.14.9}$$

where the repeated suffix r implies summation from 1 to n.

Now

$$\begin{aligned} \dot{q}_r\frac{d}{dt}\left(\frac{\partial T}{\partial \dot{q}_r}\right) - \dot{q}_r\frac{\partial T}{\partial q_r} &= \frac{d}{dt}\left(\dot{q}_r\frac{\partial T}{\partial \dot{q}_r}\right) - \left(\dot{q}_r\frac{\partial T}{\partial q_r} + \ddot{q}_r\frac{\partial T}{\partial \dot{q}_r}\right) \\ &= \frac{d}{dt}(2T - T) = \frac{dT}{dt}, \end{aligned} \tag{8.14.10}$$

and

$$\frac{\partial V}{\partial q_r}\dot{q}_r = \frac{dV}{dt} = -\frac{dT}{dt}, \tag{8.14.11}$$

where we have used (8.14.3) and the relation $\dot{q}_r \dfrac{\partial T}{\partial \dot{q}_r} = 2T$. Thus (8.14.9) takes the form

$$(2 + \mu)\frac{dT}{dt} = -\mu\frac{dT}{dt} - \frac{d\mu}{dt}(2T), \tag{8.14.12}$$

whence

$$\frac{d}{dt}\{(1 + \mu)T\} = 0. \tag{8.14.13}$$

It follows that

$$(1 + \mu)T = c, \tag{8.14.14}$$

and $c = 0$, since $\mu = -1$ at $t = \bar{\theta}$. Thus $\mu = -1$ for all values of t, and the Euler equations for F are simply the Lagrangian equations for $T - V$. This completes the proof.

8.15 Livens's theorem

Hamilton's principle in classical dynamics is concerned with the q-space, the space of the Lagrangian coordinates $q_1, q_2 \ldots, q_k$. The motion on the actual path in the q-space is compared with motion along neighbouring paths in the q-space. Liven's theorem, closely related to Hamilton's principle, is concerned with motion in the phase-space, a space of $2k$ dimensions, with coordinates $q_1, q_2, \ldots, q_k, p_1, p_2, \ldots, p_k$. The dynamical system with which we deal is a holonomic system, and the Lagrangian function L does not contain t explicitly,

$$L = L(q_1, q_2, \ldots, q_k, \dot{q}_1, \dot{q}_2, \ldots, \dot{q}_k) = L(q, \dot{q}). \tag{8.15.1}$$

Hamilton's principle asserts that

$$\int_\theta^{\bar{\theta}} L(q, \dot{q})\, dt \tag{8.15.2}$$

is stationary for an orbit in the q-space, compared with neighbouring orbits having the same end-points, say Q and $\bar{Q}$, and the same times of departure and arrival, say θ and $\bar{\theta}$.

We can interpret the principle in terms of a $2k$-fold with coordinates $q_1, q_2, \ldots, q_k, \omega_1, \omega_2, \ldots, \omega_k$. The integral

$$\int_{\theta}^{\bar{\theta}} L(q, \omega)\, dt \tag{8.15.3}$$

is stationary for the actual motion, the class of curves considered being those satisfying the conditions

$$g^r \equiv \dot{q}_r - \omega_r = 0, \qquad (r = 1, 2, \ldots, k). \tag{8.15.4}$$

The values of θ, Q, $\bar{\theta}$, $\bar{Q}$ are fixed at the end-points; but the values of the ω's are free. In the notation of §8.1

$$n = 2k, \quad m = k, \quad p = 2k + 2 = n + 2. \tag{8.15.5}$$

Now, in virtue of the multiplier rule, the orbits in the $2k$-fold space of (q, ω) satisfy Euler's equations for the integrand

$$L(q, \omega) + \sum_{r=1}^{k} \mu_r(\dot{q}_r - \omega_r), \tag{8.15.6}$$

where the multipliers $\mu_1, \mu_2, \ldots, \mu_k$ are functions of t to be determined. Euler's equations for (8.15.6) are

$$\frac{d\mu_r}{dt} = \frac{\partial L}{\partial q_r}, \quad \frac{\partial L}{\partial \omega_r} = \mu_r, \tag{8.15.7}$$

so that μ_r can be interpreted as the momentum-component p_r, where $p_r = \dfrac{\partial L}{\partial \omega_r}$. (If we eliminate μ from the equations (8.15.7), and use (8.15.4), we recover Lagrange's equation of motion, which is of course just what we expect.)

The next step is to interpret the result in terms of the phase-space of (q, p) instead of the $2k$-fold space of (q, ω). Now free variation of q's and ω's is equivalent to free variation of q's and p's, so if we write $H(q, p)$ for the function

$$\sum_{r=1}^{k} p_r\, \omega_r - L(q, \omega) \tag{8.15.8}$$

expressed in terms of q's and p's (instead of q's and ω's) we have the theorem that *the integral*

$$\int_{0}^{\theta} (H - \sum_{r=1}^{k} p_r \dot{q}_r)\, dt \tag{8.15.9}$$

is stationary for the actual motion in the phase-space. This is Livens's theorem. The end-conditions are that the values of t and the q's are fixed at the end-points, but not the values of the p's.

The function H, the Hamiltonian function, is constructed from (8.15.8) by suppressing the ω's in favour of the p's by means of the equations $p_r = \dfrac{\partial L}{\partial \omega_r}$. In the case with which we are concerned in the classical dynamics these equations are *linear* equations for $\omega_1, \omega_2, \ldots, \omega_k$, and the process is simple.

The Euler equations for the stationary integral (8.15.9) are

$$\dot{q}_r = \frac{\partial H}{\partial p_r}, \qquad \dot{p}_r = -\frac{\partial H}{\partial q_r}, \qquad (r = 1, 2, \ldots, k),$$

and these are Hamilton's equations of motion.

What information do we derive from the end-conditions in Livens's theorem? None whatever! Since the p's are free at the end-points the end-conditions require V_r to vanish at θ and at $\bar{\theta}$ for $r = k+1, k+2, \ldots, 2k$ (taking the dependent variables in the order $q_1, q_2, \ldots, q_k, p_1, p_2, \ldots, p_k$); but all these V_r's vanish identically since H does not contain $\dot{p}_r$'s.

8.16 A note on non-holonomic systems

Consider a dynamical system described by Lagrangian coordinates $q_1, q_2, \ldots, q_n$. If the system is holonomic we can choose $n = k$, where k is the number of degrees of freedom of the system. If the system is not holonomic we cannot describe it by k Lagrangian coordinates; the least possible value for n is $k + l$, where l is the number of non-integrable constraints. These numbers k and l are invariants of the system, independent of the particular coordinates chosen. For a non-holonomic system there are l equations of constraint

$$\text{(8.16.1)} \qquad \sum_{s=1}^{n} B_{rs}\dot{q}_s + B_r = 0, \qquad r = 1, 2, \ldots, l,$$

where the coefficients B_{rs} and B_r are functions of the q's (and possibly also of t) of class C_1.

We may be tempted to expect that a theorem analogous to Hamilton's principle may hold in the class κ' of curves satisfying the equations of constraint, i.e. we may expect $\int_{\theta}^{\bar{\theta}} L\,dt$ to be stationary (the end-points in space and time being fixed) in the class κ'. It comes as something of a shock to discover that this is not true. The orbits are not minimizing curves for $\int_{\theta}^{\bar{\theta}} L\,dt$ in the class κ'. If they were, the equations of motion could be found from the multiplier rule.

A different extension of Hamilton's principle *is* valid for non-holonomic systems. In this principle the variation from the point $(q_1, q_2, \ldots, q_n)$ on the original orbit to the contemporaneous point $(q_1 + \delta q_1, q_2 + \delta q_2, \ldots, q_n + \delta q_n)$ on the varied orbit is a virtual displacement satisfying the equations

$$\sum_{s=1}^{n} B_{rs}\delta q_s = 0, \qquad r = 1, 2, \ldots, l. \tag{8.16.2}$$

The δq's are functions of t of class C_2. The equations of motion are

$$\frac{d}{dt}\left(\frac{\partial L}{\partial \dot{q}_r}\right) - \frac{\partial L}{\partial q_r} = \sum_{m=1}^{l} \lambda_m B_{mr}, \qquad r = 1, 2, \ldots, n, \tag{8.16.3}$$

where $\lambda_1, \lambda_2, \ldots, \lambda_l$ are l multipliers. The equations (8.16.3), together with the equations of constraint (8.16.1), determine the motion. But the varied path, formed in the way described, does not itself satisfy the equations of constraint.

CHAPTER IX

The Parametric Problem

9.1 Properties of the integrand

We now consider curves defined parametrically, confining our attention to begin with to plane curves

$$(9.1.1)\qquad x = \varphi(t), \qquad y = \psi(t),$$

where the parameter t increases steadily from T to $\overline{T}$. We shall usually indicate differentiations with respect to t by dots: thus $\dot{x}$ stands for $\dfrac{dx}{dt}$, $\dot{\varphi}(t)$ for $\dfrac{d}{dt}\varphi(t)$, and so on. We assume always that $\dot{\varphi}(t)$ and $\dot{\psi}(t)$ never vanish for the same value of t, so that

$$(9.1.2)\qquad [\dot{\varphi}(t)]^2 + [\dot{\psi}(t)]^2 > 0.$$

The class of curves (9.1.1) joining A to B in the *parametric* problem is wider than the class of curves $y = \chi(x)$ joining A to B in the *ordinary* problem, as we have noticed already (§1.4). In the ordinary problem the curves lie in the strip $X \leqslant x \leqslant \overline{X}$, and cut each line $x = \xi$ in the strip only once. The curves contemplated in the parametric problem are not subject to these restrictions, and there are many problems of the Calculus of Variations, especially problems of geometry, which cannot be handled satisfactorily without the parametric form. One such problem is the geodesic problem, as we have noticed already (§1.4). Another example already mentioned (§3.8) occurs in the problem of minimizing $\int y\,ds$ or $\int \sqrt{y}\,ds$, where we need the parametric form to produce the Goldschmidt solution. On the other hand, for applications in dynamics, where there is no question of two different configurations for the same value of t, the ordinary problem is better (as we have already noticed in a simple case in §3.4). We need both the ordinary and the parametric problem for an adequate discussion of the subject as a whole.

We shall find that the parametric problem has some special features which distinguish it sharply from the ordinary problem. These special features arise from the fact that a curve can be represented parametrically in many different ways, whereas the value of the integral must be the same whatever parametric representation of the curve we choose to employ. This implies that the integrand is restricted to functions of a particular type. Explicitly, the properties of the integrand that must be satisfied if the value of the integral is to be independent of the particular parametric representation used, are (i) the integrand cannot contain t explicitly, and (ii) the integrand is positive-homogeneous of degree 1 in $\dot{x}$ and $\dot{y}$. Thus the integral must have the form

(9.1.3) $$\int_T^{\bar{T}} f(x, y, \dot{x}, \dot{y})\, dt,$$

and

(9.1.4) $$f(x, y, k\dot{x}, k\dot{y}) = kf(x, y, \dot{x}, \dot{y})$$

for all positive values of k.

These properties are almost evident intuitively. To establish them formally we proceed as follows. Let us suppose for the moment that the integrand does contain t explicitly,

(9.1.5) $$I = \int_T^{\bar{T}} f(t, x, y, \dot{x}, \dot{y})\, dt,$$

and let us introduce a new parameter θ, where

(9.1.6) $$t = \tau(\theta),$$

and $\tau \in C_1$. When we consider such a change of parameter we shall always choose a function τ that is monotone increasing,

(9.1.7) $$\tau'(\theta) > 0,$$

so the sense of description of the curve as the parameter increases is fixed once for all. If the formulae defining the curve in terms of the new parameter are

(9.1.8) $$x = \lambda(\theta), \qquad y = \mu(\theta),$$

the invariance of the integral implies

(9.1.9)
$$\int_T^{\bar{T}} f\{t, \varphi(t), \psi(t), \dot{\varphi}(t), \dot{\psi}(t)\}\, dt = \int_\Theta^{\bar{\Theta}} f\{\theta, \lambda(\theta), \mu(\theta), \lambda'(\theta), \mu'(\theta)\}\, d\theta$$

where

(9.1.10) $$T = \tau(\Theta), \qquad \bar{T} = \tau(\bar{\Theta}),$$

(9.1.11) $$\lambda(\theta) = \varphi[\tau(\theta)], \qquad \mu(\theta) = \psi[\tau(\theta)],$$

and

(9.1.12) $$\lambda'(\theta) = \tau'(\theta)\dot{\varphi}[\tau(\theta)], \qquad \mu'(\theta) = \tau'(\theta)\dot{\psi}[\tau(\theta)].$$

Consider in particular the substitution

(9.1.13) $$kt = \theta + c,$$

where $k > 0$. Then

(9.1.14) $$\lambda(\theta) = \varphi\left(\frac{\theta + c}{k}\right), \qquad \mu(\theta) = \psi\left(\frac{\theta + c}{k}\right),$$

(9.1.15) $$\lambda'(\theta) = \frac{1}{k}\dot{\varphi}\left(\frac{\theta + c}{k}\right), \qquad \mu'(\theta) = \frac{1}{k}\dot{\psi}\left(\frac{\theta + c}{k}\right).$$

If we transform the first member of (9.1.9) by the substitution (9.1.13) we have

(9.1.16) $$\int_{\Theta}^{\bar{\Theta}} \frac{1}{k} f\left(\frac{\theta + c}{k}, \lambda(\theta), \mu(\theta), k\lambda'(\theta), k\mu'(\theta)\right) d\theta = \int_{\Theta}^{\bar{\Theta}} f(\theta, \lambda(\theta), \mu(\theta), \lambda'(\theta), \mu'(\theta))\, d\theta,$$

and since this holds for all values of $\bar{\Theta}$ the two integrands must be identical. The case $k = 1$ shows that t cannot appear explicitly in f, and then the general case, where k has any positive value, implies (9.1.4). This completes the proof that the integral must have the form (9.1.3) subject to (9.1.4).

The assumptions that we shall make about the integrand $f(x, y, \dot{x}, \dot{y})$, and about the curves (9.1.1) admitted to competition, are very similar to those made for the ordinary problem in §1.3.

We assume that $f \in C_4$, and that f satisfies (9.1.4), in a domain R of the $(x, y, \dot{x}, \dot{y})$-space. The domain R must contain no point of the plane $\dot{x} = \dot{y} = 0$, i.e. for all points of R, $\dot{x}^2 + \dot{y}^2 > 0$; and if $(x, y, \dot{x}, \dot{y})$ lies in R, so do the related points $(x, y, k\dot{x}, k\dot{y})$ for all positive values of k. The curves (9.1.1) belong to a prescribed class κ, and we shall usually take for κ the class of curves for which $\varphi(t)$ and $\psi(t)$ are of class D_1 in $(T, \bar{T})$, i.e. $\varphi(t)$ and $\psi(t)$ are continuous, and $\dot{\varphi}(t)$ and $\dot{\psi}(t)$ are piecewise continuous. The curves have continuously turning tangents, except possibly at a finite number of corners. We may speak of this as the class D^1.

It will be observed that the curves considered are rectifiable, the arc-length s measured from the end A to the point t_1 being

(9.1.17) $$s = \int_T^{t_1} \sqrt{(\dot{x}^2 + \dot{y}^2)}\, dt.$$

The total length of the curve from A to B is

(9.1.18) $$l = \int_T^{\bar{T}} \sqrt{(\dot{x}^2 + \dot{y}^2)}\, dt.$$

If we take s as parameter we have

$$\dot{x}^2 + \dot{y}^2 = 1 \tag{9.1.19}$$

for all values of t; and if we take s/l as parameter (so that the range of values of the parameter is from 0 to 1) we have

$$\dot{x}^2 + \dot{y}^2 = l^2. \tag{9.1.20}$$

We speak of the ordered pair (x, y) as a *point* of the curve, of the ratio $\dot{y}/\dot{x}$ as the *slope* of the curve, and of the ordered quadruple $(x, y, \dot{x}, \dot{y})$ as an *element* of the curve.

9.2 Relation to the ordinary problem

If we take the ordinary problem for which the integral is

$$\int_X^{\overline{X}} F(x, y, y')\, dx \tag{9.2.1}$$

we can express the curve parametrically and write the integral in the form

$$\int_T^{\overline{T}} F\left(x, y, \frac{\dot{y}}{\dot{x}}\right) \dot{x}\, dt, \tag{9.2.2}$$

and we can discuss the parametric problem so found. If the original curve, whose minimizing properties we wish to test, is $y = \chi(x)$, a simple parametric representation is given by

$$x = t, \qquad y = \chi(t), \qquad X \leqslant t \leqslant \overline{X}. \tag{9.2.3}$$

More generally, we can express the curve in the form

$$x = \varphi(t), \qquad y = \psi(t), \qquad T \leqslant t \leqslant \overline{T}, \tag{9.2.4}$$

where we assume

$$\dot{\varphi}(t) \geqslant k > 0, \tag{9.2.5}$$

in $(T, \overline{T})$. If we consider the neighbouring curve

$$x = \varphi(t) + \alpha\xi(t), \qquad y = \psi(t) + \alpha\eta(t), \tag{9.2.6}$$

where $\xi(t)$ and $\eta(t)$ vanish both at T and at $\overline{T}$, we notice that $\dot{x} > 0$ for sufficiently small values of α, and the varied curve (9.2.6) is still expressible in the form $y = \chi(x)$. The variation is a weak variation in which δx, δy, $\delta\dot{x}$, $\delta\dot{y}$ are all small for small values of α.

It must be borne in mind, however, that the ordinary problem presented by (9.2.1) and the parametric problem presented by (9.2.2) are not precisely equivalent. A curve which is a minimizing curve for the first problem is not necessarily a minimizing curve for the second.

Consider, as a concrete illustration, the ordinary problem for

(9.2.7) $$I = \int_0^1 \frac{y'^2}{1 + y'^2}\, dx,$$

where A is (0, 0) and B is (1, 0). It is clear that the line-segment AB is a minimizing curve; the value of I for this segment is zero, and for any other curve $y = \chi(x)$, $I > 0$.

But the line-segment AB is not minimizing, not even in the sense of a strong relative minimum, for the corresponding parametric problem, where the integral is

(9.2.8) $$J = \int \frac{\dot{y}^2}{\dot{x}^2 + \dot{y}^2}\, \dot{x}\, dt.$$

The integral has the value zero for the line-segment. But for the path ACB shown in the figure the value of J is

(9.2.9) $$-\frac{h}{2\{(1 + h)^2 + h^2\}} < 0.$$

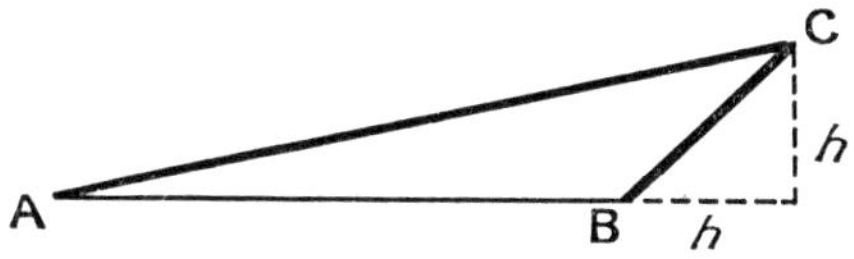

Fig. 9.2*a*

(The parametric representation of ACB can be taken as

(9.2.10) $$\begin{cases} x = \dfrac{1+h}{1-h}\, t, & y = \dfrac{h}{1-h}\, t, \quad \text{for } 0 \leqslant t \leqslant 1 - h, \\ x = 2 - t, & y = 1 - t, \quad \text{for } 1 - h \leqslant t \leqslant 1.) \end{cases}$$

Or, as a second illustration, consider the integral

(9.2.11) $$I = \int_0^1 y'^2\, dx$$

with the end-points $A(0, 0)$ and $B(1, 1)$, as in Example 1 of §3.3. The straight line L joining A to B is surely a minimizing curve in the ordinary problem, and for this curve $I = 1$. But in the associated parametric problem

(9.2.12) $$J = \int_T^{\overline{T}} \frac{\dot{y}^2}{\dot{x}}\, dt$$

we can find a path arbitrarily near to L on which $\dot{y}/\dot{x}$ has sometimes the value 0 and sometimes the value -1 (such as the paths shown in Fig. 9.2*b*) and for such a path $J = -1$. Indeed, we can find a path

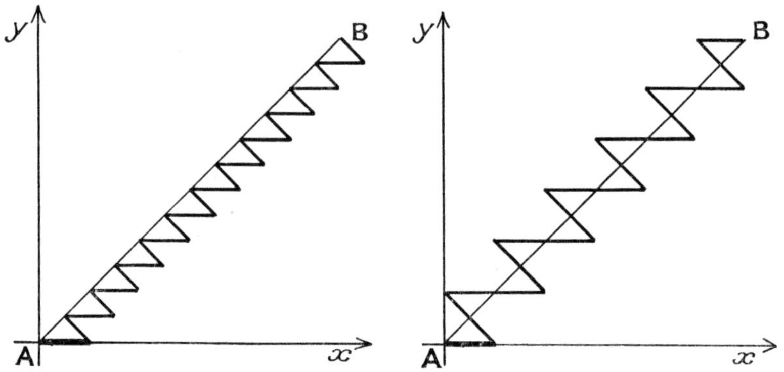

Fig. 9.2*b*

arbitrarily near to L on which $\dot{y}/\dot{x}$ has sometimes the value 0 and sometimes the value $-P$, where P is as large as we please, and for such a path $J = -P$. The line L is not a minimizing curve in the parametric problem, since $J(L) = 1$.

However, if we restrict our attention to weak variations, the ordinary problem presented by (9.2.1) and the parametric problem presented by (9.2.2) are equivalent, and it is useful to compare the formulae obtained in the ordinary problem and in the corresponding parametric problem. We suppose the original curve (whose minimizing properties we wish to test) to be given by (9.2.4–5). The relation between the integrands is

$$f(x, y, \dot{x}, \dot{y}) = \dot{x}F\left(x, y, \frac{\dot{y}}{\dot{x}}\right) \tag{9.2.13}$$

and we construct a dictionary correlating the formulae in the two problems. We have

$$f_{\dot{x}} = F - \frac{\dot{y}}{\dot{x}} F_{y'}, \; f_{\dot{y}} = F_{y'}, \tag{9.2.14}$$

where the arguments in F and its derivatives are $x, y, \dfrac{\dot{y}}{\dot{x}}$. Thus, when we transfer our attention from the parametric problem to the ordinary problem from which it is derived we have

$$f_{\dot{x}} \to U, \qquad f_{\dot{y}} \to V. \tag{9.2.15}$$

In a similar way we see that

$$(9.2.16) \qquad f_{x\dot{y}} \to F_{xy'}, \quad f_{y\dot{x}} \to F_y - y'F_{yy'}.$$

9.3 Further properties of the integrand

Since $f(x, y, \dot{x}, \dot{y})$ is positive-homogeneous of degree 1,

$$(9.3.1) \qquad \dot{x}f_{\dot{x}} + \dot{y}f_{\dot{y}} = f$$

identically. Further, $f_{\dot{x}}$ and $f_{\dot{y}}$ are themselves positive-homogeneous of degree zero, so

$$(9.3.2) \qquad \dot{x}f_{\dot{x}\dot{x}} + \dot{y}f_{\dot{x}\dot{y}} = 0, \quad \dot{x}f_{\dot{y}\dot{x}} + \dot{y}f_{\dot{y}\dot{y}} = 0,$$

identically. It follows that

$$(9.3.3) \qquad \frac{f_{\dot{x}\dot{x}}}{\dot{y}^2} = \frac{f_{\dot{x}\dot{y}}}{-\dot{x}\dot{y}} = \frac{f_{\dot{y}\dot{y}}}{\dot{x}^2}.$$

If we call the common value of these three expressions g, a known function of $(x, y, \dot{x}, \dot{y})$, we notice that g is positive-homogeneous of degree -3.

We can now make another entry in the dictionary mentioned above; if we transfer our attention from the parametric to the corresponding ordinary problem,

$$(9.3.4) \qquad g\dot{x}^3 \to F_{y'y'} = N.$$

As a simple illustration of the calculation of g, let

$$(9.3.5) \qquad f = \lambda(x, y)\sqrt{(\dot{x}^2 + \dot{y}^2)}.$$

Then

$$(9.3.6) \qquad f_{\dot{x}} = \frac{\lambda\dot{x}}{\sqrt{(\dot{x}^2 + \dot{y}^2)}}, \qquad f_{\dot{y}} = \frac{\lambda\dot{y}}{\sqrt{(\dot{x}^2 + \dot{y}^2)}}$$

and

$$(9.3.7) \qquad g = \frac{\lambda}{(\dot{x}^2 + \dot{y}^2)^{3/2}}.$$

9.4 Necessary conditions for a weak relative minimum

We suppose that the curve K_0, joining the fixed end-points A and B,

$$(9.4.1) \qquad x = \varphi(t), \quad y = \psi(t),$$

is a minimizing curve. Let us consider the one-parameter family whose typical member K_α has the form

$$x = \varphi(t) + \alpha\xi(t), \quad y = \psi(t) + \alpha\eta(t), \tag{9.4.2}$$

where $\xi, \eta \in D_1$, and ξ, η both vanish at T and at $\overline{T}$. We write

$$\chi(\alpha) = I(K_\alpha) = \int_T^{\overline{T}} f(\varphi + \alpha\xi, \psi + \alpha\eta, \dot\varphi + \alpha\dot\xi, \dot\psi + \alpha\dot\eta)\, dt, \tag{9.4.3}$$

and the argument is now familiar. The curve K_0 is minimizing in the one-parameter family, and a necessary condition for a minimum is

$$\chi'(0) = 0, \tag{9.4.4}$$

which leads to

$$\int_T^{\overline{T}} (\xi f_x + \eta f_y + \dot\xi f_{\dot x} + \dot\eta f_{\dot y})\, dt = 0, \tag{9.4.5}$$

where the arguments in the derivatives of f are the elements $(\varphi, \psi, \dot\varphi, \dot\psi)$ of K_0. We derive the equations of du Bois-Reymond as in §7.1,

$$\begin{cases} f_{\dot x}\{\varphi(t), \psi(t), \dot\varphi(t), \dot\psi(t)\} = \int_T^t f_x\{\varphi(\theta), \psi(\theta), \dot\varphi(\theta), \dot\psi(\theta)\}\, d\theta + C, \\ f_{\dot y}\{\varphi(t), \psi(t), \dot\varphi(t), \dot\psi(t)\} = \int_T^t f_y\{\varphi(\theta), \psi(\theta), \dot\varphi(\theta), \dot\psi(\theta)\}\, d\theta + D. \end{cases} \tag{9.4.6}$$

On an arc between consecutive corners, on which the integrands in the second members of (9.4.6) are continuous, the functions $\varphi(t)$, $\psi(t)$ satisfy Euler's equations,

$$\begin{cases} \dfrac{d}{dt} f_{\dot x}\{\varphi(t), \psi(t), \dot\varphi(t), \dot\psi(t)\} = f_x\{\varphi(t), \psi(t), \dot\varphi(t), \dot\psi(t)\}, \\ \dfrac{d}{dt} f_{\dot y}\{\varphi(t), \psi(t), \dot\varphi(t), \dot\psi(t)\} = f_y\{\varphi(t), \psi(t), \dot\varphi(t), \dot\psi(t)\}. \end{cases} \tag{9.4.7}$$

On an arc on which $\dot\varphi(t)$, $\dot\psi(t)$ are not merely continuous, but also differentiable, we can write Euler's equations in the developed form

$$\begin{cases} f_{\dot x x}\dot\varphi + f_{\dot x y}\dot\psi + f_{\dot x \dot x}\ddot\varphi + f_{\dot x \dot y}\ddot\psi = f_x, \\ f_{\dot y x}\dot\varphi + f_{\dot y y}\dot\psi + f_{\dot y \dot x}\ddot\varphi + f_{\dot y \dot y}\ddot\psi = f_y, \end{cases} \tag{9.4.8}$$

the arguments in the derivatives of f being the elements $(\varphi, \psi, \dot\varphi, \dot\psi)$ of K_0.

We now meet another point at which the parametric problem in the plane differs from the ordinary problem for curves in space. For the ordinary problem the Euler equations (7.1.16) are independent; for the parametric problem the Euler equations (9.4.7) are not independent. The proof of this fact is immediate, for

$$\dot{x}\left(\frac{d}{dt}f_{\dot{x}} - f_x\right) + \dot{y}\left(\frac{d}{dt}f_{\dot{y}} - f_y\right) = \frac{d}{dt}\left(\dot{x}f_{\dot{x}} + \dot{y}f_{\dot{y}} - f\right). \tag{9.4.9}$$

This is the process, familiar in classical dynamics, by which we establish Jacobi's integral from Lagrange's equations. But in the parametric problem the "energy function" $\dot{x}f_{\dot{x}} + \dot{y}f_{\dot{y}} - f$ is identically zero in virtue of (9.3.1). Thus the second member of (9.4.9) vanishes identically, and the fact that the two Euler equations are not independent is now clear. We have essentially only one differential equation, not two as we might expect at first sight. The equations are homogeneous in $(\dot{x}, \dot{y})$; they define a curve, but not the parametric representation of the curve. In practice, only one of the Euler equations need be found. The curves of class C^2 (i.e. the curves for which $\varphi(t)$ and $\psi(t)$ are of class C_2) satisfying Euler's equations are the extremals for the problem.

The extremals satisfy a third differential equation, which is equivalent to Euler's equations and is symmetrical in form. The first Euler equation can be written (assuming now that $\ddot{x}$ and $\ddot{y}$ exist) in the form

$$f_{\dot{x}x}\dot{x} + f_{\dot{x}y}\dot{y} + f_{\dot{x}\dot{x}}\ddot{x} + f_{\dot{x}\dot{y}}\ddot{y} - f_x = 0. \tag{9.4.10}$$

Now f_x is positive-homogeneous of degree 1 in $(\dot{x}, \dot{y})$, so

$$f_x = f_{x\dot{x}}\dot{x} + f_{x\dot{y}}\dot{y}, \tag{9.4.11}$$

and substituting this value in (9.4.10), and remembering that $f_{\dot{x}x} = f_{x\dot{x}}$, we have

$$(f_{\dot{x}y} - f_{x\dot{y}})\dot{y} + f_{\dot{x}\dot{x}}\ddot{x} + f_{\dot{x}\dot{y}}\ddot{y} = 0. \tag{9.4.12}$$

Finally we substitute for $f_{\dot{x}\dot{x}}$ and $f_{\dot{x}\dot{y}}$, in terms of the function $g(x, y, \dot{x}, \dot{y})$, from (9.3.3), and on removing a factor $\dot{y}$, assumed not identically zero, we obtain the required differential equation,

$$f_{x\dot{y}} - f_{y\dot{x}} + g(\dot{x}\ddot{y} - \dot{y}\ddot{x}) = 0. \tag{9.4.13}$$

This is Weierstrass's symmetrical form of Euler's equations for the parametric problem.

The geometrical significance of (9.4.13) is that it determines the curvature $\mathscr{C}$ of the extremal when the position (x, y) in the plane, and the slope $\dot{y}/\dot{x}$, are known. For

(9.4.14) $$\mathscr{C} = \frac{\dot{x}\ddot{y} - \dot{y}\ddot{x}}{(\dot{x}^2 + \dot{y}^2)^{3/2}},$$

and therefore, in virtue of (9.4.13),

(9.4.15) $$\mathscr{C} = -\frac{f_{x\dot{y}} - f_{y\dot{x}}}{g(\dot{x}^2 + \dot{y}^2)^{3/2}}.$$

The second member of (9.4.15) is a known function of $(x, y, \dot{y}/\dot{x})$.

Some special cases should be noticed (cf. §7.1). If x does not appear explicitly in f the first of du Bois-Reymond's equations (9.4.6) leads to

(9.4.16) $$f_{\dot{x}} = \text{constant},$$

and similarly, if y does not appear explicitly in f,

(9.4.17) $$f_{\dot{y}} = \text{constant}.$$

These are first integrals of Euler's equations. (Since t never appears explicitly in f we might be tempted to expect a first integral analogous to that derived from (7.1.19),

(9.4.18) $$f - \dot{x}f_{\dot{x}} - \dot{y}f_{\dot{y}} = \text{constant},$$

but, as we know, the first member of (9.4.18) is identically zero.)

Another property of Euler's equations in the parametric problem may be worthy of notice. Let us suppose that $x = \varphi(t)$, $y = \psi(t)$ are solutions of Euler's equations valid in the interval $T < t < \bar{T}$. Let $u(t)$ be a monotone strictly increasing function of t, of class C_2, and let $\lambda(t) = \varphi\{u(t)\}$ and $\mu(t) = \psi\{u(t)\}$. Then $\lambda(t)$, $\mu(t)$ are solutions of Euler's equations valid in the interval $\alpha < t < \bar{\alpha}$, where $u(\alpha) = T$ and $u(\bar{\alpha}) = \bar{T}$. The result is evident intuitively, since the same curve can be represented parametrically in various ways: the whole problem is invariant under suitable changes of parameter. To construct a formal proof, we appeal to the homogeneity properties of $f_x, f_y, f_{\dot{x}}, f_{\dot{y}}$. Taking the first of Euler's equations we have

$$\frac{d}{dt} f_{\dot{x}}(\lambda, \mu, \dot{\lambda}, \dot{\mu}) - f_x(\lambda, \mu, \dot{\lambda}, \dot{\mu})$$

$$= \frac{d}{dt} f_{\dot{x}}(\lambda, \mu, \dot{u}\lambda'(u), \dot{u}\mu'(u)) - f_x(\lambda, \mu, \dot{u}\lambda'(u), \dot{u}\mu'(u))$$

$$= \frac{d}{dt} f_{\dot{x}}(\lambda, \mu, \lambda', \mu') - \dot{u}f_x(\lambda, \mu, \lambda', \mu')$$

$$= \dot{u}\left\{\frac{d}{du} f_{\dot{x}}(\lambda, \mu, \lambda', \mu') - f_x(\lambda, \mu, \lambda', \mu')\right\},$$

and the last expression is identically zero.

9.5 The corner conditions

The corner conditions are simpler for the parametric problem than for the ordinary problem. This is in fact what we should expect, since in the parametric problem the two coordinates x and y are on the same footing, and we do not need the two separate types of argument that we used for the ordinary problem in §2.5 and §2.6. The second members of du Bois-Reymond's equations (9.4.6) are continuous even at a corner (where $\dot{\phi}$ or $\dot{\psi}$ is discontinuous) so the first members are also continuous. We thus obtain the simple result that *$f_{\dot{x}}$ and $f_{\dot{y}}$ are continuous at a corner on a minimizing curve.* We know that $f_{\dot{x}}$ and $f_{\dot{y}}$ depend only on the slope (i.e. on $\dot{y}/\dot{x}$) not on the particular parametric representation that is used.

We readily deduce a simple proof of the now-familiar corner conditions in the ordinary problem, namely the continuity of U and of V. These results follow from the corner conditions for the parametric problem in virtue of (9.2.15).

9.6 Euler's equations

We consider a parametric problem which has been derived from an ordinary problem, as in §9.2. It may be of interest to ask what forms the two equations of Euler, and the equation of Weierstrass take, when we change back from the parametric to the ordinary problem from which it was derived. Starting from (9.2.13), the proviso (9.2.5) being understood, the first of Euler's equations takes the form

$$\frac{d}{dt}\left(F - \frac{\dot{y}}{\dot{x}}F_{y'}\right) = \dot{x}F_x, \tag{9.6.1}$$

using (9.2.14); the arguments in F and its derivatives are $(x, y, \dot{y}/\dot{x})$. For the ordinary problem, (9.6.1) is equivalent to

$$\frac{d}{dx}(F - y'F_{y'}) = F_x, \tag{9.6.2}$$

which is the same as (2.9.3), and this result is equivalent to Euler's equation for the ordinary problem.

The second of Euler's equations for the parametric form is

$$\frac{d}{dt}F_{y'} = \dot{x}F_y, \tag{9.6.3}$$

and this is immediately equivalent to Euler's equation for the ordinary problem

$$\frac{d}{dx}F_{y'} = F_y. \tag{9.6.4}$$

We now turn to Weierstrass's form (9.4.13), which becomes, in virtue of (9.2.16) and (9.3.4),

$$F_{xy'} + \frac{\dot{y}}{\dot{x}} F_{yy'} + \frac{\dot{x}\ddot{y} - \dot{y}\ddot{x}}{\dot{x}^3} F_{y'y'} = F_y. \tag{9.6.5}$$

But

$$\frac{d}{dt} F_{y'} = F_{y'x}\dot{x} + F_{y'y}\dot{y} + F_{y'y'} \frac{\dot{x}\ddot{y} - \dot{y}\ddot{x}}{\dot{x}^2}, \tag{9.6.6}$$

and using this result (9.6.5) takes the form (9.6.3).

9.7 Some concrete illustrations

We now consider the application of the theory to some illustrative problems in the parametric form; we begin with some problems for which the ordinary form has been considered already.

EXAMPLE 1. *The geodesics in a plane.* The integral is

$$I = \int_T^{\overline{T}} \sqrt{(\dot{x}^2 + \dot{y}^2)}\, dt, \tag{9.7.1}$$

and the problem has already been solved without appeal to the general theory for the parametric problem (§1.4). If we attack the problem from the point of view of the theory developed in §9.4, we notice that x and y are both absent from the integrand, and the equations (9.4.16) and (9.4.17) are

$$\frac{\dot{x}}{\sqrt{(\dot{x}^2 + \dot{y}^2)}} = \text{constant}, \qquad \frac{\dot{y}}{\sqrt{(\dot{x}^2 + \dot{y}^2)}} = \text{constant}. \tag{9.7.2}$$

Hence $\dot{y}/\dot{x}$ = constant, and the geodesics are the straight lines.

EXAMPLE 2. We consider the integral

$$I = \int_T^{\overline{T}} \sqrt{\{y(\dot{x}^2 + \dot{y}^2)\}}\, dt, \qquad (y \geqslant 0). \tag{9.7.3}$$

The ordinary form of this problem was considered in §3.8. The extremals are the orbits of a particle in a uniform field of force.

Since x does not appear explicitly in the integrand the first equation of du Bois-Reymond gives $f_{\dot{x}}$ = constant, whence

$$y \frac{\dot{x}^2}{\dot{x}^2 + \dot{y}^2} = b, \qquad (b \geqslant 0). \tag{9.7.4}$$

If $b = 0$ we have either $\dot{x} = 0$ or $y = 0$, and this leads to the Goldschmidt solution, the three straight lines AM, MN, NB, where AM and BN are the perpendiculars from A and B on Ox (Fig. 3.8f). This solution we have anticipated in §3.8 and in §5.18.

If $b > 0$ we have

$$y = b \sec^2 \psi \tag{9.7.5}$$

as in (3.8.1), and this leads to

$$(x - a)^2 = 4b(y - b) \tag{9.7.6}$$

as in (3.8.4).

The second of Euler's equations, as we have seen, is not independent of the first, but it may nevertheless be of interest to examine it,

$$\frac{d}{dt}\left\{\dot{y}\sqrt{\left(\frac{y}{\dot{x}^2 + \dot{y}^2}\right)}\right\} = \frac{1}{2}\sqrt{\left(\frac{\dot{x}^2 + \dot{y}^2}{y}\right)}. \tag{9.7.7}$$

If we write

$$z = \dot{y}\sqrt{\left(\frac{y}{\dot{x}^2 + \dot{y}^2}\right)} \tag{9.7.8}$$

the equation (9.7.7) becomes

$$2z\dot{z} = \dot{y} \tag{9.7.9}$$

and the integration is now simple,

$$z^2 = y - b,$$

which is equivalent to (9.7.4).

Finally let us consider Weierstrass's form (9.4.13) of the differential equation. We have

$$g = \frac{\sqrt{y}}{(\dot{x}^2 + \dot{y}^2)^{3/2}}, \tag{9.7.10}$$

and (9.4.13) becomes

$$\frac{\dot{x}\ddot{y} - \dot{y}\ddot{x}}{\dot{x}^3} = \frac{1}{2y}\,\frac{\dot{x}^2 + \dot{y}^2}{\dot{x}^2}. \tag{9.7.11}$$

The equation defines a relation between x and y, but, as we expect, it gives no information about the parametric representation of x and y as functions of t. We can write (9.7.11) in the form

$$\frac{1}{\dot{x}}\frac{d}{dt}\left(\frac{\dot{y}}{\dot{x}}\right) = \frac{1}{2y}\left(1 + \frac{\dot{y}^2}{\dot{x}^2}\right), \tag{9.7.12}$$

which is equivalent to

$$y'' = \frac{1}{2y}(1 + y'^2), \tag{9.7.13}$$

and this leads again to (9.7.5).

As we have noticed already (§3.9) the Goldschmidt curve also appears in the solution of the problem of the surface of revolution of minimum area, for which the integrand is $y\sqrt{(\dot{x}^2 + \dot{y}^2)}$.

EXAMPLE 3. *Brachistochrone.* We have considered the ordinary form of this problem already (§3.7); let us now consider the parametric form. As before, we take the axis Ox on the energy level, and the axis Oy vertically downwards, so that the speed of the particle is $\sqrt{(2gy)}$. The points A and B lie in the region $y > 0$. The integral to be minimized is

$$I = \int_{T}^{\overline{T}} \frac{\sqrt{(\dot{x}^2 + \dot{y}^2)}}{\sqrt{y}}\, dt, \tag{9.7.14}$$

where the parameter t may be, but is not necessarily, the time. The integrand does not contain x, and the first integral $f_{\dot{x}}$ = constant is

$$\frac{\dot{x}}{\sqrt{\{y(\dot{x}^2 + \dot{y}^2)\}}} = \text{constant}. \tag{9.7.15}$$

If we introduce the angle ψ where

$$\frac{\dot{x}}{\sqrt{(\dot{x}^2 + \dot{y}^2)}} = \cos\psi, \quad \frac{\dot{y}}{\sqrt{(\dot{x}^2 + \dot{y}^2)}} = \sin\psi, \tag{9.7.16}$$

we have

$$y = b\cos^2\psi = \tfrac{1}{2}b(1 + \cos 2\psi), \qquad (b > 0) \tag{9.7.17}$$

as in (3.7.9), and, using the formula $dx = \cot\psi\, dy$, we easily complete the integration as in §3.7.

EXAMPLE 4. Consider the integral

$$I = \int_{T}^{\overline{T}} \{\tfrac{1}{2}(x\dot{y} - y\dot{x}) - \lambda\sqrt{(\dot{x}^2 + \dot{y}^2)}\}\, dt \tag{9.7.18}$$

where λ is a given positive number. The end-points A and B are prescribed. We observe that the integrand has the requisite property (9.1.4). We observe also that we could replace the integrand by

$$x\dot{y} - \lambda\sqrt{(\dot{x}^2 + \dot{y}^2)} \tag{9.7.19}$$

without effectively changing the problem, but it is perhaps more natural to use the symmetrical form (9.7.18). Each of the differential equations for (9.7.18) (the two equations of Euler and the equation of Weierstrass) is equivalent to

$$\frac{\dot{x}\ddot{y} - \dot{y}\ddot{x}}{(\dot{x}^2 + \dot{y}^2)^{3/2}} = \frac{1}{\lambda}, \tag{9.7.20}$$

which we can write in the form

$$\frac{d\psi}{ds} = \frac{1}{\lambda}, \tag{9.7.21}$$

and the extremals are arcs of circles of radius λ described in the positive sense. If $|AB| < 2\lambda$, there are two extremals through A and B, if $|AB| = 2\lambda$ there is one extremal, if $|AB| > 2\lambda$ there are none.

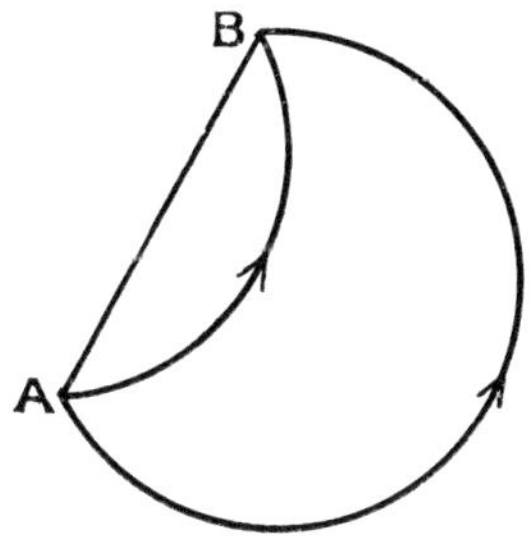

Fig. 9.7

Alternatively, if we use the integrand (9.7.19), we have (since y is not now present explicitly) the first integral $f_{\dot{y}}$ = constant,

(9.7.22) $$x - a = \lambda \frac{\dot{y}}{\sqrt{(\dot{x}^2 + \dot{y}^2)}} = \lambda \sin \psi.$$

Then

(9.7.23) $$dy = \tan \psi \, dx = \lambda \sin \psi \, d\psi,$$

giving

(9.7.24) $$y - b = -\lambda \cos \psi,$$

and the formulae (9.7.22) and (9.7.24) give arcs of circles of radius λ as before.

EXAMPLE 5. *The geodesics on a surface.* The position of a point on the surface is defined by the values of the parameters (u, v),

(9.7.25) $$x = x(u, v), \quad y = y(u, v), \quad z = z(u, v)$$

where the functions $x(u, v)$, $y(u, v)$, and $z(u, v)$ are of class C_2 in an appropriate domain of (u, v). The element of length ds on the surface is given by

(9.7.26) $$ds^2 = E\,du^2 + 2F\,du\,dv + G\,dv^2,$$

where

(9.7.27) $$E = E(u, v) = x_u^2 + y_u^2 + z_u^2, \quad F = x_u x_v + y_u y_v + z_u z_v,$$
$$G = x_v^2 + y_v^2 + z_v^2.$$

If further

$$A = y_u z_v - y_v z_u, \quad B = z_u x_v - z_v x_u, \quad C = x_u y_v - x_v y_u, \tag{9.7.28}$$

then A, B, C are proportional to the direction cosines of the normal to the surface at (u, v), and

$$EG - F^2 = A^2 + B^2 + C^2. \tag{9.7.29}$$

The length of the curve $u(t)$, $v(t)$ on the surface is

$$I = \int_{\underline{T}}^{\overline{T}} \sqrt{(E\dot{u}^2 + 2F\dot{u}\dot{v} + G\dot{v}^2)}\, dt, \tag{9.7.30}$$

the end-points being fixed. We have therefore a problem of the type under discussion, the curve being thought of, for the moment, as a curve in the (u, v)-plane. Euler's equations, assuming $u(t)$ and $v(t)$ to be of class C_2, are

$$\begin{cases} \dfrac{d}{dt}\left(\dfrac{E\dot{u} + F\dot{v}}{\sigma}\right) = \dfrac{1}{2\sigma}(E_u\dot{u}^2 + 2F_u\dot{u}\dot{v} + G_u\dot{v}^2), \\ \dfrac{d}{dt}\left(\dfrac{F\dot{u} + G\dot{v}}{\sigma}\right) = \dfrac{1}{2\sigma}(E_v\dot{u}^2 + 2F_v\dot{u}\dot{v} + G_v\dot{v}^2), \end{cases} \tag{9.7.31}$$

where σ is written for $\sqrt{(E\dot{u}^2 + 2F\dot{u}\dot{v} + G\dot{v}^2)}$ for the sake of compactness. Since $\sigma\, dt = ds$ we can write these equations in the forms

$$\begin{cases} \dfrac{d}{ds}(Eu' + Fv') = \tfrac{1}{2}(E_u u'^2 + 2F_u u'v' + G_u v'^2), \\ \dfrac{d}{ds}(Fu' + Gv') = \tfrac{1}{2}(E_v u'^2 + 2F_v u'v' + G_v v'^2), \end{cases} \tag{9.7.32}$$

where accents denote differentiations with respect to s (u' means $\dfrac{du}{ds}$ and so on) and we have in effect taken the arc-length s as the parameter for points on the curve.

The detailed discussion of the equations (9.7.32) will be found in treatises on differential geometry, but one important comment on the geometrical significance may be made here. We have

$$Eu' + Fv' = \Sigma x_u(x_u u' + x_v v'), \tag{9.7.33}$$

where Σ denotes summation over x, y, z. We can write (9.7.33) in the form

$$Eu' + Fv' = \Sigma x_u x', \tag{9.7.34}$$

where

$$x' = \frac{dx}{ds} = x_u u' + x_v v'. \tag{9.7.35}$$

Thus

$$\frac{d}{ds}(Eu' + Fv') = \Sigma x_u x'' + \Sigma(x_{uu}u' + x_{uv}v')(x_u u' + x_v v') \tag{9.7.36}$$
$$= \Sigma x_u x'' + \tfrac{1}{2}(E_u u'^2 + 2F_u u'v' + G_u v'^2),$$

and the first of the equations (9.7.32) is equivalent to

$$x_u x'' + y_u y'' + z_u z'' = 0. \tag{9.7.37}$$

Similarly the second of Euler's equations is equivalent to

$$x_v x'' + y_v y'' + z_v z'' = 0. \tag{9.7.38}$$

From (9.7.37) and (9.7.38) we have

$$\frac{x''}{A} = \frac{y''}{B} = \frac{z''}{C}, \tag{9.7.39}$$

and this means that the principal normal to the curve coincides, at each point of the curve, with the normal to the surface at that point. This is the fundamental property of geodesics on a surface (cf. §8.13).

EXAMPLE 6. *Zermelo's problem.* A ship (or aeroplane) moves in the (x, y)-plane, the components of velocity of the stream at (x, y) being u_1 and u_2, where u_1 and u_2 are prescribed functions of (x, y, t). The speed of the ship relative to the stream has the constant positive value k. The problem is to find the path $\{x(t), y(t)\}$ from a given initial point A to a given terminal point B so that the journey is accomplished in the shortest possible time.

The time for the journey is

$$\int \frac{ds}{v} = \int \frac{\sqrt{(\dot{x}^2 + \dot{y}^2)}}{v}\, dt = \int f\, dt, \tag{9.7.40}$$

where $v = \sqrt{(v_1^2 + v_2^2)}$, and v_1, v_2 are components of velocity

$$\begin{cases} v_1 = u_1 + k\cos\varphi = v\dfrac{\dot{x}}{\sqrt{(\dot{x}^2 + \dot{y}^2)}} = \dfrac{\dot{x}}{f}, \\[2ex] v_2 = u_2 + k\sin\varphi = v\dfrac{\dot{y}}{\sqrt{(\dot{x}^2 + \dot{y}^2)}} = \dfrac{\dot{y}}{f}. \end{cases} \tag{9.7.41}$$

Thus the integrand f is the positive root of the equation

$$k^2 = \left(\frac{\dot{x}}{f} - u_1\right)^2 + \left(\frac{\dot{y}}{f} - u_2\right)^2, \tag{9.7.42}$$

whence

$$f = \frac{-(u_1\dot{x} + u_2\dot{y}) + \sqrt{\{k^2(\dot{x}^2 + \dot{y}^2) - (u_2\dot{x} - u_1\dot{y})^2\}}}{k^2 - u_1^2 - u_2^2}. \tag{9.7.43}$$

It will be observed that, in the general case in which u_1 and u_2 depend on t as well as on x and y, the problem is not properly a parametric problem, since f contains t explicitly. But in the special case in which the fluid motion is steady (i.e. u_1 and u_2 are functions of position only, not of time) the integrand f satisfies the conditions demanded in §9.1. The integrand is unaltered if we change the independent variable to another variable which is a function of the time (increasing monotonically with the time).

Let us consider the particular problem in which the fluid velocity is parallel to Ox and proportional to the distance from Ox,

$$u_1 = ky/b, \qquad u_2 = 0, \qquad (b > 0). \tag{9.7.44}$$

In this case

$$f = \frac{b}{k}\frac{1}{(b^2 - y^2)}[-y\dot{x} + \sqrt{\{b^2\dot{x}^2 + (b^2 - y^2)\dot{y}^2\}}], \tag{9.7.45}$$

and the time taken in the journey is $\int f\,dt$.

So far the independent variable t represents the time. But at this stage it is convenient to take advantage of our freedom to use another independent variable, and from now on t represents this new independent variable. Since x does not occur explicitly in f we have the first integral $f_{\dot{x}}$ = constant, which leads to

$$\frac{b^2\dot{x}}{\sqrt{\{b^2\dot{x}^2 + (b^2 - y^2)\dot{y}^2\}}} = \frac{b^2 - y^2 + ay}{a}. \tag{9.7.46}$$

We can take the new independent variable t such that

$$\dot{x} = \frac{u}{ab}(b^2 - y^2 + ay), \tag{9.7.47}$$

$$\sqrt{\{b^2\dot{x}^2 + (b^2 - y^2)\dot{y}^2\}} = bu, \tag{9.7.48}$$

where u is a chosen function of t; in fact we shall make the simplest choice in which u is constant and equal to a, and then

(9.7.49) $$\dot{x} = \frac{1}{b}(b^2 - y^2 + ay),$$

(9.7.50) $$\sqrt{\{b^2\dot{x}^2 + (b^2 - y^2)\dot{y}^2\}} = ab.$$

If we eliminate $\dot{x}$ from the equations (9.7.49) and (9.7.50) we get

(9.7.51) $$\dot{y}^2 = (y - a)^2 - b^2$$

whence, since $\dfrac{d}{dy}(\tfrac{1}{2}\dot{y}^2) = \ddot{y}$, we have

(9.7.52) $$\ddot{y} = y - a.$$

The solution is

(9.7.53) $$y - a = \tfrac{1}{2}Ae^t + \tfrac{1}{2}Be^{-t},$$

where, to satisfy (9.7.51), $AB = b^2$.

If now we make a suitable choice for the zero of the t-scale we can make $A = B = \lambda b$, where $\lambda = \pm 1$, and (9.7.53) becomes

(9.7.54) $$y = a + \lambda b \cosh t.$$

It is now easy to express x also in terms of t. If we substitute the value (9.7.54) of y in the second member of (9.7.49) we get

(9.7.55) $$\dot{x} = -\lambda a \cosh t - b \sinh^2 t,$$

giving

(9.7.56) $$x = x_0 - \lambda a \sinh t - \tfrac{1}{2}b(\cosh t \sinh t - t),$$

where x_0 is the value of x when $t = 0$.

What is the relation between the parameter t that we have used and the time, which we will now denote by θ? From (9.7.45), (9.7.49) and (9.7.50) we have

(9.7.57) $$f = \frac{1}{k}(a - y) = -\lambda \frac{b}{k} \cosh t.$$

Now $d\theta = f\,dt$, and we need $\lambda = -1$ (since θ increases steadily with t) so

(9.7.58) $$\theta = \frac{b}{k} \sinh t,$$

if $t = 0$ when $\theta = 0$.

If y_0 is the value of y when $t = 0$, then $a = b + y_0$, and the extremal is expressed in terms of the parameter t by the formulae

$$\begin{cases} x = x_0 + (b + y_0)\sinh t - \tfrac{1}{2}b(\cosh t \sinh t - t), \\ y = y_0 - b(\cosh t - 1). \end{cases} \tag{9.7.59}$$

Finally we can express the extremal in terms of the time θ. If we write σ for $\sinh t$ we have

$$\begin{gathered} \sinh t = \sigma = (k/b)\theta, \quad \cosh t = \sqrt{(1 + \sigma^2)}, \\ e^t = \sigma + \sqrt{(1 + \sigma^2)}, \end{gathered} \tag{9.7.60}$$

and if we write αb for x_0 and βb for y_0 the formulae (9.7.59) become

$$\begin{cases} \dfrac{x}{b} = \alpha + (\beta + 1)\sigma - \tfrac{1}{2}\sigma\sqrt{(1 + \sigma^2)} \\ \qquad + \tfrac{1}{2}\log\{\sigma + \sqrt{(1 + \sigma^2)}\}, \\ \dfrac{y}{b} = \beta + 1 - \sqrt{(1 + \sigma^2)}. \end{cases} \tag{9.7.61}$$

In these formulae, σ denotes the time measured on an appropriate scale, $\sigma = (k/b)\theta$. In the classification of these curves the limit curves arising from $\beta = -1$ are of particular significance.*

9.8 Variable end-points

We now determine the variation of I that results when we vary from a minimizing curve to a neighbouring curve. The formula for the variation is much easier to establish than the corresponding formula (4.2.12) for the ordinary problem; the reason is that here the parts played by the two coordinates x and y are entirely similar, whereas in the ordinary problem they were dissimilar, x being an independent and y a dependent variable. Indeed it might be argued that the simplest way to establish the formula (4.2.12) is to derive it from the corresponding result for the parametric problem.

We consider then a family of curves of which the typical member K_α is given by

$$x = \varphi(t, \alpha), \quad y = \psi(t, \alpha). \tag{9.8.1}$$

We assume that K_0, namely

$$x = \varphi(t, 0), \quad y = \psi(t, 0), \tag{9.8.2}$$

*A diagram showing some curves of the type (9.7.61) will be found in **5**, p. 242.

satisfies the equations of du Bois-Reymond (9.4.6). We will suppose that the parametric representation is so arranged that the parameters of the end-points do not change; the end A moves, in the neighbourhood of $\alpha = 0$, on the curve $t = T$, and the end B moves on the curve $t = \overline{T}$. The functions $\varphi(t, \alpha)$ and $\psi(t, \alpha)$ are assumed to be of class C_1 in a neighbourhood $\mathcal{N}$ of the segment

$$(9.8.3) \qquad T \leqslant t \leqslant \overline{T}, \quad \alpha = 0,$$

and $\dfrac{\partial^2\varphi}{\partial t\, \partial\alpha}$ is assumed to be continuous in the same domain. As usual we write $\dot{\varphi}_\alpha$ for $\dfrac{\partial^2\varphi}{\partial t\, \partial\alpha}$, and we recall that $\dfrac{\partial^2\varphi}{\partial t\, \partial\alpha} = \dfrac{\partial^2\varphi}{\partial\alpha\, \partial t}$ in $\mathcal{N}$.

Let

$$(9.8.4) \quad \Omega(\alpha) = I(K_\alpha) = \int_T^{\overline{T}} f\{\varphi(t, \alpha), \psi(t, \alpha), \dot{\varphi}(t, \alpha), \dot{\psi}(t, \alpha)\}\, dt.$$

Then, since the limits of integration are not changed,

$$(9.8.5) \quad \Omega'(0) = \int_T^{\overline{T}} \{f_x\varphi_\alpha(t, 0) + f_y\psi_\alpha(t, 0) + f_{\dot{x}}\dot{\varphi}_\alpha(t, 0) + f_{\dot{y}}\dot{\psi}_\alpha(t, 0)\}\, dt,$$

where the arguments in the derivatives of f are $\varphi(t, 0)$, $\psi(t, 0)$, $\dot{\varphi}(t, 0)$, $\dot{\psi}(t, 0)$. Now, from (9.4.6),

$$(9.8.6) \quad f_{\dot{x}}\{\varphi(t, 0), \psi(t, 0), \dot{\varphi}(t, 0), \dot{\psi}(t, 0)\} = \int_T^t f_x\{\varphi(\theta, 0), \psi(\theta, 0), \dot{\varphi}(\theta, 0), \dot{\psi}(\theta, 0)\}\, d\theta + C,$$

$$(9.8.7) \quad f_{\dot{y}}\{\varphi(t, 0), \psi(t, 0), \dot{\varphi}(t, 0), \dot{\psi}(t, 0)\} = \int_T^t f_y\{\varphi(\theta, 0), \psi(\theta, 0), \dot{\varphi}(\theta, 0), \dot{\psi}(\theta, 0)\}\, d\theta + D.$$

If we denote each member of (9.8.6) by $\sigma(t)$, and each member of (9.8.7) by $\tau(t)$, the formula for $\Omega'(0)$ in (9.8.5) becomes

$$(9.8.8) \quad \begin{aligned} \Omega'(0) &= \int_T^{\overline{T}} \{\dot{\sigma}(t)\varphi_\alpha(t, 0) + \dot{\tau}(t)\psi_\alpha(t, 0) + \sigma(t)\dot{\varphi}_\alpha(t, 0) \\ &\qquad + \tau(t)\dot{\psi}_\alpha(t, 0)\}\, dt \\ &= \sigma(t)\varphi_\alpha(t, 0) + \tau(t)\psi_\alpha(t, 0)\Big|_T^{\overline{T}} \\ &= f_{\dot{x}}\varphi_\alpha + f_{\dot{y}}\psi_\alpha\Big|_T^{\overline{T}}, \end{aligned}$$

where the arguments in $f_{\dot{x}}$ and $f_{\dot{y}}$ are the elements of K_0 at A and B.

Thus finally

(9.8.9) $$dI = \Omega'(0)\, d\alpha = f_{\dot{x}}\, dx + f_{\dot{y}}\, dy \Big|_A^B ,$$

where (dX, dY) represents the displacement of A and $(d\bar{X}, d\bar{Y})$ the displacement of B, and this is the variable end-point theorem for the parametric problem. It is worthy of remark that the proof just given makes no reference to the non-tangency condition.

The corresponding theorem for the ordinary problem follows immediately from (9.8.9) by reason of (9.2.15).

In the proof just given of the variable end-point theorem (9.8.9) the notation was so chosen that the displacement of the end-point A, for example, involved no change in the parameter t; this displacement, on the curve $t = T$, is the displacement from A to A' in Fig. 9.8. The

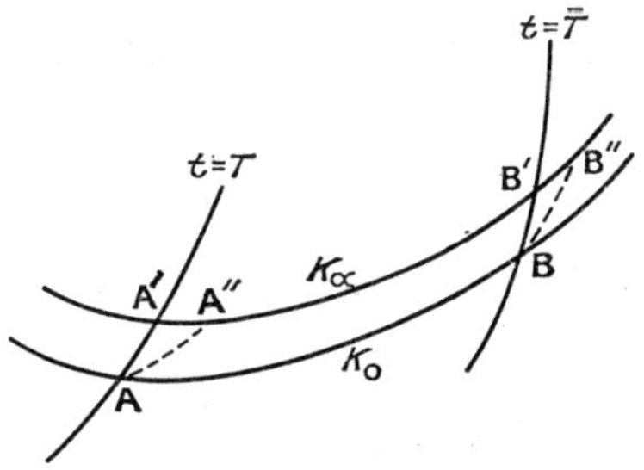

Fig. 9.8

question naturally suggests itself, what happens if we also allow the range of the parameter t to vary? The displacement is now from A to A'' in Fig. 9.8.

In this case

(9.8.10) $$I(K_\alpha) = \Omega(\alpha, T, \bar{T}),$$

and

(9.8.11) $$dI = \frac{\partial\Omega}{\partial\alpha}\, d\alpha + \frac{\partial\Omega}{\partial T}\, dT + \frac{\partial\Omega}{\partial\bar{T}}\, d\bar{T}$$

$$= f_{\dot{x}}\, \delta x + f_{\dot{y}}\, \delta y \Big|_A^B + f\, dt \Big|_A^B ,$$

where the term $\dfrac{\partial\Omega}{\partial\alpha}\, d\alpha$ is interpreted from (9.8.9). Now if the displacement of A is (dX, dY) we have

(9.8.12) $$\delta X = \frac{\partial X}{\partial\alpha}\, d\alpha = dX - \frac{\partial X}{\partial T}\, dT,\ \delta Y = \frac{\partial Y}{\partial\alpha}\, d\alpha = dY - \frac{\partial Y}{\partial T}\, dT,$$

and there are similar results for the end-point B. Thus

(9.8.13) $$dI = f_{\dot{x}}\,dx + f_{\dot{y}}\,dy\Big|_A^B + (f - \dot{x}f_{\dot{x}} - \dot{y}f_{\dot{y}})\,dt\Big|_A^B.$$

But the last term on the right in (9.8.13) vanishes because $f - \dot{x}f_{\dot{x}} - \dot{y}f_{\dot{y}}$ is identically zero, by (9.3.1), and the formula for dI is precisely the same as it was before in (9.8.9). Of course the result could have been foreseen. The value of I does not depend on what particular parametric representation of the curves we choose to employ; the parameter is, as it were, only a convenient scaffolding used in the course of construction, and the result found by the first argument (with T and $\bar{T}$ unvaried) must hold always.

COROLLARY. We have proved the theorem (9.8.9) for a curve without corners. But $f_{\dot{x}}$ and $f_{\dot{y}}$ are continuous at a corner on a minimizing curve (§9.5) and it follows (as in §4.2) that the theorem is still valid if the original curve (and therefore also the varied curve) has a corner.

9.9 Weierstrass's necessary condition

The proof of Weierstrass's necessary condition for a minimizing curve is very similar to the proof of the corresponding result for the ordinary problem (§4.4), and we may refer to the figure (Fig. 4.4*a*) previously used. Let P be the point $t = T$ on an arc K between corners on a minimizing curve, and let Q be another point $t = \bar{T}$ of the same arc, where $\bar{T} > T$. Let Γ be another curve through P, the typical point R on Γ $\{\xi(\alpha), \eta(\alpha)\}$ being defined by a parameter α, and let Δ_α be an arc joining R to Q. We choose the notation so that $\alpha = 0$ when R is at P, and we suppose that R moves on Γ in the direction of α increasing. We define the arcs Δ_α so that Δ_α coincides with the arc K_{PQ} when $\alpha = 0$, i.e. when R is at P. A simple way of achieving this end is to use a device similar to that used in §4.4, defining the point with parameter t on Δ_α $(T \leqslant t \leqslant \bar{T})$ by the formulae

(9.9.1) $$\begin{cases} x = \varphi(t) + \left\{\dfrac{\xi(\alpha) - \varphi(T)}{\bar{T} - T}\right\}(\bar{T} - t), \\[2ex] y = \psi(t) + \left\{\dfrac{\eta(\alpha) - \psi(T)}{\bar{T} - T}\right\}(\bar{T} - t). \end{cases}$$

If $\chi(\alpha)$ is the value of the integral I for the path PRQ, we have

(9.9.2) $$\chi'(0)\,d\alpha = -\{f_{\dot{x}}(x, y, \dot{x}, \dot{y})\,dX + f_{\dot{y}}(x, y, \dot{x}, \dot{y})\,dY\} + f(x, y, \dot{X}, \dot{Y})\,d\alpha,$$

where $(x, y, \dot{x}, \dot{y})$ represents the element of K at P, and $(x, y, \dot{X}, \dot{Y})$ the element of Γ at P, and (dX, dY) is the displacement of the end-point R. We introduce the symbols $\dot{X}$, $\dot{Y}$, and write $dX = \dot{X}\,d\alpha$, $dY = \dot{Y}\,d\alpha$; since K is minimizing, $\chi'(0) \geqslant 0$, so we have

$$(9.9.3) \quad E(x, y, \dot{x}, \dot{y}, \dot{X}, \dot{Y}) \equiv f(x, y, \dot{X}, \dot{Y}) - \dot{X} f_{\dot{x}}(x, y, \dot{x}, \dot{y}) - \dot{Y} f_{\dot{y}}(x, y, \dot{x}, \dot{y}) \geqslant 0.$$

This is Weierstrass's necessary condition. The function E, the *excess function*, can also be written in the form

$$(9.9.4) \quad E = \dot{X}\{f_{\dot{x}}(x, y, \dot{X}, \dot{Y}) - f_{\dot{x}}(x, y, \dot{x}, \dot{y})\} + \dot{Y}\{f_{\dot{y}}(x, y, \dot{X}, \dot{Y}) - f_{\dot{y}}(x, y, \dot{x}, \dot{y})\}.$$

The condition $E \geqslant 0$ must hold at every point of a minimizing arc, for arbitrary values of $\dot{X}$, $\dot{Y}$. It will be observed that E is positive-homogeneous of degree 1 in $\dot{X}$, $\dot{Y}$, and if the condition is satisfied for $(\dot{X}, \dot{Y})$ it is also satisfied for $(k\dot{X}, k\dot{Y})$ if $k > 0$.

There is a third formula for E which is worthy of notice. We know that $f_{\dot{x}}(x, y, \dot{x}, \dot{y})$ depends only on the ratio $\dot{y}/\dot{x}$, so we do not alter the value of $f_{\dot{x}}$ if we write $\cos\psi$ for $\dot{x}$, and $\sin\psi$ for $\dot{y}$, where $\tan\psi = \dot{y}/\dot{x}$: and a similar remark holds for $f_{\dot{y}}$. Thus, if $\dot{Y}/\dot{X} = \tan\chi$, we have

$$(9.9.5) \quad E(x, y, \cos\psi, \sin\psi, \cos\chi, \sin\chi) = \frac{E(x, y, \dot{x}, \dot{y}, \dot{X}, \dot{Y})}{\sqrt{(\dot{X}^2 + \dot{Y}^2)}}$$

$$= \cos\chi\{f_{\dot{x}}(x, y, \cos\chi, \sin\chi) - f_{\dot{x}}(x, y, \cos\psi, \sin\psi)\} + \sin\chi\{f_{\dot{y}}(x, y, \cos\chi, \sin\chi) - f_{\dot{y}}(x, y, \cos\psi, \sin\psi)\},$$

which is the formula mentioned.

Two further properties of the excess function may be noticed at this point.

(i) Since $f_{\dot{x}}$ and $f_{\dot{y}}$ are continuous at a corner on a minimizing curve, we see, from (9.9.5), that

$$(9.9.6) \quad E(x, y, \cos\psi, \sin\psi, \cos\chi, \sin\chi) = 0,$$

where ψ, χ are the slopes to left and right of a corner (x, y) on a minimizing curve (cf. (2.6.18)).

(ii) If $f(x, y, \dot{x}, \dot{y})$ has the form $\dot{x}F\left(x, y, \dfrac{\dot{y}}{\dot{x}}\right)$ the excess function E takes the form

$$(9.9.7) \quad \dot{X}\{F(x, y, \varpi) - F(x, y, p) - (\varpi - p)F_{y'}(x, y, p)\},$$

where $p = \dot{y}/\dot{x}$ and $\varpi = \dot{Y}/\dot{X}$. When we transfer from the parametric to the ordinary problem we may take $\dot{X} = 1$, and (9.9.7) becomes the excess function for the ordinary problem.

9.10 Further necessary conditions

Let us consider again the formula (9.9.5) for E. The expression

$$(9.10.1) \quad f_{\dot{x}}(x, y, \cos\chi, \sin\chi) - f_{\dot{x}}(x, y, \cos\psi, \sin\psi) = \int_{\psi}^{\chi} \frac{d}{d\tau} f_{\dot{x}}(x, y, \cos\tau, \sin\tau)\, d\tau,$$

and the integrand in the second member of (9.10.1) is

$$(9.10.2) \quad -\sin\tau f_{\dot{x}\dot{x}}(x, y, \cos\tau, \sin\tau) + \cos\tau f_{\dot{x}\dot{y}}(x, y, \cos\tau, \sin\tau).$$

If we now use the expressions for $f_{\dot{x}\dot{x}}$ and $f_{\dot{x}\dot{y}}$ in terms of the function g, (9.10.2) becomes

$$(9.10.3) \quad -\sin\tau\, g(x, y, \cos\tau, \sin\tau).$$

Thus

$$(9.10.4) \quad f_{\dot{x}}(x, y, \cos\chi, \sin\chi) - f_{\dot{x}}(x, y, \cos\psi, \sin\psi) = -\int_{\psi}^{\chi} \sin\tau\, g(x, y, \cos\tau, \sin\tau)\, d\tau,$$

and similarly

$$(9.10.5) \quad f_{\dot{y}}(x, y, \cos\chi, \sin\chi) - f_{\dot{y}}(x, y, \cos\psi, \sin\psi) = \int_{\psi}^{\chi} \cos\tau\, g(x, y, \cos\tau, \sin\tau)\, d\tau,$$

and therefore (9.9.5) takes the form

$$(9.10.6) \quad E(x, y, \cos\psi, \sin\psi, \cos\chi, \sin\chi) = \int_{\psi}^{\chi} \sin(\chi - \tau) g(x, y, \cos\tau, \sin\tau)\, d\tau.$$

Suppose now that $0 < \chi - \psi < \pi$. Then, using the mean value theorem for integrals, we can express the second member of (9.10.6) in the form

$$(9.10.7) \quad g(x, y, \cos\xi, \sin\xi)\int_{\psi}^{\chi} \sin(\chi - \tau)\, d\tau = g(x, y, \cos\xi, \sin\xi)\{1 - \cos(\chi - \psi)\},$$

where ξ lies between ψ and χ. Hence

$$(9.10.8) \quad \frac{E(x, y, \cos\psi, \sin\psi, \cos\chi, \sin\chi)}{1 - \cos(\chi - \psi)} = g(x, y, \cos\xi, \sin\xi).$$

But if $(x, y, \cos\psi, \sin\psi)$ is an element of a minimizing curve,

$$E(x, y, \cos\psi, \sin\psi, \cos\chi, \sin\chi) \geqslant 0 \tag{9.10.9}$$

for all values of χ; so letting $\chi \to \psi$ from above in (9.10.8) we find

$$g(x, y, \cos\psi, \sin\psi) \geqslant 0. \tag{9.10.10}$$

Hence

$$g(x, y, \dot{x}, \dot{y}) \geqslant 0 \tag{9.10.11}$$

is a necessary condition which must be satisfied by any element $(x, y, \dot{x}, \dot{y})$ of a minimizing curve.

Consider now a problem in which $g(x, y, \dot{x}, \dot{y}) > 0$ for all values of the variables. In such a problem no minimizing curve can have a corner; because for a corner the first member of (9.10.8) vanishes in virtue of (9.9.6), which is impossible if $g > 0$ always.

Legendre's necessary condition for a minimizing curve has a form similar to that found in §7.7 for curves in space. The condition is

$$f_{\dot{x}\dot{x}}\lambda^2 + 2f_{\dot{x}\dot{y}}\lambda\mu + f_{\dot{y}\dot{y}}\mu^2 \geqslant 0 \tag{9.10.12}$$

for all values of (λ, μ) other than $(k\dot{x}, k\dot{y})$. The arguments in the coefficients $f_{\dot{x}\dot{x}}, f_{\dot{x}\dot{y}}, f_{\dot{y}\dot{y}}$ are the values of $x, y, \dot{x}, \dot{y}$ at a point of a minimizing curve. Now from (9.9.3), using (9.3.1), we see that

$$\begin{aligned} E(x, y, \dot{x}, \dot{y}, \dot{X}, \dot{Y}) &= f(x, y, \dot{X}, \dot{Y}) - f(x, y, \dot{x}, \dot{y}) \\ &\quad - (\dot{X} - \dot{x})f_{\dot{x}}(x, y, \dot{x}, \dot{y}) - (\dot{Y} - \dot{y})f_{\dot{y}}(x, y, \dot{x}, \dot{y}), \end{aligned} \tag{9.10.13}$$

and therefore, by Taylor's theorem,

$$\begin{aligned} 2E(x, y, \dot{x}, \dot{y}, \dot{X}, \dot{Y}) &= (\dot{X} - \dot{x})^2 f_{\dot{x}\dot{x}}(x, y, \xi, \eta) \\ &\quad + 2(\dot{X} - \dot{x})(\dot{Y} - \dot{y})f_{\dot{x}\dot{y}}(x, y, \xi, \eta) + (\dot{Y} - \dot{y})^2 f_{\dot{y}\dot{y}}(x, y, \xi, \eta), \end{aligned} \tag{9.10.14}$$

where ξ lies between $\dot{x}$ and $\dot{X}$, and η lies between $\dot{y}$ and $\dot{Y}$. If we put $\dot{x} + \lambda\varepsilon$, $\dot{y} + \mu\varepsilon$ for $\dot{X}$, $\dot{Y}$, and then let $\varepsilon \to 0$, we find that (9.10.14) and (9.9.3) together imply (9.10.12). Alternatively we can deduce (9.10.12) from (9.10.11) since the first member of (9.10.12) is equal to $(\lambda\dot{y} - \mu\dot{x})^2 g(x, y, \dot{x}, \dot{y})$.

9.11 Examples of the calculation of E

Example 1. Consider again the first of the two problems considered in §9.2, where

$$f = \frac{\dot{x}\dot{y}^2}{\dot{x}^2 + \dot{y}^2}. \tag{9.11.1}$$

We easily find, using the formula (9.9.4),

$$E = \frac{(\dot{x}\dot{Y} - \dot{y}\dot{X})^2\{(\dot{x}^2 - \dot{y}^2)\dot{X} - 2\dot{x}\dot{y}\dot{Y}\}}{(\dot{X}^2 + \dot{Y}^2)(\dot{x}^2 + \dot{y}^2)^2}. \tag{9.11.2}$$

If we take again the problem discussed in §9.2, where A is (0, 0) and B is (1, 0), we see that, for an element of the line-segment AB,

$$E = \frac{\dot{X}\dot{Y}^2}{\dot{X}^2 + \dot{Y}^2}, \tag{9.11.3}$$

which is $f(\dot{X}, \dot{Y})$. (We can see the result also from the form for E given in (9.9.3), since $f_{\dot{x}}$ and $f_{\dot{y}}$ both vanish for elements of the line-segment.) Weierstrass's necessary condition is not satisfied, and the line-segment is not a minimizing curve, as we have noticed already.

EXAMPLE 2. In the second problem considered in §9.2

$$f = \frac{\dot{y}^2}{\dot{x}} \tag{9.11.4}$$

and the end-points are $A(0, 0)$ and $B(1,1)$. In this case

$$E = \frac{1}{\dot{X}\dot{x}^2}(\dot{x}\dot{Y} - \dot{y}\dot{X})^2 \tag{9.11.5}$$

On the line-segment AB

$$E = \frac{1}{\dot{X}}(\dot{X} - \dot{Y})^2, \tag{9.11.6}$$

and Weierstrass's necessary condition is not satisfied. The line-segment is not a minimizing curve, as we have noticed already.

EXAMPLE 3. Consider again the integral

$$\lambda(x, y)\sqrt{(\dot{x}^2 + \dot{y}^2)}, \tag{9.11.7}$$

already mentioned in (9.3.5). Here

$$f_{\dot{x}} = \frac{\lambda\dot{x}}{\sqrt{(\dot{x}^2 + \dot{y}^2)}} = \lambda \cos \psi, \quad f_{\dot{y}} = \frac{\lambda\dot{y}}{\sqrt{(\dot{x}^2 + \dot{y}^2)}} = \lambda \sin \psi, \tag{9.11.8}$$

and, from (9.9.5),

$$\begin{aligned} &E(x, y, \cos \psi, \sin \psi, \cos \chi, \sin \chi) \\ &\quad = \lambda\{\cos \chi(\cos \chi - \cos \psi) + \sin \chi(\sin \chi - \sin \psi)\} \\ &\quad = \lambda\{1 - \cos (\chi - \psi)\}. \end{aligned} \tag{9.11.9}$$

If $\lambda > 0$ for all values of (x, y), Weierstrass's necessary condition is satisfied.

9.12 Fields and the invariant integral

The notion of a field in the parametric problem differs from that in the ordinary problem only in the fact that the curves are no longer restricted to be of the form $y = \chi(x)$. A field Φ is a region of the plane with which is associated a one-parameter family of extremals, one and only one of which passes through each point of Φ. Explicitly we have a family of curves

$$x = \varphi(t, \alpha), \qquad y = \psi(t, \alpha), \tag{9.12.1}$$

which satisfy Euler's equations for each value of α. The functions φ, ψ are assumed to be of class C_2 in the corresponding region $\mathscr{A}$ of (t, α), defined by equations of the form

$$\alpha_1 < \alpha < \alpha_2, \qquad T(\alpha) < t < \overline{T}(\alpha), \tag{9.12.2}$$

and the Jacobian $\dfrac{\partial(\varphi, \psi)}{\partial(t, \alpha)}$ is assumed not to vanish in $\mathscr{A}$. We can therefore solve the equations (9.12.1) for t and α,

$$t = \tau(x, y), \qquad \alpha = \lambda(x, y), \tag{9.12.3}$$

and one and only one of the curves (9.12.1) passes through each point of Φ.

The slope functions of the field

$$p = \dot{\varphi}\{\tau(x, y), \lambda(x, y)\}, \quad q = \dot{\psi}\{\tau(x, y), \lambda(x, y)\}, \tag{9.12.4}$$

are uniquely defined in Φ so long as the parametric representation of the extremals is fixed. These functions change if we change to another parametric representation, but the ratio q/p is uniquely defined; the value of q/p at (x, y) is independent of the particular parametric representation used.

Now let us return to the variable end-point theorem. The formula for dI,

$$dI = f_{\dot{x}}\, dx + f_{\dot{y}}\, dy \Big|_A^B \tag{9.12.5}$$

involves the comparison of the value of I for an extremal with its value for a neighbouring curve which is not in general an extremal. Suppose now that we can construct a field and that the given extremal is one extremal of this field. Then we can express the change in I as the curve of integration varies from one extremal arc $K_{A_1B_1}$ of the field to another $K_{A_2B_2}$ in terms of the integral

$$H = \int u\,dx + v\,dy, \tag{9.12.6}$$

where

$$u = f_{\dot{x}}\{x, y, p(x, y), q(x, y)\}, \quad v = f_{\dot{y}}\{x, y, p(x, y), q(x, y)\}. \tag{9.12.7}$$

We notice that the functions u and v are uniquely defined functions of position in Φ, independent of the particular parametric representation of the extremals, since $f_{\dot{x}}$ and $f_{\dot{y}}$ are positive-homogeneous of degree zero in $(\dot{x}, \dot{y})$: in other words, $f_{\dot{x}}$ and $f_{\dot{y}}$ can be expressed in terms of the three variables $x, y, \dot{y}/\dot{x}$. By the same argument as before (§5.1) we have

$$I(K_{A_2B_2}) - I(K_{A_1B_1}) = H(\Delta_{B_1B_2}) - H(\Gamma_{A_1A_2}), \tag{9.12.8}$$

where $\Delta_{B_1B_2}$ is the path of the end-point B from B_1 to B_2, and $\Gamma_{A_1A_2}$ is the path of the end-point A from A_1 to A_2. (Cf. Fig. 5.1.) The curves Γ and Δ may have a finite number of corners. It follows as before that the integral H is invariant, a function only of its end-points in the field, not of the path in the field from one end-point to the other.

The Pfaffian form $u\,dx + v\,dy$ must be a perfect differential, and it may be of interest to verify this fact independently. The corresponding exercise for the ordinary problem has already been carried out in §5.3; as we should expect, the proof for the parametric problem is simpler, because in the parametric problem x and y have the same status. We have

$$u = f_{\dot{x}}(x, y, p, q), \qquad v = f_{\dot{y}}(x, y, p, q), \tag{9.12.9}$$

and

$$\frac{\partial v}{\partial x} - \frac{\partial u}{\partial y} = f_{\dot{y}x} + f_{\dot{y}\dot{x}}\frac{\partial p}{\partial x} + f_{\dot{y}\dot{y}}\frac{\partial q}{\partial x} - \left(f_{\dot{x}y} + f_{\dot{x}\dot{x}}\frac{\partial p}{\partial y} + f_{\dot{x}\dot{y}}\frac{\partial q}{\partial y}\right), \tag{9.12.10}$$

the arguments in the derivatives of f being (x, y, p, q). Now, using the formulae (9.3.3), the second member of (9.12.10) becomes

$$\begin{aligned} & f_{\dot{y}x} - f_{\dot{x}y} + g\left(-pq\frac{\partial p}{\partial x} + p^2\frac{\partial q}{\partial x} - q^2\frac{\partial p}{\partial y} + pq\frac{\partial q}{\partial y}\right) \\ &= f_{\dot{y}x} - f_{\dot{x}y} + g\left\{p\left(p\frac{\partial q}{\partial x} + q\frac{\partial q}{\partial y}\right) - q\left(p\frac{\partial p}{\partial x} + q\frac{\partial p}{\partial y}\right)\right\}, \end{aligned} \tag{9.12.11}$$

and, interpreting the formulae in terms of the particular extremal through (x, y), we have

$$\frac{\partial v}{\partial x} - \frac{\partial u}{\partial y} = f_{\dot{y}x} - f_{\dot{x}y} + g(\dot{x}\ddot{y} - \dot{y}\ddot{x}). \tag{9.12.12}$$

The second member of (9.12.12) is zero by Weierstrass's form of the differential equation of an extremal (9.4.13).

We notice as before that for an extremal arc $H = I$. For, if the path is an extremal,

$$H = \int_A^B u\,dx + v\,dy = \int_T^{\overline{T}} (\dot{x}f_{\dot{x}} + \dot{y}f_{\dot{y}})\,dt = \int_T^{\overline{T}} f\,dt = I, \tag{9.12.13}$$

where we have used the fact that, for the extremal, $\dot{x} = p$ and $\dot{y} = q$.

9.13 The fundamental sufficiency theorem

Let A, B be two points on the extremal arc K of the field. We want to know in what circumstances the value of I for the arc of K from A to B is smaller than the value for any other curve Γ (which may have a finite number of corners) lying in the field. Now

$$I(\Gamma) - I(K) = I(\Gamma) - H(K) = I(\Gamma) - H(\Gamma), \tag{9.13.1}$$

and the difference $I(\Gamma) - I(K)$ is expressed as an integral along Γ. Thus

$$I(\Gamma) - I(K) = \int_T^{\overline{T}} \{f(x, y, \dot{x}, \dot{y}) - \dot{x}f_{\dot{x}}(x, y, p, q) - \dot{y}f_{\dot{y}}(x, y, p, q)\}\,dt, \tag{9.13.2}$$

the integral in the second member being taken along Γ. Thus

$$I(\Gamma) - I(K) = \int_T^{\overline{T}} E(x, y, p, q, \dot{x}, \dot{y})\,dt. \tag{9.13.3}$$

The integrand in the second member is a function of the four variables $x, y, \dot{x}, \dot{y}$, since p and q are known functions of (x, y),

$$\mathscr{W}(x, y, \dot{x}, \dot{y}) = E(x, y, p, q, \dot{x}, \dot{y}), \tag{9.13.4}$$

and $\mathscr{W}$ is uniquely defined when the function $f(x, y, \dot{x}, \dot{y})$ is known and the field has been constructed. If, therefore,

$$\mathscr{W}(x, y, \dot{x}, \dot{y}) > 0 \tag{9.13.5}$$

for all points (x, y) of the field, and for arbitrary values of $(\dot{x}, \dot{y})$, then

$$I(\Gamma) > I(K), \tag{9.13.6}$$

and the extremal arc K from A to B gives a smaller value to I than does any other curve from A to B in the field.

9.14 Newton's problem

The point $B(h, k)$ is prescribed, $h > 0$ and $k > 0$. It is required to find a curve in the upper half-plane joining O to B, and such that the solid of revolution formed by rotating the curve about the axis Ox shall encounter the least possible resistance when it moves steadily to the left through the air.

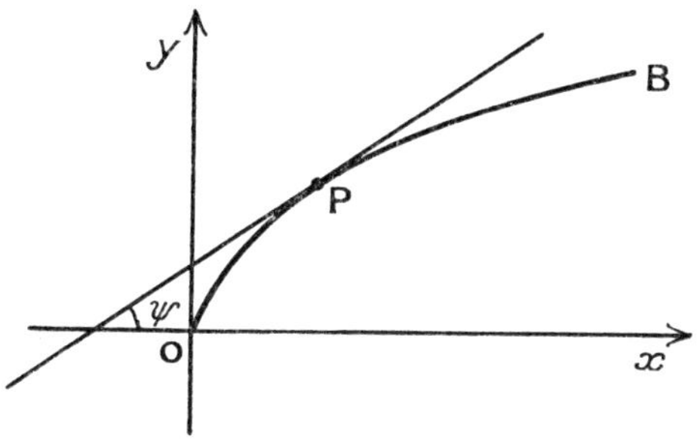

Fig. 9.14*a*

Let us consider the equivalent problem when the solid is at rest in a steady stream. The stream is thought of as an assembly of particles, each of mass m, each moving to the right with velocity V. Suppose that when a particle strikes the surface there is a frictionless inelastic impact. The normal component of momentum is destroyed, giving a normal impulse $mV \sin \psi$ on the solid, and this impulse has a component $mV \sin^2 \psi$ in the direction Ox. The components of impulse perpendicular to the axis of symmetry in the meridian planes have zero resultant, by symmetry, so the resultant force on the solid is along the axis, and is measured by the impulse per second

$$\int (2\pi y \, dy NV) mV \sin^2 \psi,$$

where N is the number of particles in unit volume, assumed uniform. Putting $mN = \rho$, the density of the gas, we get as the resisting force

(9.14.1) $$2\pi\rho V^2 \int_0^k y \sin^2 \psi \, dy,$$

so, removing the constant positive multiplier, the integral we have to handle is

(9.14.2) $$I = \int_0^k y \sin^2 \psi \, dy.$$

As we have mentioned already, the result is not in fact in good agreement with the experimental results.

We now introduce, on physical grounds, some further restrictions. We assume that the curve lies in the first quadrant, $x \geqslant 0$, and that $0 \leqslant \psi \leqslant \frac{1}{2}\pi$ throughout. We may therefore suppose $y \geqslant 0$, $\dot{x} \geqslant 0$, $\dot{y} \geqslant 0$ in $(T, \overline{T})$. It is worth noticing that, without these restrictions we can find a curve to make the integral as small as we please. For the curves shown in Fig. 9.14*b*, consisting of segments of straight lines inclined at angles α and $\pi - \alpha$ to Ox, we have

$$I = \sin^2 \alpha \int_0^k y\, dy = \tfrac{1}{2}k^2 \sin^2 \alpha, \tag{9.14.3}$$

which we can make as small as we please by choice of α.

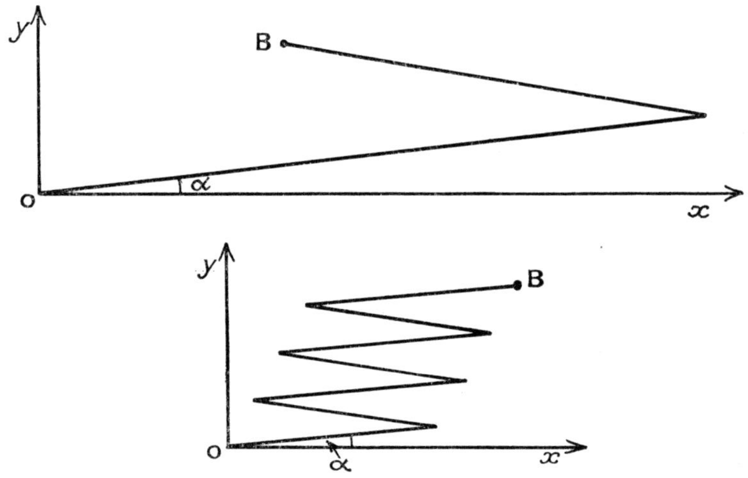

Fig. 9.14*b*

The problem, then, expressed in parametric form, is to find a minimizing curve for the integral

$$I = \int_T^{\overline{T}} y \frac{\dot{y}^3}{\dot{x}^2 + \dot{y}^2}\, dt. \tag{9.14.4}$$

The curves admitted are of class D^1 with $\dot{x} \geqslant 0$, $\dot{y} \geqslant 0$. Since x is absent from the integrand the first of du Bois-Reymond's equations is

(9.14.5) $$\frac{y\dot{y}^3\dot{x}}{(\dot{x}^2+\dot{y}^2)^2} = a, \qquad a > 0.$$

If $a = 0$ we have either $\dot{x} = 0$ or $\dot{y} = 0$, lines parallel to the axes. If $a > 0$ we have

(9.14.6) $$y = \frac{a}{\sin^3 \psi \cos \psi} = a\,\frac{(1+q^2)^2}{q},$$

where the parameter q is $\cot \psi = \dot{x}/\dot{y}$. To express x in terms of the same parameter we have $dx = q\,dy$, whence

(9.14.7) $$x = qy - \int y\,dq = a(q^2 + \tfrac{3}{4}q^4 - \log q) + b.$$

The general curve defined by (9.14.7) and (9.14.6) is obtained from the special curve

(9.14.8) $$X(q) = q^2 + \tfrac{3}{4}q^4 - \log q, \qquad Y(q) = (1+q^2)^2/q,$$

by the transformation (a magnification and translation) given by

(9.14.9) $$x = aX + b, \qquad y = aY.$$

Let us consider the curve (9.14.8). We notice first that as $q \to \infty$ (i.e. as $\psi \to 0$), $Y/X \to 0$; and as $q \to 0$ (i.e. as $\psi \to \frac{1}{2}\pi$), $Y/X \to \infty$. Also

(9.14.10) $$X'(q) = \frac{(3q^2-1)(q^2+1)}{q}, \qquad Y'(q) = \frac{1}{q}X'(q) = \frac{(3q^2-1)(q^2+1)}{q^2}.$$

As q increases from 0 to ∞ (i.e. as ψ decreases from $\frac{1}{2}\pi$ to 0) $X(q)$ decreases steadily from ∞ to a minimum (when $q = 1/\sqrt{3}$) and then increases steadily to ∞; $Y(q)$ also decreases steadily from ∞ to a minimum (when $q = 1/\sqrt{3}$) and then increases steadily to ∞. At the minimum point Q

(9.14.11) $$X = \tfrac{1}{3} + \tfrac{31}{49} + \tfrac{1}{2}\log 3 = \cdot 97, \qquad Y = \sqrt{3}(1+\tfrac{1}{3})^2 = 3{\cdot}08, \text{ approx.}$$

There is a cusp at Q, and the tangent at this point makes an angle of

60° with Ox. The curve has a part PQ convex to Ox and a part QS concave to Ox (Fig. 9.14c).

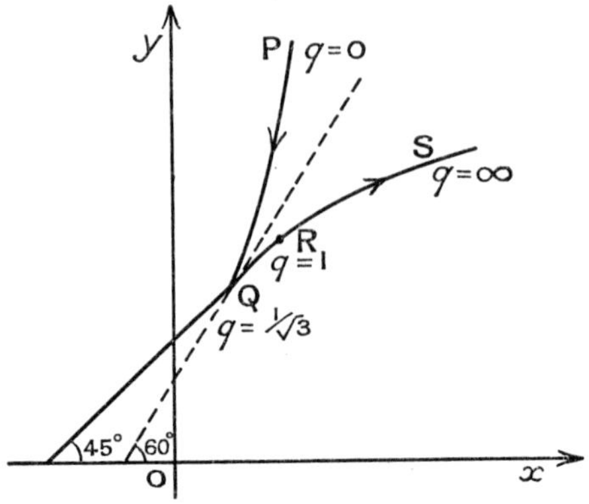

Fig. 9.14*c*

To find the curvature $\mathscr{C}$ we have

(9.14.12) $$\cot \psi = q, \quad -\operatorname{cosec}^2 \psi \frac{d\psi}{ds} = \frac{dq}{ds},$$

whence

(9.14.13) $$\mathscr{C} = \frac{d\psi}{ds} = -\frac{1}{(q^2+1)\sqrt{(X'^2+Y'^2)}}$$

$$= -\frac{q^2}{(q^2+1)^{5/2}\,|3q^2-1|},$$

if s is measured throughout in the direction of increasing q; $\mathscr{C} < 0$ always, since ψ always decreases as s increases. We can also find $\mathscr{C}$ from the formula (9.4.15), since

(9.14.14) $$g = \frac{2y\dot{y}(3\dot{x}^2 - \dot{y}^2)}{(\dot{x}^2+\dot{y}^2)^3}.$$

The necessary condition (9.10.11) shows that only the part of the curve for which $q \geqslant 1/\sqrt{3}$ can be part of a minimizing curve, i.e. the part concave to Ox, and this was to be expected on physical grounds. But in fact the more exacting necessary condition of Weierstrass restricts still further the part that is relevant. Since

(9.14.15) $$f_{\dot{x}} = -\frac{2y\dot{x}\dot{y}^3}{(\dot{x}^2+\dot{y}^2)^2}, \quad f_{\dot{y}} = \frac{y\dot{y}^2}{(\dot{x}^2+\dot{y}^2)^2}\{(\dot{x}^2+\dot{y}^2)+2\dot{x}^2\},$$

the formula (9.9.5) gives

$$
\begin{aligned}
(9.14.16)\quad & E(x, y, \cos\psi, \sin\psi, \cos\chi, \sin\chi)\\
&= y\cos\chi(-2\cos\chi\sin^3\chi + 2\cos\psi\sin^3\psi)\\
&\quad + y\sin\chi(\sin^2\chi + 2\cos^2\chi\sin^2\chi - \sin^2\psi - 2\cos^2\psi\sin^2\psi)\\
&= y\sin\chi(\sin^2\chi - \sin^2\psi)\\
&\quad + 2y\cos\psi\sin^2\psi(\cos\chi\sin\psi - \sin\chi\cos\psi)\\
&= y\sin\chi\sin(\chi-\psi)\sin(\chi+\psi)\\
&\quad - 2y\cos\psi\sin^2\psi\sin(\chi-\psi)\\
&= y\sin(\chi-\psi)\{\sin\chi\sin(\chi+\psi) - \sin 2\psi\sin\psi\}\\
&= y\sin^2(\chi-\psi)\sin(\chi+2\psi).
\end{aligned}
$$

It is clear that, strictly speaking, if $y > 0$, we can make $E < 0$ by taking $\chi + 2\psi > \pi$; however in this problem we are concerned only with curves for which $0 \leqslant \chi \leqslant \frac{1}{2}\pi$, and therefore we need $\psi \leqslant \pi/4$. A minimizing curve can contain only that part of (9.14.8) for which $q \geqslant 1$. The arc starts at $(7/4, 4)$ at an angle $\pi/4$ with Ox, and the parameter q increases from 1 to ∞; this is the arc RS in Fig. 9.14*c*. We speak of this arc, and the associated arc (9.14.9), as a Newtonian arc N.

9.15 The minimizing curve

The Newtonian arc does not reach the axis Ox, so the minimizing curve (if it exists) must be of class D^1, and must consist of Newtonian arcs N, segments x = constant parallel to Oy (which we will call X), and segments y = constant parallel to Ox (which we will call Y). The required curve from O to B may contain segments of all these types. But in fact of all the possible combinations the only one that can actually occur is the one that we denote by the symbol XN, a segment parallel to Oy and a Newtonian arc.

To see this, let us consider the various possibilities. The combination YX, consisting of a horizontal segment PQ and a vertical segment QR, cannot appear in the minimizing curve, since the straight line PR gives a smaller value to the integral than the broken line PQR. And similarly XY cannot occur.

The combination $N'N''$ of two Newtonian arcs abutting cannot occur. For at a corner $E = 0$, whereas (9.14.16) implies $\chi = \psi$, where ψ and χ are the angles of slope to left and to right of the corner. Alternatively the result can be deduced from (9.10.8); for

$$(9.15.1)\qquad g(x, y, \cos\xi, \sin\xi) = 2y\sin\xi\,(3\cos^2\xi - \sin^2\xi),$$

where ξ lies between ψ and χ. Both ψ and χ lie in the interval $(0, \pi/4)$, and therefore ξ lies in the same interval. But the second member of (9.15.1) does not vanish anywhere in this range.

The combination *YN*, a line parallel to *Ox* abutting on a Newtonian arc, is impossible. The continuity of $f_{\dot{x}}$ at a corner would imply

$$0 = -2y \cos \psi \sin^3 \psi,$$

which cannot be satisfied with $y > 0$ and $0 < \psi \leqslant \pi/4$. And similarly the combination *NY* cannot occur.

The combination *NX*, a Newtonian arc abutting on *a* segment parallel to *Oy*, cannot occur. The continuity of $f_{\dot{y}}$ requires

$$(9.15.2) \qquad y = y \sin^2 \psi(1 + 2\cos^2 \psi) = y\,\frac{(3q^2 + 1)}{(q^2 + 1)^2},$$

which cannot be satisfied with $\psi < \pi/4$, $q > 1$.

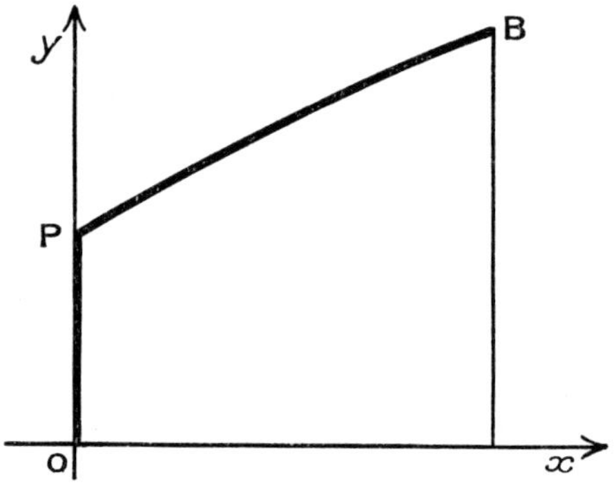

Fig. 9.15

But, finally, the combination *XN*, a vertical line abutting on a Newtonian arc, *can* occur, for (9.15.2) is satisfied if $q = 1$. The Newtonian arc leaves the vertical segment at an inclination of $\pi/4$ to *Ox*. (Notice the rather troublesome point that the other corner condition, the continuity of $f_{\dot{x}}$, is violated. This anomaly arises from the stipulation that $\dot{x} \geqslant 0$ for all the curves considered, so free variation of the curve in the *x*-direction is not permissible, whereas it is from such a variation that this condition arises.)

Finally then we are left with a segment *OP* of the axis *Oy*, and a Newtonian arc *PB* with slope $\pi/4$ at *P*. The arc (9.14.9) has $x = 0$ when $q = 1$, giving $b = -7a/4$, and the required arc is therefore

$$(9.15.3) \quad x = a(\tfrac{3}{4}t^4 + t^2 - \log t - \tfrac{7}{4}),\ y = a(t^2 + 1)^2/t, \qquad t \geqslant 1.$$

The point P is $(0, 4a)$. The curve (9.15.3) goes through $B(\overline{X}, \overline{Y})$ for precisely one value of a. A simple way of seeing this is to notice that x/y increases monotonically from 0 to ∞ as t increases from 1 to ∞. Thus x/y passes just once through the given value $\overline{X}/\overline{Y}$ say at $t = \tau$, and a is determined from (9.15.3) with $(t, x, y) = (\tau, \overline{X}, \overline{Y})$.

Thus the minimizing curve (if it exists) consists of the segment OP, of length $4a$, of the y-axis, and a Newtonian arc PB leaving Oy at 45° (Fig. 9.15).

9.16 Proof that the solution gives a minimum value to I

The curves defined by (9.15.3) for different positive values of a constitute a field in the domain $x > 0$, $y > 0$. To prove that the solution we have found is actually minimizing (in the class of curves satisfying the condition $0 \leqslant \psi \leqslant \frac{1}{2}\pi$) we need a suitable modification of the argument used in establishing the fundamental sufficiency theorem.

Let $B(\overline{X}, \overline{Y})$ denote, for the moment, a variable point in the positive quadrant, and let K_{OPB} be the discontinuous solution, of the type just found, through B. Thus K_{OPB} consists of a segment OP of the axis Oy, and a Newtonian arc PB. Let $u(B)$ be the value of the integral I for the path K_{OPB}; then if B varies,

(9.16.1) $$du = f_{\dot{x}}\, d\overline{X} + f_{\dot{y}}\, d\overline{Y},$$

where the arguments in $f_{\dot{x}}$ and $f_{\dot{y}}$ are the elements of the Newtonian arc at B. (The discontinuity in $f_{\dot{x}}$ at P does not invalidate the application of the variable end-point theorem to the composite arc, because the displacement of P in the x-direction is zero.) Thus if B moves to C along any curve Δ of the prescribed type in the positive quadrant

(9.16.2) $$u(C) - u(B) = \int f_{\dot{x}}\, dx + f_{\dot{y}}\, dy = H(\Delta_{BC}).$$

We can now deduce that the path K_{OPB} does in fact give a smaller value to I than does any other curve which lies in the region $x \geqslant 0$, $y \geqslant 0$, and for which $0 \leqslant \psi \leqslant \frac{1}{2}\pi$. Let Γ_{OHB} be any other path of this type, consisting of a segment OH of the axis Oy and a curve of class D^1 joining H to B. (Of course in a special case H may coincide with O.) Let B' move along the arc Γ_{HB}, and let $K_{OP'B'}$ be the discontinuous solution through B' (consisting of a segment OP' of Oy and a Newtonian arc joining P' to B') as in Fig. 9.16.

Now let us consider the value of the integral I taken along the composite path $K_{OP'B'} + \Gamma_{B'B}$: let us denote this value by $J(B')$. We notice that

$$J(H) = I(\Gamma_{OHB}), \tag{9.16.3}$$

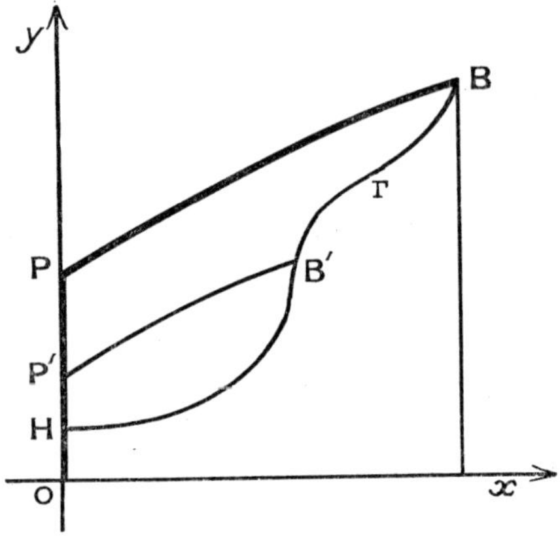

Fig. 9.16

and that

$$J(B) = I(K_{OPB}). \tag{9.16.4}$$

Now

$$\begin{aligned} J(B') - J(B) &= I(K_{OP'B'}) + I(\Gamma_{B'B}) - I(K_{OPB}) \\ &= I(\Gamma_{B'B}) - H(\Gamma_{B'B}) \end{aligned} \tag{9.16.5}$$

which is positive (as in §9.13) since $E > 0$, by (9.14.16), unless $\chi = \psi$. In particular

$$J(H) > J(B), \tag{9.16.6}$$

which is equivalent to

$$I(\Gamma_{OHB}) > I(K_{OPB}), \tag{9.16.7}$$

and this completes the proof that K_{OPB} is the minimizing curve.

9.17 Comparison of the resistances for various curves

Let us examine how the value of the resistance for the minimizing curve compares with the value for some other curves: for simplicity we confine our attention to the special case where B is the point (h, h).

For the circular cylinder, with generators parallel to the

airstream,

(9.17.1) $$I = \tfrac{1}{2}h^2.$$

For the cone with spike at O,

(9.17.2) $$I = \int_0^h y \sin^2 \psi \, dy = \tfrac{1}{4}h^2.$$

For the hemisphere

(9.17.3) $$\int_0^h y \sin^2 \psi \, dy = h^2 \int_0^{\frac{1}{2}\pi} \cos \psi \sin^3 \psi \, d\psi = \tfrac{1}{4}h^2.$$

For the parabola

(9.17.4) $$y^2 = hx,$$

as the meridian curve,

(9.17.5) $$y' = \frac{h}{2y}, \quad \sin^2 \psi = \frac{h^2}{4y^2 + h^2},$$

whence

(9.17.6) $$I = \int_0^h \frac{h^2 y \, dy}{4y^2 + h^2} = \frac{h^2}{8} \log 5 = \cdot 201h^2.$$

For the truncated cone, whose meridian curve contains the two linear segments shown in Fig. 9.17,

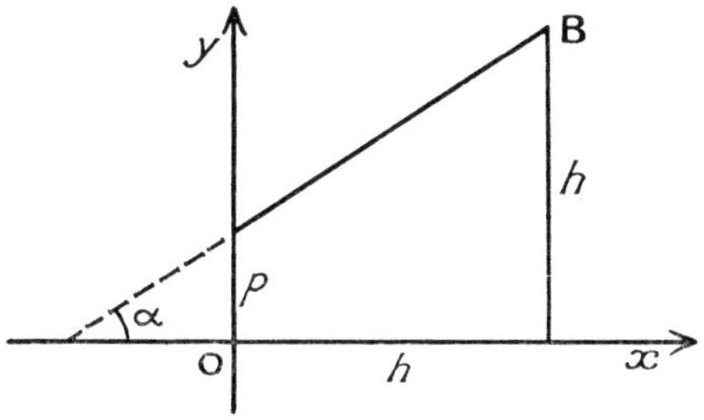

Fig. 9.17

(9.17.7) $$I = \int y \sin^2 \psi \, dy = \tfrac{1}{2}p^2 + \sin^2 \alpha \, \tfrac{1}{2}(h^2 - p^2)$$
$$= \tfrac{1}{2}(p^2 \cos^2 \alpha + h^2 \sin^2 \alpha).$$

Now

(9.17.8) $$p = h(1 - \tan \alpha),$$

whence

(9.17.9) $$I = \tfrac{1}{2}h^2\{(\cos \alpha - \sin \alpha)^2 + \sin^2 \alpha\}$$
$$= \tfrac{1}{2}h^2(\tfrac{3}{2} - \sin 2\alpha - \tfrac{1}{2} \cos 2\alpha)$$
$$= \tfrac{1}{4}h^2(3 - \sqrt{5} \sin (2\alpha + \beta)),$$

where $\tan \beta = \frac{1}{2}$. Thus I has a minimum value

$$\frac{1}{4}h^2(3 - \sqrt{5}) = \cdot 191h^2 \tag{9.17.10}$$

when $\tan 2\alpha = 2$, $\alpha = 31^\circ\, 43'$.

Finally, for the minimizing curve found in §9.15,

$$I = \int_0^{4a} y\, dy + \int_1^{\tau} \frac{y\dot{y}^3}{\dot{x}^2 + \dot{y}^2}\, dt, \tag{9.17.11}$$

where, in the second integral, x and y are given by (9.15.3), and τ is given by $x = y$, i.e. by the equation

$$\frac{3}{4}\tau^4 + \tau^2 - \log \tau - \frac{7}{4} = \frac{1}{\tau}(\tau^2 + 1)^2. \tag{9.17.12}$$

Thus

$$\begin{aligned} I &= 8a^2 + a^2\int_1^{\tau}\left(3t^3 + 5t + \frac{1}{t} - \frac{1}{t^3}\right) dt \\ &= a^2\left(\frac{3}{4}\tau^4 + \frac{5}{2}\tau^2 + \log \tau + \frac{17}{4} + \frac{1}{2\tau^2}\right). \end{aligned} \tag{9.17.13}$$

This can be simplified somewhat by substituting for $\log \tau$ from (9.17.12). which gives

$$I = \frac{a^2(\tau^2 + 1)^2}{2\tau^2}(3\tau^2 - 2\tau + 1). \tag{9.17.14}$$

But

$$h = a\frac{(\tau^2 + 1)^2}{\tau}, \tag{9.17.15}$$

and (9.17.14) becomes

$$I = \frac{h^2}{2(\tau^2 + 1)^2}(3\tau^2 - 2\tau + 1). \tag{9.17.16}$$

The solution of (9.17.12) is, to a good approximation, $\tau = 1{\cdot}917$, and substituting this value in (9.17.16) we find

$$I = \cdot 1874h^2 \tag{9.17.17}$$

Now the resistance to the motion of the solid is $2\pi\rho V^2 I$ so the resistance for the cylinder is $\pi\rho h^2 V^2$. The values of the resistance for the solids derived from the other curves considered, expressed as fractions of the value for the cylinder, are as shown in the following table:

Cylinder	1·000
Cone, Hemisphere	·500
Paraboloid	·402
Truncated cone (best value)	·382
True minimizing curve	·375

9.18 The isoperimetrical problem in parametric form

We start with the fixed end-point problem. Our object is to find a minimizing curve for

$$\int_T^{\overline{T}} f(x, y, \dot{x}, \dot{y})\, dt \tag{9.18.1}$$

among the curves of the class κ'. These curves have the form

$$x = \varphi(t), \quad y = \psi(t), \tag{9.18.2}$$

where φ and ψ are of class D_1; the curves pass through the prescribed end-points A and B, and are such that

$$\int_T^{\overline{T}} h(x, y, \dot{x}, \dot{y})\, dt = l. \tag{9.18.3}$$

The functions f and h have the properties demanded of the function f in §9.1.

The fundamental result is *Euler's rule.* The minimizing curve, if it exists, is minimizing for the integral

$$\int_T^{\overline{T}} (f - \lambda h)\, dt, \tag{9.18.4}$$

where λ is a constant. The minimizing curve satisfies the equations of du Bois-Reymond for

$$f^* = f - \lambda h, \tag{9.18.5}$$

and an arc between consecutive corners satisfies Euler's equations for f^*. In general the extremals have the form

$$x = \varphi(u(t);\ a, b, c, d;\ \lambda), \qquad y = \psi(u(t);\ a, b, c, d;\ \lambda), \tag{9.18.6}$$

and in the simple cases we can find values of a, b, c, d, λ so that the curve (9.18.6) passes through the prescribed end-points and satisfies the isoperimetrical condition (9.18.3).

The proof of Euler's rule is substantially the same as for the ordinary problem (§6.5).

Now consider the problem with variable end-points. We will suppose, for the sake of simplicity, that φ and ψ are of class C_2, that B is fixed, and that A is constrained to lie on a given curve Γ. Then the minimizing curve satisfies Euler's equations for f^* for some definite value of λ, and the end-condition at A is

$$f^*_{\dot{x}}\,dX + f^*_{\dot{y}}\,dY = 0, \tag{9.18.7}$$

where the arguments in $f^*_{\dot{x}}$ and $f^*_{\dot{y}}$ are the elements of the extremal at A, and (dX, dY) is a displacement on Γ. The same λ occurs in Euler's equations and in the end-condition (9.18.7). The proof follows the same lines as that given for the ordinary problem in §6.12, and need not be repeated here.

EXAMPLE 1. *The chord-and-arc problem.* We seek an arc of given length $2l$ in the upper half-plane joining A $(a, 0)$ to B $(-a, 0)$ and such that the area bounded by the segment AB and the arc is a maximum (cf. §6.8.)

We can use for the area either of the formulae

$$\int_T^{\overline{T}} \tfrac{1}{2}(x\dot{y} - y\dot{x})\,dt, \tag{9.18.8}$$

or

$$\int_T^{\overline{T}} x\dot{y}\,dt, \tag{9.18.9}$$

and the isoperimetrical condition is

$$\int_T^{\overline{T}} \sqrt{(\dot{x}^2 + \dot{y}^2)}\,dt = 2l. \tag{9.18.10}$$

According to Euler's rule we need the extremals for the integrand

$$f^* = \tfrac{1}{2}(x\dot{y} - y\dot{x}) - \lambda\sqrt{(\dot{x}^2 + \dot{y}^2)}, \tag{9.18.11}$$

or for

$$f^* = x\dot{y} - \lambda\sqrt{(\dot{x}^2 + \dot{y}^2)}. \tag{9.18.12}$$

As we have seen (Example 4 of §9.7) the extremal is a circular arc of radius $|\lambda|$. For an arc of length $2l$ through A and B the curve is given by the formulae

$$x = \lambda \sin\psi, \quad y = \lambda(\cos\beta - \cos\psi) \tag{9.18.13}$$

where $\lambda > 0$, $\psi = \beta$ at A and $\psi = 2\pi - \beta$ at B, $a = \lambda \sin\beta$, and

$\lambda(\pi - \beta) = l$. The angle β, lying in $(0, \pi)$, is uniquely determined by the equation

$$\frac{a}{l} = \frac{\sin \beta}{\pi - \beta} = \frac{\sin \alpha}{\alpha}, \tag{9.18.14}$$

where $\alpha = \pi - \beta$. If $1 < \frac{l}{a} < \frac{1}{2}\pi$ the angle β is obtuse, and if $\frac{1}{2}\pi < \frac{l}{a}$ the angle β is acute (Fig. 9.18). When β has been found from (9.18.14),

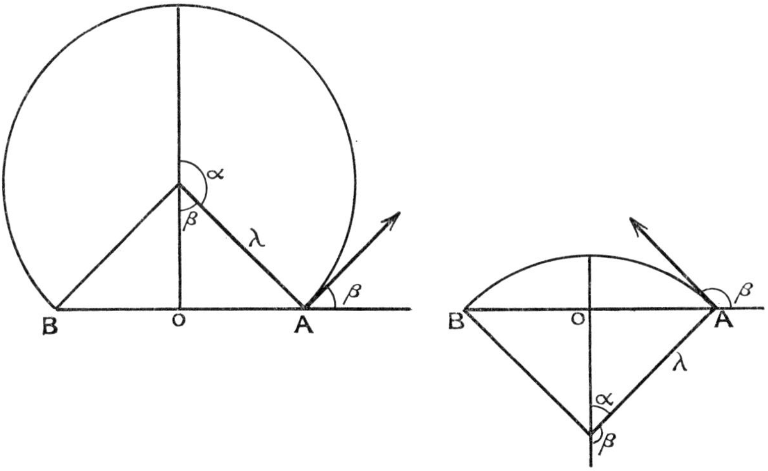

Fig. 9.18

λ is uniquely determined from either of the formulae

$$\lambda = \frac{a}{\sin \alpha}, \qquad \lambda = \frac{l}{\alpha}. \tag{9.18.15}$$

The area is

$$\Delta = \int_{\beta}^{2\pi - \beta} x \frac{dy}{d\psi}\, d\psi, \tag{9.18.16}$$

where we now take ψ as the parameter defining the curve as in (9.18.13). Thus the maximum area attainable is

$$\Delta = \int_{\beta}^{2\pi - \beta} \lambda^2 \sin^2 \psi \, d\psi = \tfrac{1}{2}\lambda^2(2\alpha - \sin 2\alpha) \tag{9.18.17}$$

$$= a^2 \frac{2\alpha - \sin 2\alpha}{1 - \cos 2\alpha},$$

a formula already noticed in §6.8.

EXAMPLE 2. To prove that the surface of revolution of given area and enclosing maximum volume is a sphere (cf. Example 4 of §6.13).

Consider an arc $\{x(t), y(t)\}$ in the upper half-plane joining the point A on the positive x-axis to the origin B. The point A is not specified in advance, so we have a variable end-point problem. The volume enclosed by the surface of revolution formed by rotating the curve about the x-axis is

$$V = \int_T^{\overline{T}} - \pi y^2 \dot{x} \, dt, \tag{9.18.18}$$

where $t = T$ at A and $t = \overline{T}$ at B. We wish to maximize (9.18.18) subject to the isoperimetrical condition

$$\int_T^{\overline{T}} 2\pi y \sqrt{(\dot{x}^2 + \dot{y}^2)} \, dt = \Delta, \tag{9.18.19}$$

where Δ is the prescribed area of the surface of revolution. If

$$f^* = -y^2\dot{x} - \lambda y \sqrt{(\dot{x}^2 + \dot{y}^2)} \tag{9.18.20}$$

we have $f^*_{\dot{x}} = C$, and the end-condition at the variable end-point A gives $C = 0$, so

$$-y^2 - \lambda y \frac{\dot{x}}{\sqrt{(\dot{x}^2 + \dot{y}^2)}} = 0, \tag{9.18.21}$$

whence

$$y = -\lambda \cos \psi. \tag{9.18.22}$$

It is clear now that $\lambda > 0$ and that ψ increases from $\pi/2$ to $3\pi/2$. Moreover

$$dx = \cot \psi \, dy = \lambda \cos \psi \, d\psi, \tag{9.18.23}$$

$$x - x_0 = \lambda \sin \psi, \tag{9.18.24}$$

and $x_0 = \lambda$ (since $x = 0$ when $\psi = 3\pi/2$). The curve is the semi-circle

$$x = \lambda(1 + \sin \psi), \quad y = -\lambda \cos \psi, \tag{9.18.25}$$

for $\pi/2 \leqslant \psi \leqslant 3\pi/2$, and the required surface of revolution is a sphere. This surface encloses the maximum volume among all surfaces of revolution of given area Δ, and we readily deduce the isoperimetrical inequality

$$V^2 \leqslant \Delta^3/36\pi. \tag{9.18.26}$$

CHAPTER X

Multiple Integrals

10.1 The analogue of Euler's differential equation

We now consider problems of the Calculus of Variations in which there are several (usually two or three) independent variables and one dependent variable.

In the case of two independent variables we have a bounded domain Δ of the (x, y)-plane whose boundary is a simple closed curve β. We assume that β has a continuously turning tangent, except possibly at a finite number of corners, has no cusps, and cuts any straight line in a finite number of points or intervals. For example, Δ might be the circular disc domain $x^2 + y^2 < 1$, and β the unit circle, $x^2 + y^2 = 1$; or Δ might be the square domain $|x| < 1$, $|y| < 1$, and β the bounding square. A real-valued boundary value function g is prescribed as a function of position on β, and varies continuously on β. We consider the real-valued functions $\varphi(x, y)$ which are continuous in $\Delta + \beta$, belong to a prescribed class κ, and take the values g on β. As in the problems previously discussed, various choices are open to us for the class κ; but in all cases we require that $\varphi(x, y)$ is continuous in $\Delta + \beta$, that the first derivatives φ_x and φ_y exist at least almost everywhere in Δ, and that the elements $(x, y, \varphi, \varphi_x, \varphi_y)$ belong to a certain domain R of the five-fold space. Our object is to determine among these *admissible functions* φ one which minimizes the integral

$$I(\varphi) = \iint_{\Delta} f(x, y, \varphi, \varphi_x, \varphi_y)\, dx\, dy. \tag{10.1.1}$$

The function f is a given function of its five arguments, of a sufficiently simple type: for our immediate purpose it will suffice to assume that f is of class C_2 in R.

Just as in the theory for simple integrals (one independent variable) the theory for multiple integrals (several independent variables) will depend markedly on the choice we make for the class κ. The two choices for κ which we shall consider are as follows.

(i) We may choose for κ the class of functions of class C_2 (i.e. with continuous second derivatives) in a domain $\mathscr{D}$ containing $\Delta + \beta$.

Notice at once that this choice implies a restriction, beyond that of mere continuity already imposed on the function g defining the boundary values on β. In particular the fact that $\varphi \in C_2$ in $\mathscr{D}$ implies the existence of $d\varphi/ds$ on the boundary curve β, where s is the arc-length, whereas the condition that g is continuous on β may be fulfilled when dg/ds does not exist. Perhaps the simplest way of defining the necessary restriction is to say that g must be such that there is at least one function φ_0 which is of class C_2 in $\mathscr{D}$ and which takes the values g on β.

With this choice of κ the derivatives φ_x and φ_y are continuous in the bounded closed region $\Delta + \beta$. Therefore they are bounded in this region, and the integral $I(\varphi)$ has a finite value.

(ii) We may choose for κ the class of functions continuous in $\Delta + \beta$ and of class D_1 in Δ. The class D_1 is the class of functions possessing derivatives φ_x and φ_y which are continuous in Δ, except possibly on a finite number of arcs with continuously turning tangents, or at a finite number of isolated points.

Similar remarks apply to the case of three independent variables. We have a bounded domain Δ of the (x, y, z)-space whose boundary is a simple closed surface β. We assume that β is a surface having two finite principal curvatures at each point, except possibly on a finite number of arcs or at a finite number of isolated points. For example β might be a sphere or an ellipsoid or a cube. A boundary value function g is prescribed as a function of position on β, and varies continuously on β. We consider the functions $\varphi(x, y, z)$ which are continuous in $\Delta + \beta$, belong to a prescribed class κ, and take the values g on β. Our object is to determine among these *admissible functions* φ one which minimizes the integral

$$(10.1.2) \qquad I(\varphi) = \iiint_{\Delta} f(x, y, z, \varphi, \varphi_x, \varphi_y, \varphi_z)\, dx\, dy\, dz.$$

The function $f \in C_2$ in an appropriate domain R of the seven-fold space, and the elements $(x, y, z, \varphi, \varphi_x, \varphi_y, \varphi_z)$ of the admissible functions lie in R.

It is easy to apply the technique previously used for functions of one independent variable. Let us consider the integral (10.1.2), and let us make for κ the simple choice of functions of class C_2 in a domain $\mathscr{D}$ containing $\Delta + \beta$. We readily find a necessary condition for a minimizing function. Let us suppose that $\varphi(x, y, z)$ is a minimizing function (among the admissible functions) for the integral

(10.1.2), and let us consider the one-parameter family of functions $\varphi(x, y, z) + \alpha\eta(x, y, z)$, where $\eta \in C_2$ in $\mathscr{D}$, and $\eta = 0$ on β. Then if

(10.1.3)
$$\psi(\alpha) = \iiint\limits_{\Delta} f(x, y, z, \varphi + \alpha\eta, \varphi_x + \alpha\eta_x, \varphi_y + \alpha\eta_y, \varphi_z + \alpha\eta_z)\, d\tau,$$

where $d\tau$ stands for the volume element $dx\, dy\, dz$, a necessary condition for a minimum is

(10.1.4)
$$\psi'(0) = 0.$$

Now

(10.1.5)
$$\psi'(0) = \iiint\limits_{\Delta} (\eta f_\varphi + \eta_x f_{\varphi_x} + \eta_y f_{\varphi_y} + \eta_z f_{\varphi_z})\, d\tau,$$

where the arguments in the derivatives of f are the elements $(x, y, z, \varphi, \varphi_x, \varphi_y, \varphi_z)$ of the minimizing function φ. Thus

(10.1.6)
$$\psi'(0) = \iiint\limits_{\Delta} \eta\left(f_\varphi - \frac{\partial}{\partial x} f_{\varphi_x} - \frac{\partial}{\partial y} f_{\varphi_y} - \frac{\partial}{\partial z} f_{\varphi_z}\right) d\tau$$
$$+ \iiint\limits_{\Delta} \left\{\frac{\partial}{\partial x}(\eta f_{\varphi_x}) + \frac{\partial}{\partial y}(\eta f_{\varphi_y}) + \frac{\partial}{\partial z}(\eta f_{\varphi_z})\right\} d\tau.$$

The second integral on the right is equal, by Green's lemma, to

(10.1.7)
$$\iint\limits_{\beta} \eta(l f_{\varphi_x} + m f_{\varphi_y} + n f_{\varphi_z})\, dS,$$

where l, m, n are direction cosines of the outward normal to β, and dS is an element of area of β. But (10.1.7) vanishes, since $\eta = 0$ on β, so the condition $\psi'(0) = 0$ implies

(10.1.8)
$$\iiint\limits_{\Delta} \eta\left(f_\varphi - \frac{\partial}{\partial x} f_{\varphi_x} - \frac{\partial}{\partial y} f_{\varphi_y} - \frac{\partial}{\partial z} f_{\varphi_z}\right) d\tau = 0,$$

and this holds for all admissible η. It follows, by the analogue for multiple integrals of Lemma 1 of §2.1, that

(10.1.9)
$$f_\varphi - \frac{\partial}{\partial x} f_{\varphi_x} - \frac{\partial}{\partial y} f_{\varphi_y} - \frac{\partial}{\partial z} f_{\varphi_z} = 0$$

at all points of Δ.

The equation (10.1.9) is a partial differential equation of the second order satisfied by φ: it is linear in the second derivatives of φ. Its status is similar to that of Euler's equation for simple integrals. Notice that the term $\frac{\partial}{\partial x} f_{\varphi_x}$, for example, written *in extenso*, means

$$f_{\varphi_x x} + f_{\varphi_x \varphi}\varphi_x + f_{\varphi_x\varphi_x}\varphi_{xx} + f_{\varphi_x\varphi_y}\varphi_{yx} + f_{\varphi_x\varphi_z}\varphi_{zx}. \tag{10.1.10}$$

For the problem with two independent variables (10.1.1), if

$$\psi(\alpha) = \iint_\Delta f(x, y, \varphi + \alpha\eta, \varphi_x + \alpha\eta_x, \varphi_y + \alpha\eta_y)\, dS, \tag{10.1.11}$$

the formula corresponding to (10.1.6–7) is

$$\psi'(0) = \iint_\Delta \eta\left(f_\varphi - \frac{\partial}{\partial x} f_{\varphi_x} - \frac{\partial}{\partial y} f_{\varphi_y}\right) dS + \int_\beta \eta(lf_{\varphi_x} + mf_{\varphi_y})\, ds. \tag{10.1.12}$$

In the ordinary case, where $\eta = 0$ on β, we obtain at once the differential equation corresponding to (10.1.9), namely

$$f_\varphi - \frac{\partial}{\partial x} f_{\varphi_x} - \frac{\partial}{\partial y} f_{\varphi_y} = 0. \tag{10.1.13}$$

There are exceptional cases in which η does not vanish everywhere on β (cf. §10.12 and §10.13) and then we need the complete formula (10.1.12).

The condition we have found, the differential equation (10.1.9) or (10.1.13) is of course only a necessary condition, but, as in the theory for one independent variable, it may lead in simple special cases to a complete solution of the problem. We may be able to find a solution of the differential equation satisfying the prescribed boundary condition, and then we may be able to construct an *ad hoc* proof that this actually makes the integral a minimum. But this technique is only applicable in very simple cases. As a concrete example consider the integral

$$I(\varphi) = \iint (x^2\varphi_y^2 + y^2\varphi_x^2)\, dx\, dy, \tag{10.1.14}$$

where the integral is over the region $x^2 + y^2 < 1$, and the boundary condition on $x^2 + y^2 = 1$ is $\varphi = x^2$. The differential equation (10.1.13) for a minimizing φ is

$$y^2\varphi_{xx} + x^2\varphi_{yy} = 0, \tag{10.1.15}$$

and the solution taking the value x^2 on the unit circle is

$$\varphi = \tfrac{1}{2}(x^4 - y^4 + 1). \tag{10.1.16}$$

The value of the integral for this function is $\pi/16$, and this is genuinely a minimum. For if $\zeta(x, y) \in C_2$, and $\zeta = 0$ on β, we have

$$\begin{aligned} I(\varphi + \zeta) - I(\varphi) &= \iint (x^2\zeta_y^2 + y^2\zeta_x^2)\, dS \\ &\quad + 4\iint (y^2x^3\zeta_x - x^2y^3\zeta_y)\, dS, \end{aligned} \tag{10.1.17}$$

where dS stands for the element of area $dx\, dy$. The last integral on the right in (10.1.17) is

(10.1.18)

$$4\iint_{\Delta} \left\{\frac{\partial}{\partial x}(y^2x^3\zeta) - \frac{\partial}{\partial y}(x^2y^3\zeta)\right\} dS = 4\int_\beta x^2y^2\zeta(y\, dx + x\, dy),$$

and this vanishes since $\zeta = 0$ on β. Therefore

$$I(\varphi + \zeta) > I(\varphi) \tag{10.1.19}$$

unless ζ vanishes identically, and this completes the proof that (10.1.16) actually minimizes I.

10.2 Direct methods

In the preceding section we proved the existence of a minimizing function in a simple special case by an *ad hoc* argument of a type we have sometimes used in the theory for one independent variable. But in general the line of development of the theory for multiple integrals diverges sharply from that for simple integrals. In particular, we have no analogue for multiple integrals of the fundamental sufficiency theorem for simple integrals. One new feature in the theory for multiple integrals is the important part taken by the so-called *direct methods*. In the direct methods we start, in general, from a boundary value problem of partial differential equations, and this problem is replaced by an equivalent extremum problem in the Calculus of Variations. This procedure is in a sense the opposite to that familiar in the classical theory for simple integrals, where we normally start from an extremum problem and derive a differential equation satisfied by the minimizing function.

A famous and important example of this procedure occurs in potential theory. We are given a domain Δ (in the plane or in space) with boundary β, and the problem is to find a *potential function* or *harmonic function* in Δ (i.e. a solution of Laplace's equation $\nabla^2\varphi = 0$) taking the prescribed values g on β. This problem is known as *Dirichlet's problem.* Let us consider (in the case of three independent variables) *Dirichlet's integral*

$$D(\varphi) = D_\Delta(\varphi) = \iiint_\Delta (\varphi_x^2 + \varphi_y^2 + \varphi_z^2)\, d\tau, \tag{10.2.1}$$

where the functions φ admitted to competition at this stage are of class C_2 in a domain $\mathscr{D}$ containing $\Delta + \beta$, and take the prescribed values g on β. As we have noticed already, the boundary value function g must be of a suitably restricted type. A minimizing function must satisfy (10.1.9), which in this case takes the form

$$\nabla^2\varphi \equiv \varphi_{xx} + \varphi_{yy} + \varphi_{zz} = 0. \tag{10.2.2}$$

If therefore a minimizing function for (10.2.1) exists it must be a harmonic function taking the values g on β. (We shall see in the next section that if such a function exists it is unique.) Thus the minimizing function for (10.2.1) is also the solution of the boundary value problem proposed.

Now the integrand in (10.2.1) is non-negative, so $D(\varphi)$ is bounded below; let us denote the infimum (greatest lower bound) by m. If there is a function φ such that $D(\varphi) = m$, this function provides the solution of the boundary value problem. The early workers in this field, notably Gauss and Kelvin, assumed that the infimum is always attained, and they deduced that in consequence the boundary value problem must always have a solution. The same reasoning was used by Dirichlet, and Riemann, who was an ardent disciple of Dirichlet, used the idea extensively and fruitfully, and gave it the name of *Dirichlet's principle.* Dirichlet's principle asserts that there must be a function φ such that $D(\varphi) = m$, and that this same function must be the unique harmonic function taking the prescribed values g on β.

But in fact, as Weierstrass pointed out, the crucial assumption made in Dirichlet's principle, that the infimum is actually attained, cannot be made without further investigation. We have met many problems (cf. §1.5) in which an integral $\int_X^{\bar{X}} F(x, y, y')\, dx$, where

$y = \varphi(x)$, is bounded below for all admissible φ, but where there is no function φ for which $I(\varphi) = m$. The examples previously noticed were of problems with one independent variable, but the same phenomenon appears in problems with several independent variables, as is shown by the following simple example. Consider the problem of finding a function $\varphi(x, y)$ of class D_1 in Δ, where Δ is the domain $x^2 + y^2 < 1$, such that the surface $z = \varphi(x, y)$ passes through the unit circle in the plane $z = 0$, and through the point V (0, 0, 1) on the z-axis, and has minimum area. Thus $\varphi = 0$ on $x^2 + y^2 = 1$, and $\varphi(0, 0) = 1$. The infimum for the area is the area of the unit circle itself, namely π, and we can find surfaces with area exceeding π by as little as we please. For example, consider the surface consisting of the annulus in the plane $z = 0$ between the circles $r = \varepsilon$ and $r = 1$ (where $r = \sqrt{(x^2 + y^2)}$) and the cone whose generators join the points of the circle $r = \varepsilon$ to the vertex V. The area of this surface is

$$\pi\{1 - \varepsilon^2 + \varepsilon\sqrt{(1 + \varepsilon^2)}\} < \pi(1 + \varepsilon). \tag{10.2.3}$$

The area exceeds the infimum value π by as little as we please, but there is no surface for which the infimum is actually attained.

10.3 Dirichlet's principle, elementary theory

In the case of three independent variables we have a domain Δ inside a closed surface β of sufficiently simple type. The functions φ considered in this section are of class C_2 in a domain $\mathscr{D}$ containing $\Delta + \beta$, and they take the values g on β, where g is suitably restricted. We seek a function φ which minimizes

$$D(\varphi) = \iiint_{\Delta} (\varphi_x^2 + \varphi_y^2 + \varphi_z^2)\, dz. \tag{10.3.1}$$

If such a function exists it must be, as we have seen, the harmonic function which is regular in Δ and which takes the values g on the bounding surface β.

We easily establish the two results following:

(i) If φ exists such that $D(\varphi) = m$, it is unique. For suppose on the contrary that there is another function $\varphi + \psi$ such that $D(\varphi + \psi) = m$, where $\psi \in C_2$ in $\mathscr{D}$, and ψ vanishes on β. Now

(10.3.2)

$$D(\varphi + \psi) - D(\varphi) = D(\psi) + 2\iiint_{\Delta} (\varphi_x\psi_x + \varphi_y\psi_y + \varphi_z\psi_z)\, d\tau.$$

The last integral on the right is equal, by Green's theorem, to

$$(10.3.3) \qquad \iint_{\beta} \psi \frac{\partial \varphi}{\partial n}\, dS - \iiint_{\Delta} \psi \nabla^2 \varphi \, d\tau,$$

where $\partial\varphi/\partial n$ is the rate of change of φ along the outward normal to β. The first integral in (10.3.3) vanishes because $\psi = 0$ on β, and the second vanishes because, as we have seen in the preceding paragraph, $\nabla^2\varphi = 0$ in Δ. Thus, since $D(\varphi + \psi) = D(\varphi) = m$, we have

$$(10.3.4) \qquad D(\psi) = 0,$$

and therefore ψ must be constant in Δ. But in fact ψ must vanish everywhere in Δ, since it is continuous in $\Delta + \beta$ and vanishes on the boundary. Thus if a function φ exists which makes $D(\varphi) = m$, it is unique.

(ii) If φ exists such that $\nabla^2\varphi = 0$ in $\mathscr{D}$ and $\varphi = g$ on β, then $D(\varphi) = m$. For let $\varphi + \psi$ be any other function of class C_2 in $\mathscr{D}$, with $\psi = 0$ on β. Then, by the argument used in (i),

$$(10.3.5) \qquad D(\varphi + \psi) = D(\varphi) + D(\psi) > D(\varphi)$$

unless ψ is identically zero. It follows that $D(\varphi) = m$. For if $D(\varphi)$ had a value greater than m there would exist a function $\varphi + \psi$ such that $D(\varphi + \psi)$ had a value between $D(\varphi)$ and m. For such a function $D(\varphi + \psi) < D(\varphi)$, and we know from (10.3.5) that no such function exists.

Similar remarks hold for Dirichlet's problem for two independent variables. In this case Δ is a domain of the (x, y)-plane bounded by the simple closed curve β: a function g, of a suitably restricted type, is prescribed on β. The integral to be discussed is now

$$(10.3.6) \qquad D(\varphi) = \iint_{\Delta} (\varphi_x^2 + \varphi_y^2)\, dS,$$

and the functions φ admitted to competition are of class C_2 in a domain $\mathscr{D}$ containing $\Delta + \beta$, and take the values g on β. The argument is precisely similar to that just exhibited for the problem with three independent variables. If the infimum m of $D(\varphi)$ is attained, it is attained by a harmonic function taking the prescribed values on the boundary β. Further (i) the minimizing function, if it exists, is unique, and (ii) if, on the other hand, a harmonic function φ exists taking the prescribed values on β, then $D(\varphi) = m$.

10.4 Dirichlet's principle for functions of two variables, introductory remarks

The theory is less simple if we lighten the restrictions previously imposed.

Our first impulse is to replace the choice (i) for κ (§10.1) by the choice (ii): then the admissible functions are functions continuous in $\Delta + \beta$, of class D_1 in Δ, and taking the values g on β. But in fact if we lighten the restrictions in this way we go too far: without some further modification of the conditions, Dirichlet's principle does not hold.

The first point to notice is that, unless we impose some further condition, Dirichlet's integral may diverge. The integral is finite for any closed region F contained in Δ. Consider a monotone increasing sequence $\{F_n\}$ of closed regions converging to Δ,

$$F_n \subset F_{n+1}, \qquad F_n \to \Delta. \tag{10.4.1}$$

Then, for any admissible φ, the sequence $D_{F_n}(\varphi)$ increases steadily with n, and therefore it either tends to a limit or it tends to $+\infty$. If the sequence $D_{F_n}(\varphi)$ tends to a limit, this limit is, by definition, the Dirichlet integral $D(\varphi)$; but in some cases the sequence tends to infinity and Dirichlet's integral for Δ does not exist.

(We use $D_\delta(\varphi)$ to denote Dirichlet's integral over the region δ,

$$D_\delta(\varphi) = \iint_\delta (\varphi_x^2 + \varphi_y^2)\, dS. \tag{10.4.2}$$

The symbol $D(\varphi)$, without a suffix, means $D_\Delta(\varphi)$. Occasionally we write $D_K(\varphi)$, where K is a simple closed curve, for the integral over the interior of K. More generally, we sometimes write $\iint_K f(x, y)\, dx\, dy$ to denote the integral over the interior of K.)

The solution of Dirichlet's *problem* when β is a circle is well known in the theory of Fourier series. Let us take polar coordinates (r, θ) in the plane, let β be the unit circle $r = 1$, and let $g(\theta)$ be the prescribed boundary value. Then g is a continuous function of θ with period 2π. Let the Fourier series for g be

$$g(\theta) \sim \tfrac{1}{2}a_0 + \sum_{n=1}^{\infty} (a_n \cos n\theta + b_n \sin n\theta). \tag{10.4.3}$$

The series does not necessarily converge. But if we consider the function

(10.4.4) $$\psi(r, \theta) = \tfrac{1}{2}a_0 + \sum_{n=1}^{\infty} r^n(a_n \cos n\theta + b_n \sin n\theta)$$

for $0 \leqslant r < 1$, the series on the right is convergent at each point inside the unit circle, and the function $\psi(r, \theta)$ has the following properties: (i) $\psi(r, \theta)$ is a harmonic function, (ii) $\psi(r, \theta)$ tends uniformly to $g(\theta)$ as $r \to 1$. It follows that $\psi(r, \theta) \to g(\theta_0)$ when the point (r, θ) approaches the point $(1, \theta_0)$ from inside the circle in any way. Therefore $\psi(r, \theta)$ is the solution of Dirichlet's problem for the unit circle.

Let us now return to the statement made above, that Dirichlet's *principle* is not valid without further modification. The solution of the boundary value problem for the unit circle is given by (10.4.4), but it may happen that the extremum problem for Dirichlet's integral has no solution. If C_ρ is the circle of radius ρ about the origin we have

(10.4.5) $$D_{C_\rho}(\psi) = \pi \sum_{n=1}^{\infty} n(a_n^2 + b_n^2)\rho^{2n}$$

If $D(\psi)$ is to exist, we must have a finite limit for $D_{C_\rho}(\psi)$ as ρ tends to 1 from below, and this limit exists if and only if the series

(10.4.6) $$\pi \sum_{n=1}^{\infty} n(a_n^2 + b_n^2)$$

is convergent.

Now the series (10.4.6) may diverge, even though $g(\theta)$ is continuous. This is shown by the following example, due to Hadamard. Let the boundary value on the unit circle be given by the uniformly convergent series

(10.4.7) $$g(\theta) = \sum_{\mu=1}^{\infty} \frac{1}{\mu^2} \sin \mu!\,\theta.$$

In this example the boundary value problem has the solution

(10.4.8) $$\sum_{\mu=1}^{\infty} \frac{r^{\mu!}}{\mu^2} \sin \mu!\,\theta,$$

whereas the formula (10.4.6) yields

(10.4.9) $$\sum_{\mu=1}^{\infty} \frac{\mu!}{\mu^4},$$

which is divergent. The extremum problem has no solution.

Thus, as we have said, Dirichlet's principle is not valid until we impose some further restriction on the function g defining the boundary values. We need a restriction less drastic than that imposed in §10.1, but stronger than that of mere continuity. The assumption we shall make is that *there exists at least one admissible function for which Dirichlet's integral is finite. When the prescribed boundary values conform to this condition, Dirichlet's principle is valid.* Explicitly, let φ_0 be a function which is continuous in $\Delta + \beta$ and of class D_1 in Δ and for which Dirichlet's integral is finite. We consider the class of all functions φ which are continuous in $\Delta + \beta$, which are of class D_1 in Δ, and which take the same values g as φ_0 on β: these are the *admissible functions.* Let the infimum of $D(\varphi)$ for the admissible functions (which we know to be finite) be denoted by m. Then the problem of minimizing $D(\varphi)$ in the class of admissible functions has a unique solution ψ for which $D(\psi) = m$, and this solution ψ is identical with the unique solution of the boundary value problem, i.e. the problem of finding a function which is harmonic in Δ and continuous in $\Delta + \beta$, and which takes the same prescribed boundary values on β.

To establish this result we proceed in three stages as follows. First we establish some properties of harmonic functions that we shall need in the sequel. Then we prove Dirichlet's principle for the special case of a circular area. Finally, using an ingenious attack due in principle to Poincaré, we establish Dirichlet's principle for the general case.

10.5 Harmonic functions

Laplace's differential equation

$$\nabla^2\varphi \equiv \varphi_{xx} + \varphi_{yy} = 0 \tag{10.5.1}$$

is of fundamental importance in potential theory. The solutions of Laplace's equation of class C_2 (i.e. possessing continuous second derivatives) are called *potential functions* or *harmonic functions.* We now consider some properties of harmonic functions.

LEMMA 1. *The mean value property.* The function $u(x, y)$ is harmonic in a domain G, and P is any point of G. The circle C lies in G and P is its centre. Then the mean value of u on C is equal to the value of u at P.

It is sometimes convenient to write $u(Z)$ instead of $u(x, y)$ for the value of u at the point Z whose coordinates are (x, y). The mean value property can be expressed in the form

$$u(P) = \frac{1}{2\pi}\int_0^{2\pi} u(Q)\, d\theta, \tag{10.5.2}$$

where Q is a variable point on C, and θ is the inclination of PQ to a fixed line PA.

One method of proof depends on Green's formula

$$\int_C \frac{\partial u}{\partial r}\, ds = \iint\limits_C \nabla^2 u\, dS, \tag{10.5.3}$$

where r is the radial distance from P. Since u is harmonic

$$\int_C \frac{\partial u}{\partial r}\, d\theta = 0 \tag{10.5.4}$$

whence

$$\frac{\partial}{\partial r}\left(\int_{C_r} u\, d\theta\right) = 0, \tag{10.5.5}$$

where C_r is the circle of radius r about P. Thus the mean value of u on the circle C_r is independent of r, and the fact that its value must be $u(P)$ follows by letting r tend to zero.

Another proof, due in principle to Rayleigh, is as follows. Let $u = f(r, \theta)$, where P is taken as origin for the polar coordinates. Since $f(r, \theta)$ is harmonic, so is $f(r, \theta + \alpha)$, where α is any constant, and so also is $v = \frac{1}{2\pi}\int_0^{2\pi} f(r, \theta + \alpha)\, d\alpha$. Thus we get a new harmonic function if we replace the value of u at any point Q by the mean of its values on the circle through Q with P as centre. We thus obtain a harmonic function which is a function of r only, and the only such function (without singularity at P) is a constant. Thus the mean value of u on all the circles with P as centre is the same, and this value is the value of v at P, namely $u(P)$.

COROLLARY 1. If C is any circle with P as centre there is a point Q on C at which $u(Q) = u(P)$.

COROLLARY 2. The mean value of u over any circular disc with P as centre is also equal to $u(P)$. Indeed, the mean value property for the circles implies that for the discs, and conversely.

LEMMA 2. This is the converse of Lemma 1. If u is continuous in G, and has the mean value property for all points P of G and all circles with P as centre and of sufficiently small radius, then u has derivatives of all orders and is harmonic.

The mean value property for the circles implies that for the discs. Let $P(x, y)$ be a point of G, and $P'(x + h, y)$ a neighbouring point of G. Let C, C' be the circles of radius r with P, P' as centres, where r is so small that these circles lie in G. Then

$$u(x + h, y) - u(x, y) = \frac{1}{\pi r^2}\left(\iint_{C'} u\,dS - \iint_{C} u\,dS\right) \tag{10.5.6}$$

$$= \frac{1}{\pi r^2}\left(\iint_{L'} u\,dS - \iint_{L} u\,dS\right)$$

$$= \frac{1}{\pi r^2}\left(\iint_{L'+T} u\,dS - \iint_{L+T} u\,dS\right)$$

where L and L' are the lunes shown in Fig. 10.5, and T represents the

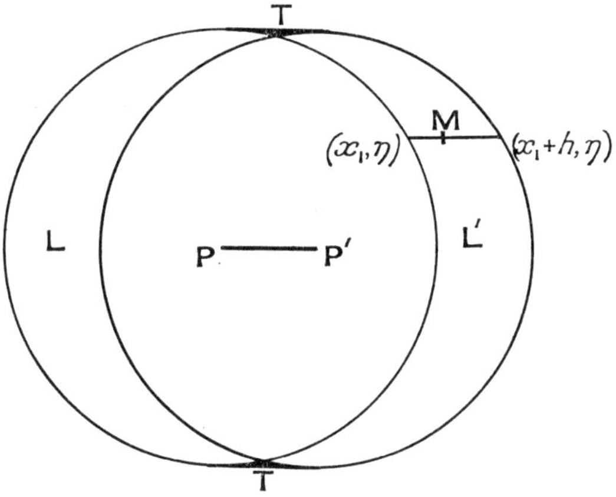

Fig. 10.5

two triangular areas. Now

$$\iint_{L'+T} u\,dS = \int_{y-r}^{y+r} d\eta \int_{x_1}^{x_1+h} u\,dx = h\int_{y-r}^{y+r} u(M)\,d\eta, \tag{10.5.7}$$

where M is a point $(x_1 + \theta h, \eta)$ with $0 < \theta < 1$. Treating the integral over $L + T$ in the same way, and letting $h \to 0$, we have

$$\frac{u(x + h, y) - u(x, y)}{h} \to \frac{1}{\pi r^2}\int_C u\,dy, \tag{10.5.8}$$

so u_x exists, and its value is $\dfrac{1}{\pi r^2}\displaystyle\int_C u\,dy$. The existence of u_y is proved similarly. The first derivatives u_x and u_y exist at all points of G.

By Green's formula

$$\int_C u\,dy = \iint_C u_x\,dx\,dy, \tag{10.5.9}$$

and therefore, combining (10.5.8) and (10.5.9)

$$u_x = \frac{1}{\pi r^2}\iint_C u_x\,dx\,dy. \tag{10.5.10}$$

Thus u_x has the same mean value property as u. The derivative u_y also has the same mean value property. It is now clear that u has derivatives of all orders.

To prove that u is harmonic, we now know that (10.5.5) is true, and this implies, as in (10.5.3),

$$\iint_C \nabla^2 u\,dS = 0, \tag{10.5.11}$$

where the integral is taken over the interior of any circle in G. Hence $\nabla^2 u = 0$ at all points of G.

LEMMA 3. The function $u(x, y)$ is harmonic in the domain G, and F is a bounded closed region lying in G. If P is a point of F

$$|u_x(P)| \leqslant 2\omega/\pi r, \tag{10.5.12}$$

where ω is the oscillation of u in F, and r is the distance of P from the boundary of F (i.e. r is inf $|PQ|$, where Q is a point of the boundary of F, and $|PQ|$ denotes the distance from P to Q).

Let C_r be the circle of radius r with P as centre, and let the maximum and minimum values of u in F be H and h. If v denotes the harmonic function

$$v = u - \tfrac{1}{2}(H + h) \tag{10.5.13}$$

then

$$|v| \leqslant \tfrac{1}{2}(H - h) = \tfrac{1}{2}\omega. \tag{10.5.14}$$

Now, recalling (10.5.8), we have

$$u_x(P) = v_x(P) = \frac{1}{\pi r^2}\int_{C_r} v\,dy = \frac{1}{\pi r}\int_0^{2\pi} v\cos\theta\,d\theta, \tag{10.5.15}$$

and therefore

$$|u_x(P)| \leqslant \frac{1}{\pi r}\int_0^{2\pi} |v||\cos\theta|\,d\theta \leqslant \frac{1}{\pi r}\cdot\frac{\omega}{2}\cdot 4 = \frac{2\omega}{\pi r}. \tag{10.5.16}$$

LEMMA 4. A sequence $\{u_n\}$ of functions harmonic in the domain G converges to a limit function u, and the convergence is uniform in every closed sub-set of G. Then

(i) u is harmonic,

(ii) $(u_n)_x$, $(u_n)_y$ converge to u_x, u_y, and the convergence is uniform in any closed region F of G,

(10.5.17) (iii) $$\underline{\lim}\, D_G(u_n) \geqslant D_G(u).$$

To prove (i), let P be a point of G, and let C_r be the circle of radius r about P: r is so small that C_r lies in G. Then, by Lemma 1,

(10.5.18) $$u_n(P) = \frac{1}{2\pi}\int_{C_r} u_n \, d\theta.$$

Hence

(10.5.19) $$u(P) = \lim_{n\to\infty} \frac{1}{2\pi}\int_{C_r} u_n \, d\theta,$$

and since the convergence is uniform on C_r (which is a closed sub-set of G)

(10.5.20) $$u(P) = \frac{1}{2\pi}\int_{C_r} (\lim u_n)\, d\theta = \frac{1}{2\pi}\int_{C_r} u \, d\theta.$$

This holds for all points P of G and for all (sufficiently small) values of r, and the fact that u is harmonic now follows from Lemma 2.

To prove (ii), let F_0 be a closed region such that $F \subset F_0 \subset G$, and such that the distance between the disjoint closed sets F and the boundary of F_0 is a positive number r. (The distance between two sets α and β is defined as $\inf |AB|$, where A is a point of α and B is a point of β. The distance between two disjoint closed sets (i.e. two closed sets with no common point), of which at least one is bounded, is always positive.) Let ω_n be the oscillation of the harmonic function $u_n - u$ in F_0. Then, if P is a point of F, we have, by Lemma 3,

(10.5.21) $$|u_{nx}(P) - u_x(P)| \leqslant 2\omega_n/\pi r,$$

where u_{nx} is written for $(u_n)_x$. It follows that u_{nx} converges uniformly to u_x in F, since r is independent of the position of P in F, and $\omega_n \to 0$ as $n \to \infty$. Similar statements hold for the derivatives with respect to y.

To prove (iii), expressing the lower semi-continuity of $D(u)$, let F

be a closed region of G. Since the derivatives of u_n converge uniformly in F to the derivatives of u

$$D_F(u) = \lim_{n\to\infty} D_F(u_n). \tag{10.5.22}$$

But

$$\lim_{n\to\infty} D_F(u_n) \leqslant \underline{\lim}\, D_G(u_n), \tag{10.5.23}$$

and from these two results

$$D_F(u) \leqslant \underline{\lim}\, D_G(u_n). \tag{10.5.24}$$

The result stated follows by letting F tend to G.

COROLLARY. If G is convex we can use convex sets throughout. Thus, u is harmonic if the convergence of the sequence $\{u_n\}$ is uniform in every convex closed region of G, and then u_{nx}, u_{ny} converge uniformly to u_x, u_y in every convex closed region F of G. (A set is convex if, when P and Q are any two points of the set, all points of the linear segment PQ belong to the set.)

LEMMA 5. The function $u(x, y)$ is harmonic in the domain G, and F is a bounded convex closed region of G. If P and Q are two points of F

$$|u(P)| - |u(Q)| \leqslant C\sqrt{\{D_G(u)\}}, \tag{10.5.25}$$

where C is a constant depending only on F (not on the positions of P and Q in F).

Let h be a positive number less than the distance between F and the boundary of G, and let l be the diameter of F. (The diameter of a set is defined as sup $|AB|$, where A and B are two points of the set.) Then, if C_h is the circle of radius h about P,

$$u_x(P) = \frac{1}{\pi h^2}\iint_{C_h} u_x\, dS, \tag{10.5.26}$$

whence, by Schwarz's inequality,

$$u_x^2(P) \leqslant \frac{1}{\pi h^2}\iint_{C_h} u_x^2\, dS. \tag{10.5.27}$$

Hence, adding the analogous result for u_y,

$$u_x^2(P) + u_y^2(P) \leqslant \frac{1}{\pi h^2} D_{C_h}(u) \leqslant \frac{1}{\pi h^2} D_G(u). \tag{10.5.28}$$

Now

$$u(P) = u(Q) + \int_Q^P u_x\, dx + u_y\, dy, \tag{10.5.29}$$

where the line-integral is taken along the straight line QP (which lies in F). Hence, remembering $|PQ| \leqslant l$, we have

(10.5.30) $$|u(P)| \leqslant |u(Q)| + \frac{l}{h\sqrt{\pi}} \sqrt{\{D_G(u)\}},$$

and (10.5.25) follows.

LEMMA 6. A sequence (u_n) of functions harmonic in the domain G is such that $D_G(u_n)$ tends to zero as n tends to infinity, and F is a convex closed region of G. If for each value of n there is a point P_n (depending on n) of F such that $u_n(P_n) \to 0$, then $u_n \to 0$ uniformly in F.

The result follows immediately from Lemma 5. If P is a given point of F

(10.5.31) $$|u_n(P)| \leqslant |u_n(P_n)| + C\sqrt{\{D_G(u_n)\}},$$

so $|u_n(P)|$ tends to zero uniformly in F.

COROLLARY. If n and p are positive integers, and there is a point P_{np} of F (depending on n and p) such that $u_p(P_{np}) - u_n(P_{np})$ tends to zero as n and p tend to infinity, then $u_p - u_n$ tends to zero uniformly in F as n and p tend to infinity.

10.6 Proof of Dirichlet's principle for the circle

Let us take the unit circle $r = 1$ as the boundary β, so that Δ is the region $r < 1$, and let the Fourier series of the prescribed boundary function g be

(10.6.1) $$g \sim \tfrac{1}{2}a_0 + \sum_{n=1}^{\infty} (a_n \cos n\theta + b_n \sin n\theta).$$

As we have noticed (§10.4) this series may not converge, but for $r < 1$ the series

(10.6.2) $$u = \tfrac{1}{2}a_0 + \sum_{r=1}^{\infty} r^n(a_n \cos n\theta + b_n \sin n\theta)$$

converges and u is a harmonic function taking the values g on β.

Now let $u + \zeta$ be any admissible function other than u for which $D(u + \zeta)$ is finite: we know by hypothesis that such a function exists. Now $\zeta = 0$ on β, and

(10.6.3) $$D(u + \zeta) = D(u) + D(\zeta) + 2R(u, \zeta),$$

where

(10.6.4) $$R(u, \zeta) = \iint_{\Delta} (u_x\zeta_x + u_y\zeta_y)\, dS.$$

If we could transform the second member of (10.6.4) by the formula of Green and Stokes, as in §10.3, we could prove that $R(u, \zeta) = 0$, and it would follow that

$$D(u + \zeta) - D(u) = D(\zeta) > 0. \tag{10.6.5}$$

But this method is no longer available, since Green's formula may not be applicable in the whole domain Δ. However, we can surmount the difficulty as follows.

Let u_N denote the *harmonic polynomial*

$$u_N = \tfrac{1}{2}a_0 + \sum_{n=1}^{N} r^n(a_n \cos n\theta + b_n \sin n\theta), \tag{10.6.6}$$

and let

$$\rho = \rho(N) = u + \zeta - u_N. \tag{10.6.7}$$

Then

$$D(u + \zeta) = D(u_N + \rho) = D(u_N) + D(\rho) + 2R(u_N, \rho), \tag{10.6.8}$$

and

$$R(u_N, \rho) = \int_\beta \rho \frac{\partial u_N}{\partial r}\, d\theta - \iint_\Delta \rho\, \nabla^2 u_N\, dS. \tag{10.6.9}$$

The second integral on the right vanishes because u_N is harmonic. The first vanishes also, because (since $\zeta = 0$ on β) $\rho = u - u_N$ on β, and the Fourier series for $u - u_N$ on β contains only terms $\cos n\theta$ and $\sin n\theta$ for $n > N$, whereas $\partial u_N/\partial r$ contains only a finite number of terms $\cos n\theta$ and $\sin n\theta$ with $n \leqslant N$. Thus

$$R(u_N, \rho) = 0, \tag{10.6.10}$$

and

$$D(u + \zeta) = D(u_N) + D(\rho) \geqslant D(u_N). \tag{10.6.11}$$

In Δ the harmonic polynomials u_N converge to the harmonic function u with the boundary values g, and the convergence is uniform in every closed region F of Δ. Hence, by Lemma 4(iii) of §10.5,

$$\underline{\lim}\, D(u_N) \geqslant D(u), \tag{10.6.12}$$

and therefore

$$D(u + \zeta) \geqslant D(u). \tag{10.6.13}$$

Thus the minimizing property of u for Dirichlet's integral is established, and it follows, as in §10.3(ii), that $D(u) = m$.

We now prove uniqueness: there is no other admissible function $u + \zeta$ for which Dirichlet's integral had the value m. For if $u + \zeta$ is admissible, so is $u + \lambda\zeta$ for all real values of λ, and therefore

(10.6.14) $$D(u + \lambda\zeta) \geqslant m.$$

Hence (since $D(u) = m$)

(10.6.15) $$2\lambda R(u, \zeta) + \lambda^2 D(\zeta) \geqslant 0,$$

and since this holds for both positive and negative values of λ,

(10.6.16) $$R(u, \zeta) = 0.$$

Thus

(10.6.17) $$D(u + \zeta) = D(u) + D(\zeta) > m$$

unless ζ vanishes identically, and this completes the proof of Dirichlet's principle for the unit circle with its centre at O. The truth of Dirichlet's principle for any circle follows easily.

10.7 Dirichlet's principle in the plane

We now turn to the third stage of the argument, the proof of Dirichlet's principle, as enunciated in §10.4, for a general bounded domain. We have seen that the principle is valid if the boundary curve β is a circle.

Now since $D(\varphi)$ for the admissible functions φ has a finite lower bound m, there exists a *minimizing sequence* of admissible functions $\{\varphi_n\}$, i.e. a sequence such that $D(\varphi_n) \to m$ as $n \to \infty$.

We may be tempted to expect that such a sequence will converge to a limit function which is the harmonic function taking the prescribed values as the boundary. If this were true the proof of Dirichlet's principle would be easy: but the expectation is not fulfilled, as is shown by the following simple example.

Let β be the unit circle $r = 1$, and let $g = 0$ at all points of the circle. The solution of Dirichlet's problem, i.e. the function u which is harmonic inside the circle, and which takes the value zero on the circle, is identically zero. The infimum for Dirichlet's integral is zero, and this value is attained by u, $D(u) = m = 0$. Now consider the sequence of admissible functions $\{\varphi_n\}$, where, for $n > 1$,

$$(10.7.1)\qquad \begin{cases} \varphi_n = 1, & \text{if } 0 \leqslant r \leqslant \dfrac{1}{n^2}, \\[2ex] \quad = -\dfrac{\log r}{\log n} - 1, & \text{if } \dfrac{1}{n^2} \leqslant r \leqslant \dfrac{1}{n}, \\[2ex] \quad = 0, & \text{if } \dfrac{1}{n} \leqslant r \leqslant 1. \end{cases}$$

Then

$$(10.7.2)\qquad D(\varphi_n) = \frac{2\pi}{\log n},$$

and $D(\varphi_n) \to m$ as $n \to \infty$. But φ_n tends to the limit function Φ which has the value 1 at the origin and the value zero elsewhere. The limit function is not identical with u: it is not even an admissible function. A minimizing sequence $\{\varphi_n)$ does not necessarily yield the solution of Dirichlet's problem by merely letting n tend to infinity.

We now prove that if $\{\varphi_n\}$ is a minimizing sequence, and n, p are two positive integers, then

$$(10.7.3)\qquad D(\varphi_p - \varphi_n) \to 0$$

as n and p tend to infinity. Explicitly, given $\varepsilon > 0$, there is an integer $N(\varepsilon)$ such that

$$(10.7.4)\qquad D(\varphi_p - \varphi_n) < \varepsilon$$

if p and n are both greater than N. To prove this, consider Dirichlet's integral for the admissible function $\varphi_n + \lambda(\varphi_p - \varphi_n)$. We have

$$(10.7.5)\qquad D\{\varphi_n + \lambda(\varphi_p - \varphi_n)\} \geqslant m,$$

whence

$$(10.7.6)\qquad \lambda^2 D(\varphi_p - \varphi_n) + 2\lambda R(\varphi_n, \varphi_p - \varphi_n) + [D(\varphi_n) - m] \geqslant 0,$$

where (as in §10.6)

$$(10.7.7)\qquad R(\psi, \chi) = \iint\limits_{\Delta} (\psi_x \chi_x + \psi_y \chi_y)\, dS.$$

Now (10.7.6) holds for all real values of λ, the quadratic form is a positive semi-definite form, and therefore

$$(10.7.8)\qquad |R(\varphi_n, \varphi_p - \varphi_n)| \leqslant \sqrt{\{D(\varphi_p - \varphi_n)[D(\varphi_n) - m]\}}.$$

But

$$(10.7.9)\qquad D(\varphi_p - \varphi_n) = R(\varphi_p, \varphi_p - \varphi_n) - R(\varphi_n, \varphi_p - \varphi_n),$$

and therefore, from (10.7.8) and the inequality obtained by interchanging n and p, we have

(10.7.10) $$D(\varphi_p - \varphi_n) \leqslant \sqrt{D(\varphi_p - \varphi_n)}\,(\sqrt{D(\varphi_n) - m} + \sqrt{D(\varphi_p) - m}).$$

Hence

(10.7.11) $$\sqrt{D(\varphi_p - \varphi_n)} \leqslant \sqrt{D(\varphi_n) - m} + \sqrt{D(\varphi_p) - m},$$

and therefore $D(\varphi_p - \varphi_n)$ tends to zero as n and p tend to infinity.

10.8 The triangle inequality

If λ and μ are two functions of class D_1 in Δ

(10.8.1) $$\sqrt{D(\lambda + \mu)} \leqslant \sqrt{D(\lambda)} + \sqrt{D(\mu)}.$$

To prove this, we notice that (10.8.1) is true if and only if

(10.8.2) $$D(\lambda) + D(\mu) + 2R(\lambda, \mu) \leqslant D(\lambda) + D(\mu) + 2\sqrt{\{D(\lambda)D(\mu)\}}$$

and this follows from Schwarz's inequality.

Let φ, ψ, χ be admissible functions. If in (10.8.1) we put $\lambda = \varphi - \psi$, $\mu = \psi - \chi$, we have

(10.8.3) $$\sqrt{D(\varphi - \chi)} \leqslant \sqrt{D(\varphi - \psi)} + \sqrt{D(\psi - \chi)}$$

which we may speak of as the *triangle inequality*. If we think of the admissible functions as points in a function space, we can give the space a metrical structure by defining a *distance function* $d(\varphi, \psi)$ by the formula

(10.8.4) $$d(\varphi, \psi) = \sqrt{D(\varphi - \psi)},$$

where φ, ψ are any two admissible functions. It is easy to see that $d(\varphi, \psi)$ has the properties characteristic of a distance. Thus

(10.8.5) $$d(\varphi, \psi) \geqslant 0,$$

and $d(\varphi, \psi) = 0$ if and only if $\varphi = \psi$. The distance function d is symmetric

(10.8.6) $$d(\varphi, \psi) = d(\psi, \varphi),$$

and, as we have seen, it satisfies the triangle inequality

(10.8.7) $$d(\varphi, \chi) \leqslant d(\varphi, \psi) + d(\psi, \chi).$$

(We notice that to establish the triangle inequality it would suffice to prove (10.8.1) for functions λ and μ which vanish on β.)

10.9 The smoothing process

Let $\{\varphi_n\}$ be a minimizing sequence of admissible functions, $D(\varphi_n) \to m$ as $n \to \infty$. As we have seen, this sequence does not necessarily converge to the solution of the boundary value problem, and our immediate purpose is to replace it by a minimizing sequence which does converge to this solution, at least in some region of Δ. To achieve this end we use a technique introduced by Poincaré. Let K be a fixed circle lying in Δ, and let ψ_n be the function defined as follows: $\psi_n = \varphi_n$ in the part of Δ outside K, and $\psi_n = u_n$ inside K, where u_n is the harmonic function taking the same values as φ_n on K. We are, as it were, smoothing out φ_n when we replace it by ψ_n. We know that u_n exists inside K, because we have already established Dirichlet's principle for the circle, and $D_K(u_n) \leqslant D_K(\varphi_n)$. Therefore $D(\psi_n) \leqslant D(\varphi_n)$, and it follows that $\{\psi_n\}$ is also a minimizing sequence. It follows, as in §10.7, that $D(\psi_p - \psi_n)$ tends to zero as n and p tend to infinity.

We now prove that $u_p - u_n$ tends to zero uniformly in any convex closed region F lying entirely inside K. To prove this it will suffice (in virtue of the Corollary to Lemma 6 of §10.5) to show that, for each number-pair (n, p), there is in F a point P_{np} such that $u_p(P_{np}) - u_n(P_{np})$ tends to zero as n and p tend to infinity. We prove the existence of such a point P_{np} as follows.

Let v be a function continuous in $\Delta + \beta$, of class D_1 in Δ, and vanishing on β. Let AB be a segment of a vertical line

$$x = \xi_1, \quad \eta_1 \leqslant y \leqslant \eta_2, \tag{10.9.1}$$

lying in F. Let $P(\xi_1, y)$ be a point of the segment AB, and let the horizontal line through P cut β in $Q(x_2, y)$, PQ lying in Δ (Fig. 10.9). Then, since $v(x_2, y) = 0$,

$$v(\xi_1, y) = -\int_{\xi_1}^{x_2} v_x(x, y)\, dx, \tag{10.9.2}$$

and therefore, by Schwarz's inequality, supposing for definiteness $\xi_1 < x_2$,

$$v^2(\xi_1, y) \leqslant (x_2 - \xi_1)\int_{\xi_1}^{x_2} v_x^2(x, y)\, dx \leqslant L\int_{\xi_1}^{x_2} v_x^2(x, y)\, dx, \tag{10.9.3}$$

where L is the diameter of the bounded set Δ. On integrating from η_1 to η_2 we have

$$\int_{\eta_1}^{\eta_2} v^2(\xi_1, y)\, dy \leqslant L\int_{\eta_1}^{\eta_2} dy\int_{\xi_1}^{x_2} v_x{}^2(x, y)\, dx \leqslant LD(v). \tag{10.9.4}$$

It follows that, at some point (ξ_1, η) of AB,

$$(10.9.5) \qquad v^2(\xi_1, \eta) \leqslant \frac{LD(v)}{\eta_2 - \eta_1}.$$

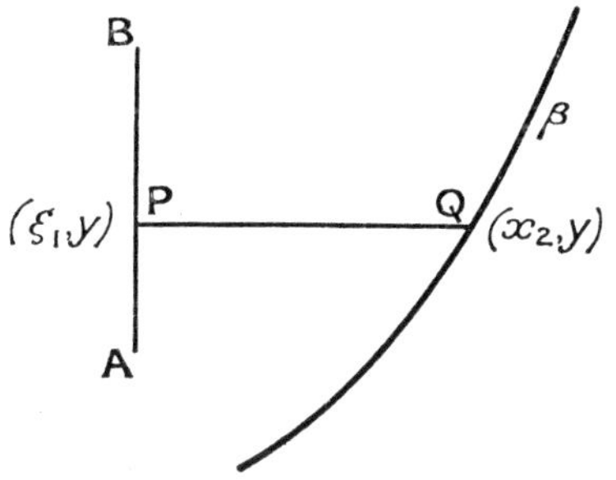

Fig. 10.9

We now take $v(x, y) = \psi_p - \psi_n$. Then $D(v)$ tends to zero as n and p tend to infinity, and therefore $v(\xi_1, \eta)$ tends to zero. Thus we may take for P_{np} the point (ξ_1, η) on AB, and therefore $u_p - u_n$ tends to zero uniformly in F. The general principle of uniform convergence now assures us that u_n tends uniformly to a limit function u in F. Since F may be chosen to include any particular point inside K, u_n tends to a limit function u inside K. In virtue of the Corollary to Lemma 4 of §10.5, u is harmonic.

10.10 The limit function

The smoothing process described in §10.9 can be applied to any circle K in Δ, and we have no reason to choose one circle rather than another. But now we come to the crux of the whole matter. Let K_1 and K_2 be two intersecting circles, and let us denote the domain common to the interiors of both circles by S. If we apply the smoothing process to K_1 we obtain a harmonic function u_1 in K_1, and if we apply it to K_2 we obtain a harmonic function u_2 in K_2. The crucial point is that $u_1 = u_2$ at each point of S.

To prove this, let $\{\psi_n{}^1\}$ be the minimizing sequence obtained from $\{\varphi_n\}$ by the smoothing process for K_1, and let $\{\psi_n{}^2\}$ be the minimizing sequence obtained from $\{\varphi_n\}$ by the smoothing process for K_2. Then the mixed sequence $\psi_1{}^1, \psi_1{}^2, \psi_2{}^1, \psi_2{}^2, \psi_3{}^1, \psi_3{}^2, \ldots$ is also a minimizing sequence. Let K_3 be a circle lying in S. Then, as in §10.9, the mixed sequence converges to a harmonic function u_3 inside K_3. But since $\{\psi_n{}^1\}$ converges to u_1 inside K_3, and $\{\psi_n{}^2\}$ converges to u_2 inside K_3, we must have $u_1 = u_3 = u_2$ inside K_3. It follows that u_1 is identical with u_2 in S.

Let F be a closed region of Δ, and let the distance between F and β be r (> 0). The interiors of the circles of radius r with their centres at points of F form an *open covering* of the bounded closed set F, i.e. each point of F belongs to at least one of the open sets which are the interiors of the circles. It follows from the Heine-Borel theorem that F can be covered by a finite number of these circles, say $C_1, C_2, \ldots, C_k$. The smoothing process applied to any one of these circles, say C_ν leads to a harmonic function inside C_ν, but since these functions agree in the common part of two overlapping circles we have a harmonic function defined in F. Since F can be chosen to contain any assigned point of Δ, we have a harmonic function u defined in Δ. We shall prove that this function provides both the solution of Dirichlet's problem and the minimizing function for Dirichlet's integral.

Consider a particular closed set F in Δ and the covering $C_1, C_2, \ldots, C_k$. We have

$$F \subseteq \sum_{\nu=1}^{k} C_\nu \subset \Delta, \tag{10.10.1}$$

and therefore, for all values of n,

$$D_F(\varphi_n - u) \leqslant \sum_{\nu=1}^{k} D_{C_\nu}(\varphi_n - u). \tag{10.10.2}$$

But for any circle C of Δ,

$$D_C(\varphi_n - u) \to 0. \tag{10.10.3}$$

For if $\{\psi_n\}$ is the minimizing sequence derived from $\{\varphi_n\}$ by the smoothing process for the circle C, the mixed sequence $\varphi_1, \psi_1, \varphi_2, \psi_2, \varphi_3, \psi_3, \ldots$ is also a minimizing sequence, and therefore (in virtue of (10.7.3)) $D_C(\varphi_n - \psi_n)$, which is equal to $D(\varphi_n - \psi_n)$, tends to zero. Now by (10.8.1)

$$\sqrt{D_C(\varphi_n - u)} \leqslant \sqrt{D_C(\varphi_n - \psi_n)} + \sqrt{D_C(\psi_n - u)}, \tag{10.10.4}$$

and (10.10.3) follows, since both terms on the right in (10.10.4) tend to zero: we have just seen that the first term tends to zero, and the second tends to zero because $\psi_n = u_n$ inside C, and the derivatives of $u_n - u$ tend uniformly to zero. Thus (10.10.3) is true for each of the k circles $C_1, C_2, \ldots, C_k$, and it therefore follows from (10.10.2) that

(10.10.5) $$D_F(\varphi_n - u) \to 0$$

as $n \to \infty$.

Using again the inequality (10.8.1) we have

(10.10.6) $$\begin{aligned}\sqrt{D_F(u)} &\leqslant \sqrt{D_F(\varphi_n - u)} + \sqrt{D_F(\varphi_n)}\\ &\leqslant \sqrt{D_F(\varphi_n - u)} + \sqrt{D(\varphi_n)}.\end{aligned}$$

The first member of this inequality is independent of n, and in the second member the first term tends to zero by (10.10.5), and the second tends to $\sqrt{m}$ as $n \to \infty$. Hence

(10.10.7) $$D_F(u) \leqslant m,$$

and letting $F \to \Delta$ we find

(10.10.8) $$D(u) \leqslant m.$$

10.11 Proof of Dirichlet's principle

Starting from the minimizing sequence $\{\varphi_n\}$ we have constructed, by the smoothing process, a function u which is harmonic in Δ. The tasks that remain are to prove (i) that u takes the prescribed boundary values, (ii) that $D(u) = m$, and (iii) that u is unique and independent of the particular minimizing sequence from which we start. We shall find that, when (i) is established, (ii) and (iii) follow easily. We therefore turn to the proof of the fact that $u(P) \to g(R)$ as a point P of Δ tends to a point R of β. We will assume that R is an ordinary point, not a corner of β, and we first prove the result for the case when P approaches R along the normal to the boundary curve.

Let us suppose then that R is a point of β, and that P is a point of Δ on the normal to β at R. We denote the distance $|RP|$ by $5h$, and we wish to prove that $u(P) \to g(R)$ as $h \to 0$. To establish this result we shall show that, if ε is a given positive number, $|u(P) - g(R)| \leqslant \varepsilon$ when h is sufficiently small. Using a procedure due in principle to Courant we draw the circle of radius $10h$ with R as centre, and we denote the part of Δ lying inside this circle by δ. We choose an integer N so large that

(10.11.1) $$D(\varphi_n - \varphi_N) < (\tfrac{1}{32}\varepsilon)^2$$

for all $n > N$. We then choose h so small that both

(10.11.2) $$D_\delta(\varphi_N) < (\tfrac{1}{32}\varepsilon)^2$$

and

(10.11.3) $$|g(R) - g(S)| < \tfrac{1}{8}\varepsilon,$$

where S is any point of β such that the distance $|RS| < 4h$: this is always possible since g is continuous on β. Then, by (10.8.1),

(10.11.4) $$\sqrt{D_\delta(\varphi_n)} \leqslant \sqrt{D_\delta(\varphi_n - \varphi_N)} + \sqrt{D_\delta(\varphi_N)}$$
$$\leqslant \sqrt{D(\varphi_n - \varphi_N)} + \sqrt{D_\delta(\varphi_N)} < \tfrac{1}{16}\varepsilon$$

for all $n > N$.

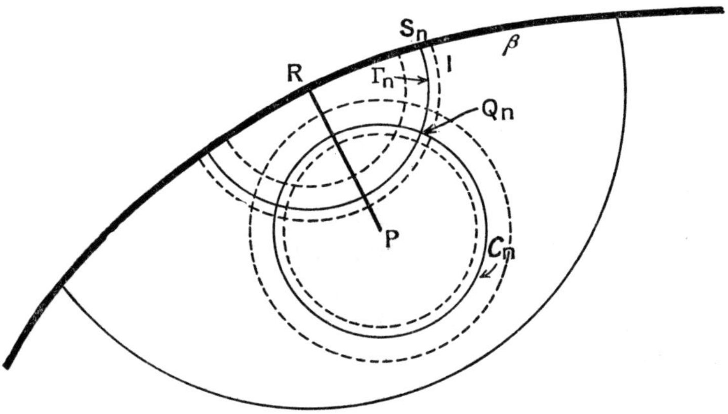

Fig. 10.11

We now consider the annulus α bounded by the circle of radius $3h$ and the circle of radius $4h$ about P; we assume that $\alpha \subset \delta$. If for the moment (to simplify the notation) we write φ instead of φ_n, we have

(10.11.5) $$\iint_\alpha \varphi_s^2 \, dr \, ds \leqslant \iint_\alpha (\varphi_r^2 + \varphi_s^2) \, dr \, ds$$
$$= D_\alpha(\varphi) \leqslant D_\delta(\varphi) < (\tfrac{1}{16}\varepsilon)^2,$$

where we use polar coordinates with P as origin, and where we write ds for $r \, d\theta$. Thus

(10.11.6) $$\int_{3h}^{4h} dr \int_0^{2\pi r} \varphi_s^2 \, ds < (\tfrac{1}{16}\varepsilon)^2,$$

and therefore there is a value $r = a$, where $3h < a < 4h$, such that

(10.11.7) $$\int_0^{2\pi r} \varphi_s^2\, ds < \frac{1}{h}(\tfrac{1}{16}\varepsilon)^2,$$

where the integral is taken along the circle C, $r = a$. Then, by Schwarz's inequality,

(10.11.8) $$\left(\int_0^{2\pi a} |\varphi_s|\, ds\right)^2 < \frac{2\pi a}{h}(\tfrac{1}{16}\varepsilon)^2 < 8\pi(\tfrac{1}{16}\varepsilon)^2,$$

and it follows that, if A_1 and A_2 are any two points on the circle C,

(10.11.9) $$|\varphi(A_1) - \varphi(A_2)| < \tfrac{1}{16}\varepsilon\sqrt{(8\pi)} < \tfrac{1}{3}\varepsilon.$$

For all $n > N$ there is a circle C_n of radius a_n about P, with $3h < a_n < 4h$, such that, for any two points A_1 and A_2 on C_n,

(10.11.10) $$|\varphi_n(A_1) - \varphi_n(A_2)| < \tfrac{1}{3}\varepsilon.$$

By the same argument there exists a circle Γ_n of radius b_n about R, where $3h < b_n < 4h$, such that for any two points B_1 and B_2 on Γ_n and in $\delta + \beta$,

(10.11.11) $$|\varphi_n(B_1) - \varphi_n(B_2)| < \tfrac{1}{3}\varepsilon.$$

Now Γ_n intersects C_n at a point Q_n, and Γ_n intersects β at a point S_n, such that S_n and Q_n are connected by an arc of Γ_n in δ. Therefore, since $\varphi_n(S_n) = g(S_n)$,

(10.11.12) $$|\varphi_n(Q_n) - g(S_n)| < \tfrac{1}{3}\varepsilon.$$

If u_n is the harmonic function in C_n obtained by the smoothing process for the minimizing sequence $\{\varphi_n\}$, then the value of u_n at P is equal to the value of φ_n at some point T_n of C_n (Corollary 1 of Lemma 1, §10.5). Thus

(10.11.13) $$|u_n(P) - \varphi_n(Q_n)| = |\varphi_n(T_n) - \varphi_n(Q_n)| < \tfrac{1}{3}\varepsilon.$$

And finally, from (10.11.3),

(10.11.14) $$|g(S_n) - g(R)| < \tfrac{1}{3}\varepsilon.$$

We now combine the inequalities (10.11.13), (10.11.12), and (10.11.14), giving

(10.11.15) $$\begin{aligned}|u_n(P) - g(R)| &\leqslant |u_n(P) - \varphi_n(Q_n)| + |\varphi_n(Q_n) - g(S_n)| \\ &\quad + |g(S_n) - g(R)| \\ &< \tfrac{1}{3}\varepsilon + \tfrac{1}{3}\varepsilon + \tfrac{1}{3}\varepsilon = \varepsilon.\end{aligned}$$

Letting $n \to \infty$ we have

(10.11.16) $$|u(P) - g(R)| \leqslant \varepsilon,$$

and this completes the proof that $u(P) \to g(R)$ as $h \to 0$.

So far we have supposed that P approaches R along the normal. But an inspection of the proof shows that, if R lies on a small segment γ of β, the convergence is uniform with respect to the position of R on γ, and it follows easily that u is a function which is continuous in $\Delta + \beta$ and which takes the prescribed values g on β.

Thus u is an admissible function, and

$$D(u) \geqslant m, \tag{10.11.17}$$

and this inequality, together with (10.10.8), shows that

$$D(u) = m. \tag{10.11.18}$$

Finally, the solution u of the boundary value problem is unique; the proof is the same as that for the special case of the circle (§10.6). It is evident therefore that we arrive at the same minimizing function whatever minimizing sequence $\{\varphi_n\}$ we start from. The proof of Dirichlet's principle for functions of two variables is complete.

10.12 Plateau's problem

Another famous problem is that of finding the surface of minimum area bounded by a given closed curve Γ in space.

If the projection of Γ on the plane $z = 0$ is a simple closed curve β, and if the surfaces considered have the form

$$z = \varphi(x, y), \tag{10.12.1}$$

the integral we wish to minimize is

$$\iint_{\Delta} \sqrt{(1 + \varphi_x^2 + \varphi_y^2)}\, dx\, dy, \tag{10.12.2}$$

where Δ is the inner domain of the (x, y)-plane bounded by β. Let us be content to consider the simple case in which the admissible functions are those functions which are of class C_2 in a domain $\mathscr{D}$ containing $\Delta + \beta$, and which take the values g on β, where g is the height of a point of Γ above the corresponding point of β.

The first-order condition (10.1.13) is

$$\frac{\partial}{\partial x}\frac{p}{\rho} + \frac{\partial}{\partial y}\frac{q}{\rho} = 0, \tag{10.12.3}$$

where

$$p = \varphi_x, \quad q = \varphi_y, \quad \rho^2 = 1 + p^2 + q^2. \tag{10.12.4}$$

Equation (10.12.3) can be written in the expanded form

$$r(1 + q^2) - 2pqs + t(1 + p^2) = 0, \tag{10.12.5}$$

where

$$r = \varphi_{xx}, \quad s = \varphi_{xy}, \quad t = \varphi_{yy}. \tag{10.12.6}$$

The equation (10.12.5) was given by Lagrange. Later Meusnier proved that this equation is equivalent to the vanishing of the mean curvature at every point of the surface,

$$\frac{1}{\rho_1} + \frac{1}{\rho_2} = 0. \tag{10.12.7}$$

The equation (10.12.7) expresses the defining property of the so-called *minimal surfaces*; the name arises from the least-area property from which we set out.

The attack is of course inadequate, since the assumptions made about Γ and about the surfaces admitted are too narrow. For a more complete discussion we must use a parametric representation of the surface, and then the integral to be minimized is

$$\iint \sqrt{(EG - F^2)}\, du\, dv. \tag{10.12.8}$$

(The functions E, F, G have already been encountered in §9.7). A fuller discussion of Plateau's problem will be found in books on differential geometry, and would be out of place here. The minimal surface for a given boundary Γ is the form taken by a soap-film bounded by a rigid wire in the form Γ, and much experimental work of great interest has been devoted, especially by Courant, to this aspect of the problem.

Plateau's problem can be regarded as a generalization of Dirichlet's problem. Suppose we have a *membrane*, stretched uniformly, and originally covering the interior Δ of a simple closed curve β in the plane $z = 0$. Now let the points of the boundary be displaced in the direction Oz through a small distance $g(x, y)$, where the function g, defined on β, is subject to the restriction mentioned in §10.4. The potential energy of the membrane is proportional to the increase in area, and the membrane will take a form for which the potential energy is a minimum, i.e. a form for which the integral (10.12.2) is a minimum. But here φ and its derivatives are small, and to a sufficient approximation the potential energy is

$$V = \tfrac{1}{2}\iint_{\Delta} \mu(\varphi_x^2 + \varphi_y^2)\, dS, \tag{10.12.9}$$

where the positive constant μ is the area tension in the membrane. Thus we need the function φ which takes the values g on β and minimizes (10.12.9), and this is precisely the problem of Dirichlet already discussed.

It may be of interest to pursue the subject of the nearly-plane membrane a little further. If the membrane is subject to an external pressure $f(x, y)$ in the direction Oz the fundamental equation of statics (the equation of virtual work) has the form

$$-\delta V + \iint_{\Delta} f\, \delta\varphi\, dS = 0, \tag{10.12.10}$$

and this leads to

$$-\iint_{\Delta} \mu(\varphi_x\, \delta\varphi_x + \varphi_y\, \delta\varphi_y)\, dS + \iint_{\Delta} f\, \delta\varphi\, dS = 0. \tag{10.12.11}$$

Now

$$\varphi_x\, \delta\varphi_x = \varphi_x \frac{\partial}{\partial x}\, \delta\varphi = \frac{\partial}{\partial x}\, (\varphi_x\, \delta\varphi) - \varphi_{xx}\, \delta\varphi, \tag{10.12.12}$$

and using this and the similar formula for $\varphi_y\, \delta\varphi_y$ we find

$$\iint_{\Delta} \Big\{[f + \mu(\varphi_{xx} + \varphi_{yy})]\, \delta\varphi - \mu\Big[\frac{\partial}{\partial x}\, (\varphi_x\, \delta\varphi) + \frac{\partial}{\partial y}\, (\varphi_y\, \delta\varphi)\Big]\Big\}\, dS = 0. \tag{10.12.13}$$

We now use Green's lemma to transform (10.12.13) into

$$\iint_{\Delta} \{f + \mu(\varphi_{xx} + \varphi_{yy})\}\, \delta\varphi\, dS - \int_{\beta} \mu\varphi_n\, \delta\varphi\, ds = 0, \tag{10.12.14}$$

where φ_n $(= l\varphi_x + m\varphi_y)$ is the rate of change of φ along the outward normal to β (cf. 10.1.7)). In our present problem, where the value of φ at all points of β is prescribed, the line-integral in (10.12.14) disappears, and we see that φ satisfies Poisson's equation

$$\varphi_{xx} + \varphi_{yy} = -f/\mu. \tag{10.12.15}$$

Alternatively we can absorb the effect of the external pressure into the potential function,

$$V' = \iint_{\Delta} \{\tfrac{1}{2}\mu(\varphi_x^2 + \varphi_y^2) - f\varphi\}\, dS, \tag{10.12.16}$$

and then the equation of virtual work is simply $-\delta V' = 0$.

Finally, suppose that the points of the boundary are free to move in the direction Oz and are tied to their undisturbed positions by elastic forces $\sigma(s)$ per unit length, i.e. the restoring force on the element ds is $\sigma\varphi\, ds$. The potential energy function is now

$$V'' = \iint_{\Delta} \{\tfrac{1}{2}\mu(\varphi_x^2 + \varphi_y^2) - f\varphi\}\, dS + \tfrac{1}{2}\int_{\beta} \sigma\varphi^2\, ds, \tag{10.12.17}$$

and the equation $-\delta V'' = 0$ leads to

$$\iint_{\Delta} \{f + \mu(\varphi_{xx} + \varphi_{yy})\}\, \delta\varphi\, dS - \int_{\beta} (\mu\varphi_n + \sigma\varphi)\, \delta\varphi\, ds = 0. \tag{10.12.18}$$

The differential equation satisfied by φ is still (10.12.15), but now, instead of having prescribed boundary values, we have to satisfy on β the boundary condition

$$\mu\varphi_n + \sigma\varphi = 0. \tag{10.12.19}$$

Of course the boundary condition (10.12.19) is evident also by considering the equilibrium of an element ds of the boundary of the membrane.

It will help to clarify the ideas if we consider a simple problem of each type. We suppose in each case that the boundary β is the circle given (in Cartesian coordinates) by $x^2 + y^2 = a^2$, or (in polar coordinates) by $r = a$. We recall that

$$\nabla^2\varphi = \varphi_{xx} + \varphi_{yy} = \frac{1}{r}\frac{\partial}{\partial r}\left(r\frac{\partial\varphi}{\partial r}\right) + \frac{1}{r^2}\frac{\partial^2\varphi}{\partial\theta^2}.$$

(i) Let the prescribed displacement of the boundary be $g = \lambda \sin^2\theta = \lambda y^2/a^2$, where λ is small. Then the displacement φ of the membrane is the harmonic function taking the value $\lambda \sin^2\theta$ on $r = a$, namely

$$\varphi = \frac{\lambda}{2a^2}(a^2 - r^2\cos 2\theta) = \frac{\lambda}{2a^2}(a^2 - x^2 + y^2).$$

(ii) If the prescribed displacement of the boundary is $\lambda \sin^2\theta$ as before, and the membrane is subject to a *uniform* external pressure (in the direction Oz) $f(x, y) = p$, the solution of (10.12.15) taking the required value on $r = a$ is

$$\varphi = \frac{p}{4\mu}(a^2 - r^2) + \frac{\lambda}{2a^2}(a^2 - r^2 \cos 2\theta).$$

(iii) If there is a uniform external pressure p, and the boundary is movable and subject to a *uniform* restoring force σ, the displacement φ of the membrane is the solution of (10.12.15) satisfying the boundary condition (10.12.19), namely

$$\varphi = \frac{pa}{2\sigma} + \frac{p}{4\mu}(a^2 - r^2).$$

10.13 The vibrating string

We consider a perfectly flexible elastic string stretched at tension b along the x-axis with its ends at $x = 0$ and at $x = l$. The line-density $\sigma(x)$ is a continuous function of x. In the fundamental problem the ends of the string are fixed at $(0, 0)$ and at $(l, 0)$. The string executes small transverse oscillations in the plane Oxy, the transverse displacement at time t of the particle of the string originally at $(x, 0)$ being $y(x, t)$. The tension b is large and is effectively constant throughout. The kinetic energy function T is $\int_0^l \frac{1}{2}\sigma(x)\dot{y}^2\, dx$, and the potential energy function V at time t is $b\,\delta l$ (where δl is the increase in length) which is, correct to order y^2, $b\int_0^l \frac{1}{2}y_x^{\,2}\, dx$.

We now appeal to Hamilton's principle, which we assume to be valid, not only for systems with a finite number of degrees of freedom, but also for continuous systems. The principle asserts that $\int_\tau^{\bar{\tau}} (T - V)\, dt$ is stationary for the actual motion. The terminal instants τ and $\bar{\tau}$ are fixed, and the configuration at each of these instants is unvaried. Thus the integral

$$I = \int_\tau^{\bar{\tau}}\int_0^l \tfrac{1}{2}(\sigma\dot{y}^2 - by_x^{\,2})\, dx\, dt \tag{10.13.1}$$

is stationary for the actual motion. We have thus an extremal problem with two independent variables x, t, and one dependent variable $y(x, t)$. The region $\Delta + \beta$ is the rectangle $0 \leqslant x \leqslant l$, $\tau \leqslant t \leqslant \bar{\tau}$, and the values of y on the boundary are prescribed. The differential equation (10.1.13) gives

$$\sigma\ddot{y} = by_{xx}. \tag{10.13.2}$$

The equation (10.13.2) can also be derived from the fundamental equation of dynamics, and it can be argued that this is the more natural approach to the problem, since Hamilton's principle is in essence merely the result of integrating the fundamental equation over an interval of time. The fundamental equation of dynamics can be written in the form

$$\int_0^l \sigma\ddot{y}\,\delta y\,dx + \delta V = 0, \tag{10.13.3}$$

where, as before, $V = b\int_0^l \frac{1}{2}y_x^2\,dx$. But

$$\begin{aligned} \delta V &= b\int_0^l y_x\,\delta y_x\,dx = b\int_0^l y_x\frac{\partial}{\partial x}\delta y\,dx \\ &= by_x\,\delta y\Big|_0^l - b\int_0^l y_{xx}\,\delta y\,dx. \end{aligned} \tag{10.13.4}$$

Hence, since $\delta y = 0$ at $x = 0$ and at $x = l$,

$$\int_0^l \sigma\ddot{y}\,\delta y\,dx - b\int_0^l y_{xx}\,\delta y\,dx = 0, \tag{10.13.5}$$

and since this holds for an arbitrary δy (assumed to be of class C_2 and to vanish at the end-points) we recover (10.13.2).

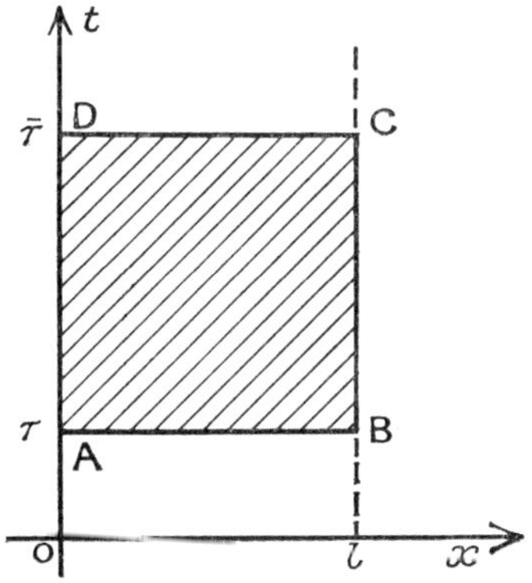

Fig. 10.13

A slightly more difficult problem is that in which the end of the string at $x = l$, instead of being fixed, is attached to a bead of mass m which slides on a smooth wire on the line $x = l$: and let us suppose further that the bead is attracted to its equilibrium position by a restoring force $k|y|$. Now in applying Hamilton's principle we may suppose that the value of y at $x = l$ is unvaried for all t in $[\tau, \bar{\tau}]$, and this implies that y still satisfies the differential equation (10.13.2).

The end condition at $x = l$ is provided by the equation of motion of the bead

$$m\ddot{z} = -kz - b\theta, \tag{10.13.6}$$

where $z(t)$ is written for $y(l, t)$ and $\theta(t)$ for $y_x(l, t)$. The simplest case is that in which both m and k are zero, and then (10.13.6) reduces to $\theta = 0$.

But we can, of course, derive the whole system of equations, (10.13.6) as well as (10.13.2), from Hamilton's principle. To achieve this end we consider a more general variation in which we abandon the restriction that y is unvaried on $x = l$ for all time. The motion is such as to give a stationary value to

$$J = \int_\tau^{\bar{\tau}}\int_0^l \tfrac{1}{2}(\sigma\dot{y}^2 - by_x^2)\,dx\,dt + \int_\tau^{\bar{\tau}} \tfrac{1}{2}(m\dot{z}^2 - kz^2)\,dt. \tag{10.13.7}$$

Let $\psi(\alpha)$ be the value of J for the varied motion $y(x, t) + \alpha\eta(x, t)$. We notice that η vanishes on three sides of the rectangle $ABCD$ (Fig. 10.13) but not on the fourth side BC. Now, quoting (10.1.12),

$$\psi'(0) = -\int_\tau^{\bar{\tau}}\int_0^l \eta(\sigma\ddot{y} - by_{xx})\,dx\,dt + \int_\tau^{\bar{\tau}} \zeta(-b\theta)\,dt + \int_\tau^{\bar{\tau}} (m\dot{z}\dot{\zeta} - kz\zeta)\,dt, \tag{10.13.8}$$

where ζ is written for $\eta(l, t)$. Since ζ vanishes at τ and at $\bar{\tau}$, (10.13.8) leads to

$$\psi'(0) = -\int_\tau^{\bar{\tau}}\int_0^l \eta(\sigma\ddot{y} - by_{xx})\,dx\,dt - \int_\tau^{\bar{\tau}} \zeta(b\theta + m\ddot{z} + kz)\,dt. \tag{10.13.9}$$

Since η is arbitrary, the differential equation (10.13.2) and the boundary condition (10.13.6) both follow from the condition $\psi'(0) = 0$.

10.14 The eigenvalues

We now turn to the task of finding a solution of the equation (10.13.2). Let us endeavour to find a solution of the form $\varphi(x)\psi(t)$. On substituting this formula in the equation we find

$$\frac{\ddot{\psi}}{\psi} = \frac{b\varphi''}{\sigma\varphi}, \tag{10.14.1}$$

and since the first member is a function of t, and the second is a function of x, the only possibility is that each has a constant value, say $-\lambda$, so that

$$b\varphi'' + \lambda\sigma\varphi = 0, \tag{10.14.2}$$

$$\ddot{\psi} + \lambda\psi = 0. \tag{10.14.3}$$

Now (10.14.2) is a simple special case of the differential equation (6.14.10) which we have discussed already. Let us consider first the case where the end-points of the string are fixed. In this case we need a solution of (10.14.2) vanishing at $x = 0$ and at $x = l$, and such a solution exists if and only if λ has one of an enumerable sequence of values $\lambda_1, \lambda_2, \lambda_3, \ldots$. These numbers are the *eigenvalues*, and we usually arrange them in ascending order of magnitude, $\lambda_1 < \lambda_2 < \lambda_3 \ldots$: the λ's are all positive, and $\lambda_n \to \infty$ with n. Corresponding to each λ_n there is a solution $\varphi_n(x)$ of (10.14.2) which vanishes at $x = 0$ and at $x = l$, and which is unique save for a constant multiplier. The solution $\varphi_n(x)$ is uniquely determined if we impose the conditions $\varphi_n'(0) > 0$ and $\int^l \sigma\varphi_n^2\,dx = 1$, and these are the *eigenfunctions*. As we have seen (§6.14) the eigenfunctions have the property of orthogonality,

$$\int_0^l \sigma\varphi_r\varphi_s\,dx = 0 \tag{10.14.4}$$

if $r \neq s$. A solution of (10.13.2) is given by the formula

$$(A\cos p_n t + B\sin p_n t)\varphi_n(x), \tag{10.14.5}$$

where $p_n = \sqrt{\lambda_n}$.

The simplest case is that of the uniform string, $\sigma(x)$ is constant. Then (10.13.2) is the *wave equation*

$$\ddot{y} = c^2 y_{xx}, \tag{10.14.6}$$

where $c^2 = b/\sigma$, and (10.14.2) becomes

$$c^2\varphi'' + \lambda\varphi = 0. \tag{10.14.7}$$

The eigenvalue λ_n is $(n\pi c/l)^2$, and the corresponding eigenfunction is

$$\varphi_n = \sqrt{\frac{2}{\sigma l}}\sin\frac{n\pi x}{l}. \tag{10.14.8}$$

We return to the general case in which $\sigma(x)$ is not constant. If we consider the second problem mentioned in §10.13, where the end $x = l$ is attached to a bead sliding on a smooth wire, the calculation needs modification. If $m = 0$ the modification is slight. The end-conditions are now $\varphi = 0$ at $x = 0$, and $k\varphi + b\varphi_x = 0$ at $x = l$, and the proof of the orthogonal property of the eigenfunctions is practically the same as that given in §6.14. But if $m > 0$ the orthogonal property takes a somewhat more complicated form. If we put $y = \varphi(x)\psi(t)$ in the end-condition (10.13.6) we get, in virtue of (10.14.3),

$$\lambda m\varphi = k\varphi + b\varphi' \tag{10.14.9}$$

at $x = l$. The orthogonality property is

$$\int_0^l \sigma\varphi_r\varphi_s\,dx + m\varphi_r(l)\varphi_s(l) = 0. \tag{10.14.10}$$

To prove this, if we multiply the first member of (10.14.10) by λ_r, and make use of (10.14.2) and (10.14.9), we find

$$\lambda_r\left(\int_0^l \sigma\varphi_r\varphi_s\,dx + m\varphi_r(l)\varphi_s(l)\right) = -b\int_0^l \varphi_s\varphi_r''\,dx + \varphi_s(l)(k\varphi_r(l) + b\varphi_r'(l)). \tag{10.14.11}$$

If we subtract from (10.14.11) the similar result obtained by multiplying by λ_s instead of λ_r we obtain

$$\begin{aligned}(\lambda_r - \lambda_s)\left(\int_0^l \sigma\varphi_r\varphi_s\,dx + m\varphi_r(l)\varphi_s(l)\right) &= b\int_0^l (\varphi_r\varphi_s'' - \varphi_s\varphi_r'')\,dx - b(\varphi_r(l)\varphi_s'(l) - \varphi_s(l)\varphi_r'(l))\\ &= b(\varphi_r\varphi_s' - \varphi_s\varphi_r')\Big|_0^l - b(\varphi_r(l)\varphi_s'(l) - \varphi_s(l)\varphi_r'(l))\\ &= 0,\end{aligned} \tag{10.14.12}$$

and (10.14.10) follows since $\lambda_r - \lambda_s \neq 0$.

10.15 The vibrating membrane

We discussed in §10.12 the problem of a membrane in equilibrium; we now consider the membrane vibrating. We use the same notation as before (§10.12.) In the undisturbed position the membrane covers the interior Δ of a simple closed curve β in the plane $z = 0$, and the motion considered is a small oscillation normal to that plane, the displacement at time t being $z = \varphi(x, y, t)$. We denote the area density, supposed uniform, by ρ. We suppose that an external pressure $f(x, y, t)$ acts on the membrane in the direction Oz, and that the boundary is free to move in the direction Oz, this motion being controlled by a restoring force $\sigma\varphi$ per unit length, where $\sigma = \sigma(s)$. We can find the equation of motion and the boundary condition either from Hamilton's principle or from the fundamental equation of dynamics. The latter is simpler, and gives

$$(10.15.1)\quad \iint\limits_{\Delta} \rho\ddot{\varphi}\,\delta\varphi\,dS - \iint\limits_{\Delta} f\,\delta\varphi\,dS + \int_{\beta} \sigma\varphi\,\delta\varphi\,ds + \delta\iint \tfrac{1}{2}\mu(\varphi_x{}^2 + \varphi_y{}^2)\,dS = 0,$$

where $\ddot{\varphi}$ means $\partial^2\varphi/\partial t^2$. Now, as before,

$$(10.15.2)\quad \delta\iint \tfrac{1}{2}\mu(\varphi_x{}^2 + \varphi_y{}^2)\,dS = -\iint\limits_{\Delta} \mu(\varphi_{xx} + \varphi_{yy})\delta\varphi\,dS + \int_{\beta} \mu\varphi_n\,\delta\varphi\,ds,$$

and we derive at once the differential equation

$$(10.15.3)\qquad \rho\ddot{\varphi} = \mu\nabla^2\varphi + f$$

and the boundary condition (the same as for the equilibrium problem)

$$(10.15.4)\qquad \mu\varphi_n + \sigma\varphi = 0.$$

Let us consider in particular the simple case where the boundary is fixed and there is no body force, so that

$$(10.15.5)\qquad \rho\ddot{\varphi} = \mu\nabla^2\varphi,$$

and $\varphi = 0$ on β. The line of argument is similar to that for the vibrating string considered in §10.13. If we seek a solution of the form

$$(10.15.6)\qquad \varphi = u(x, y)\psi(t)$$

we find, on substituting in (10.15.5),

$$(10.15.7)\qquad \frac{\ddot{\psi}}{\psi} = \frac{\mu\nabla^2 u}{\rho u},$$

and since the first member is a function of t, and the second is a function of (x, y), each must be constant, say each is equal to $-\lambda$.

Now $\lambda > 0$. To prove this, we start from the formula

$$\iint\limits_{\Delta} \left\{ \frac{\partial}{\partial x}(uu_x) + \frac{\partial}{\partial y}(uu_y) \right\} dS = \int_{\beta} uu_n \, ds = 0. \tag{10.15.8}$$

Hence

$$\iint\limits_{\Delta} (u_x^2 + u_y^2) \, dS + \iint\limits_{\Delta} u\nabla^2 u \, dS = 0, \tag{10.15.9}$$

and, since $\mu\nabla^2 u = -\lambda\rho u$, we have

$$\lambda = \frac{\mu \iint\limits_{\Delta} (u_x^2 + u_y^2) \, dS}{\rho \iint\limits_{\Delta} u^2 \, dS}, \tag{10.15.10}$$

and therefore $\lambda > 0$, since u is not identically zero. We write $\lambda = p^2$, where $p \geqslant 0$, and then

$$\ddot{\psi} + p^2\psi = 0, \tag{10.15.11}$$

$$\nabla^2 u + p^2\kappa^2 u = 0, \tag{10.15.12}$$

where $\kappa^2 = \rho/\mu$. The solution of (10.15.11) is

$$\psi = A \cos pt + B \sin pt, \tag{10.15.13}$$

and it remains to choose $\lambda(= p^2)$ so that (10.15.12) has a solution continuous in $\Delta + \beta$ and vanishing on β. There exists an infinite sequence of eigenvalues $\lambda_1, \lambda_2, \ldots$ satisfying this condition, and the corresponding functions $u_1(x, y), u_2(x, y), \ldots$ are the eigenfunctions.

The eigenfunctions possess an orthogonality property analogous to the orthogonality property (10.14.4) for the vibrating string. This property is given by the relation

$$\iint\limits_{\Delta} u_r u_s \, dS = 0 \tag{10.15.14}$$

where r and s are unequal positive integers. To prove this we notice that

$$\kappa^2(\lambda_r - \lambda_s) \iint\limits_{\Delta} u_r u_s \, dS = \iint\limits_{\Delta} (u_r\nabla^2 u_s - u_s\nabla^2 u_r) \, dS = 0, \tag{10.15.15}$$

and (10.15.14) follows since $\lambda_r - \lambda_s \neq 0$.

We follow the subject a little further for the special case in which the boundary β is the circle $r = a$. The equation (10.15.12), expressed in polar coordinates, is

$$r^2 u_{rr} + ru_r + p^2\kappa^2 r^2 u + u_{\theta\theta} = 0. \tag{10.15.16}$$

Let us seek a solution of the form

(10.15.17) $$u = f(r)g(\theta).$$

On substitution in (10.15.16) we find

(10.15.18) $$\frac{r^2}{f}\left(f_{rr} + \frac{1}{r}f_r + p^2\kappa^2 f\right) = -\frac{g_{\theta\theta}}{g},$$

and each member must be constant. But g must be periodic with period 2π, so the constant must be the square of a positive integer n, and

$$g = \alpha \cos n\theta + \beta \sin n\theta.$$

The equation satisfied by f is then

$$r^2 f_{rr} + r f_r + (p^2\kappa^2 r^2 - n^2) f = 0,$$

and the solution of this equation which is finite at 0 is a multiple of the Bessel function $J_n(p\kappa r)$.

Now the Bessel function $J_n(x)$ has an enumerable infinity of real positive zeros $x_{n1}, x_{n2}, \ldots$, and since $f(r)$ vanishes at $r = a$ we must have

$$p\kappa a = x_{nm}$$

for some integral value of m. We have thus a two-fold infinity of eigenvalues $(x_{nm}/\kappa a)^2$, and the corresponding eigenfunctions are of the form

$$J_n(x_{nm} r/a)(\alpha \cos n\theta + \beta \sin n\theta).$$

The simplest case is that in which $n = 0$, and there is circular symmetry about 0. There are a single infinity of oscillations, and in the mth of these the displacement is

$$J_0(\kappa q_m r)(A \cos q_m t + B \sin q_m t),$$

where $q_m = x_{0m}/\kappa a$.

Examples

1. *Maxwell's problem.* It is required to construct a road on a hemispherical mountain from the equator (which lies in a horizontal plane) to the summit so that a car travelling on the road will reach the summit in the shortest possible time. The speed of the car is a function $f(\alpha)$ of the inclination α of the road to the horizontal. The function $f(\alpha)$ is monotone decreasing, with $f(0) = v_0, f(\frac{1}{2}\pi) = 0$, and $\sin \alpha f(\alpha)$ has a unique maximum in $(0, \frac{1}{2}\pi)$ at $\alpha = \beta$. (The solution is a curve for which the inclination to the horizontal is β until a point is reached (at an angular distance β from the vertical) at which β is the maximum inclination of the tangent plane; from this point the path to the summit is the meridian circle.) Consider in particular the cases $f(\alpha) = v_0 \cos \alpha$, $f_0 = v_0 \cos^3 \alpha$. More generally consider the same problem for a mountain which is a surface of revolution, $z = g(r)$, with its axis vertical; here r denotes distance from the axis, and $g'(r) < 0$, except possibly at the summit.

2. Consider the integral

$$I = \int_X^{\bar{X}} \frac{1}{\sigma(x)} y'^2 \, dx,$$

where $\sigma(x)$ is a continuous function of x, positive in the (closed) interval $[X, \bar{X}]$, and the curves $y = \varphi(x)$ admitted join the fixed point $A(X, Y)$ to the fixed point $B(\bar{X}, \bar{Y})$. Prove from Schwarz's inequality that, if the functions $\varphi(x)$ are absolutely continuous, the infimum value of I is

$$(\bar{Y} - Y)^2 \Big/ \int_X^{\bar{X}} \sigma(x) \, dx.$$

Prove also that the infimum value is attained.

3. Find the most general integrand of the form

$$L(x, y)y'^2 + M(x, y)y'^3 + N(x, y)y'^4$$

for which the extremals are straight lines. (Euler's equation for the problem must be $y'' = 0$. This leads to an equation of the form $f(x, y, y') = 0$ which must be satisfied identically in x, y, y'. From this fact we easily find the solution

$$N = Ax^2 + Bx + C, \quad M = -4Axy + Dx - 2By + E,$$
$$L = 6Ay^2 - 3Dy + F,$$

where A, B, C, D, E, F are constants.)

4. Prove that if $M(x)$ is bounded in $[X, \overline{X}]$ and continuous except at a finite number of points, and if

$$\int_X^{\overline{X}} M(x)\eta'(x)\,dx = 0$$

for all functions $\eta(x)$ which belong to the class D_1, and which are such that

$$\eta(X) = \eta'(X) = \eta(\overline{X}) = \eta'(\overline{X}) = 0,$$

then there is a constant C such that

$$M(x) = C$$

at every point at which $M(x)$ is continuous. (Cf. Lemma 2, §2.1.)

5. Derive du Bois-Reymond's equation from the vanishing of the second member of (2.3.7) using for η the special form given below, without appealing to the result of Lemma 2 for a general η. The special η is defined as follows, where ξ is a number between X and $\overline{X}$, and $X < X + \varepsilon < \xi < \xi + \varepsilon < \overline{X}$:

$$\begin{aligned}
\eta(x) &= \frac{1}{\varepsilon}(x - X) && \text{for } X \leqslant x \leqslant X + \varepsilon,\\
\eta(x) &= 1 && \text{for } X + \varepsilon \leqslant x \leqslant \xi,\\
\eta(x) &= \frac{1}{\varepsilon}(\xi + \varepsilon - x) && \text{for } \xi \leqslant x \leqslant \xi + \varepsilon,\\
\eta(x) &= 0 && \text{for } \xi + \varepsilon \leqslant x \leqslant \overline{X}.
\end{aligned}$$

6. Consider the integral

$$\int_{-1}^{1} (x^2y'^2 + xy'^3)\,dx$$

along curves of class D_1 joining $A(-1, 0)$ to $B(1, 0)$. Prove that the line-segment AB is not a minimizing curve, and does not give even a strong relative minimum.

7. The refractive index μ in an optical medium is a function of y only, the axes being rectangular. Show from Fermat's principle that, for a light-ray in the plane $z = 0$, $\mu \cos \psi$ is constant along the ray. Hence find how μ varies with y (in the relevant range of values of y) if the light-path is part of (i) a sine-curve $y = a \sin nx$, (ii) an ellipse $\dfrac{x^2}{a^2} + \dfrac{y^2}{b^2} = 1$.

8. (i) A surface of revolution is such that a geodesic cuts the meridians at a constant angle α. Prove that the surface is a circular cylinder.

(ii) Find the geodesics (*a*) on a right circular cylinder, (*b*) on a right circular cone. Verify in each case that, when the surface is developed into a plane, the geodesics become straight lines.

9. A surface of revolution, whose equation in cylindrical polar coordinates is $r = \varphi(z)$, where $r = \sqrt{(x^2 + y^2)}$, is bounded by the circles $r = a, z = \pm c$, where $0 < c < a$. The function $\varphi(z)$ is chosen so that the surface integral

$$I = \iint r^{-\frac{1}{2}}\, dS$$

is stationary, dS being the element of area. Show that

$$\varphi(z) = k + \frac{z^2}{4k},$$

where

$$k = \tfrac{1}{2}\{a \pm \sqrt{(a^2 - c^2)}\}.$$

10. Show that the differential equation defining the geodesics on the paraboloid of revolution

$$x = r\cos\theta, \quad y = r\sin\theta, \quad z = r^2/(2a),$$

is

$$\frac{b^2}{a^2}\left(\frac{dr}{d\theta}\right)^2 = \frac{r^2(r^2 - b^2)}{r^2 + a^2},$$

and integrate the equation, taking $\theta = 0$ when $r = b$. (The equation is the polar equation of the projection of the geodesic on the plane $z = 0$.)

11. Find the extremals for the integral $\int e^x \sqrt{(1 + y'^2)}\, dx$, and show that there is no extremal joining two points if the difference of their ordinates is greater than π.

12. A particle moves in a plane under an attraction $n^2 r$ per unit mass to the point O, where r denotes distance from O. Deduce from Jacobi's form of the principle of Least Action (3.6.6) that the orbit is an ellipse with its centre at O.

13. Consider, in the light of Jacobi's form of the principle of Least Action, the motion of a particle in a plane under the action of a *repulsion* from O of magnitude μ/r^2 per unit mass (cf. §3.12). Prove that the orbit is a branch of a hyperbola with O as the outer focus.

14. According to the theory of relativity the path of a light-ray in the neighbourhood of the sun is such as to minimize

$$\int \sqrt{(\varphi^2\, dr^2 + \varphi r^2\, d\theta^2)},$$

where (r, θ) are polar coordinates, $\varphi = (1 - \frac{\gamma}{r})^{-1}$, and γ is constant. Prove that the differential equation of the path can be written in the form

$$\frac{d^2u}{d\theta^2} + u = \frac{3}{2}\gamma u^2,$$

where $u = 1/r$.

15. Find the curve joining the origin A (0, 0) to a variable point $B(\overline{X}, \overline{Y})$ on the curve $y^3 = a - x$, where $a > 0$, and minimizing the integral

$$I = \tfrac{1}{2}\int_0^{\overline{X}} (y'^2 - y^2)\, dx.$$

Prove that, in the special case $a = 2$, the value of $\overline{X}$ is approximately 1·83.

16. Consider the problem of the brachistochrone from a (variable) point A on a curve Γ to a (variable) point B on a curve Δ, when the velocity of the particle at A, not the total energy, is prescribed. Show that the tangent to Γ at A is parallel to the tangent to Δ at B. (The new feature in this problem is that the integrand now involves Y: it is a function of $y - Y$. Prove that the result corresponding to (4.2.12) is

$$\begin{aligned} dI &= (U_B\, d\overline{X} + V_B\, d\overline{Y}) - (U_A\, dX + V_B\, dY) \\ &= (U_B\, d\overline{X} + V_B d\overline{Y}) - (U_B\, dX + V_B\, dY).) \end{aligned}$$

17. Consider the problem of minimizing the integral $\int \frac{y'^2}{f'(x)}\, dx$ when the end-points are fixed, $f(x) \in C_2$, and $f'(x) > 0$ in $[X, \overline{X}]$. Prove that the extremals are the curves $y = af(x) + b$. Examine the fields obtained by keeping a fixed and allowing b to vary, and by keeping b fixed and allowing a to vary, and determine the transversals in each case. Discuss in particular the integrals $\int (y'^2/x)\, dx$ and $\int xy'^2\, dx$.

18. Consider the integral

$$I = \int y'^2(1 + y')^2\, dx$$

along a curve joining the fixed end-points A and B. Prove that the line-segment AB is a minimizing curve if $k \geqslant 0$ or if $k \leqslant -1$, where k is the slope of AB, but that the minimizing curve is discontinuous (in slope) if $0 > k > -1$. In what cases does the line-segment AB provide a weak relative minimum?

19. Consider the integral

$$I = \int y\sqrt{(1 - y'^2)}\, dx.$$

If A is the origin, and B is a point in the interior of the sector $x \geqslant y \geqslant 0$, prove that there is a unique extremal through A and B if we impose the condition that the extremal does not cut Ox between A and B, and prove that this extremal gives a larger value to I than any other curve $y = \varphi(x)$ in the sector. (Cf. §5.13. This is an example of the anomalous case where the slopes of the extremals through A can have only certain definite values. In this case $y'' = 0$ at A for all these extremals, but y''' can have any prescribed negative value. The integral appears in *Example* 3 of §6.13.)

20. Find the minimizing curve for the integral $\int y^2(1 + y'^2)\, dx$ when the end-points A and B lie on opposite sides of the x-axis, say A is $(-1, -\beta)$ and B is $(1, \gamma)$, where β and γ are positive (cf. §5.13). Distinguish the cases $\beta + \gamma < 2$ and $\beta + \gamma > 2$.

21. The point A lies on the given curve $\Gamma, y = f(x)$, in the upper half-plane. To find a point B on Γ, and an arc AB *of given length*, such that the area enclosed between this arc and the curve Γ is a maximum (Cf. *Example* 3 of §6.13. The required arc is a circular arc orthogonal to Γ at B.)

22. *Dido's problem.* A lamina with variable surface density $\mu(x, y)$ occupies the plane $z = 0$, where $\mu(x, y)$ is a continuous function of x and y. Two given points A and B lie on the x-axis. It is required to find a curve $y = \varphi(x)$ of given length, joining A to B, and lying in the upper half-plane, such that the mass contained between the curve and the x-axis is as great as possible. Prove that the curve is concave to Ox, and that its curvature is proportional to $\mu(x, y)$.

Consider in particular the case in which μ is a function $\mu(y)$ of y only. Show that the curve can be expressed parametrically in terms of ψ by formulae of the form

$$y = \theta(\psi),$$

where $\theta(\psi)$ is defined by the equation

$$\lambda \cos \psi = \int_0^\theta \mu(u)\, du + C,$$

and

$$x - x_0 = -\lambda \int_0^\psi \frac{\cos v}{\mu\{\theta(v)\}}\, dv.$$

(Cf. Example 3 of §6.13. The legend is that when Dido landed in N. Africa she persuaded the local chief to sell her as much land as an oxhide could contain. She then cut a hide into very narrow strips, and joined them to make a continuous thread more than two-and-a-half miles long. She was then able to enclose between the thread and the sea the land on which Carthage was built. To justify the name *Dido's problem* we may suppose that the function $\mu(x, y)$ is a measure of the fertility of the soil, and that the positions of the end-points of the thread on the coastline were prescribed!)

23. Determine among curves *of given length* joining two fixed points A and B in the upper half-plane, and lying in the upper half-plane, the curve which, with the ordinates through A and B, determines the solid of revolution of greatest volume. (The extremals are the *elastic curves* for which ρy is constant, where ρ is the radius of curvature. The curves can be represented explicitly in terms of elliptic integrals.)

24. A uniform flexible string, of length l and of weight w per unit length, has one end attached to fixed point A, and the other end attached to a bead B, of weight W. The bead slides on a smooth wire in the form of a curve Δ which lies in a vertical plane through A. Discuss the end-condition at B when the system is in equilibrium.

25. Discuss, without using the theory of Lagrange's problem, the extension of Euler's rule to the problem of minimizing

$$I = \int_X^{\overline{X}} F(x, y, y', y'')\, dx$$

subject to the isoperimetrical condition

$$J \equiv \int_X^{\overline{X}} G(x, y, y', y'')\, dx = l.$$

The end-points and the slopes at the end-points are prescribed, and, for the curves $y = \varphi(x)$ considered, $\varphi \in C_4$.

26. The point A lies on the line $x = X$ and the point B lies on the line $x = \overline{X}$. A curve in the upper half-plane joins A to B, and is such that the area bounded by the curve and by the lines $x = X$, $x = \overline{X}$, $y = 0$, is prescribed. The axis Oy being vertically upwards, find the curve for which the centre of gravity of the area lies as low as possible. Give a physical interpretation of the result.

27. A solid of uniform density ρ is bounded by the planes $x = 0$ and $x = a$ and the surface of revolution formed by rotating the

curve $y = f(x)$ about the x-axis. It has given mass M, and its moment of inertia about the x-axis is $2M^2/3\pi a\rho$. Show that if the distance $\bar{x}$ of the centre of gravity from the origin is stationary with respect to variations of the shape of the curve, then $y = f(x)$ is a parabola of semi-latus rectum $M/\pi a^2\rho$, with vertex either at the origin or at the point $(a, 0)$. Find $\bar{x}$ in each case.

28. A solid of revolution has uniform density and given mass. To find its shape if the moment of inertia about an axis at right angles to the axis of rotation is a minimum. (The axis we seek goes through the centre of gravity. The solid is an oblate spheroid, the ratio of the axes being $\sqrt{2}:1$.)

29. A curve in the upper half-plane joins the (fixed) point A to a (variable) point B which lies on the line $y = \overline{Y}$, and the curve is such that the area bounded by the curve, the ordinates through A and B, and the x-axis has a prescribed value. To find the curve of shortest length. (In this Example, and in Example 30, the device of Euler described in Example 3 of §6.13 can be used.)

30. Two lines OM, ON are given, and A is a (fixed) point on OM. A family of curves joins A to a (variable) point B on ON, and the curves are such that the area of the sector bounded by the two given lines and the curve has a prescribed value. To find the curve of this family which has the shortest length.

31. Consider the solution of the equation

$$x^4\varphi'' + \lambda\varphi = 0$$

in the range $1 \leqslant x \leqslant 2$, with the end-conditions $\varphi(1) = \varphi(2) = 0$. Transform the equation by the substitution $\psi = \varphi/x$, $t = 1/x$, and show that the eigenvalues are $\lambda = (2\pi n)^2$, where n is a positive integer. Find the corresponding eigenfunctions.

32. It is required to find a curve of class C_2 and of given length, joining two given points A and B in space, and such that the length of the orthogonal projection of the curve on a given plane is a maximum.

33. Three points O, A, and B are given. Find the curve joining A to B and minimizing the integral $\int r^2\, ds$, where r denotes distance from O. (If O, A, B are collinear, the solution is the line-segment AB. If $0 < \beta < \frac{1}{3}\pi$, where β is the angle AOB, there is a unique curve through A and B of the form $r^3 \cos(3\theta + \alpha) =$ constant, and this is the required curve. If $\theta \geqslant \frac{1}{3}\pi$, the solution is the pair of line-segments AO, OB.)

34. Determine the solid of least resistance when, instead of Newton's formula (9.14.1) for the resistance, we use the formula $\int_0^k y \sin \psi \, dy$. (This formula agrees better with the empirical results than Newton's formula. The solution again consists of a segment of the y-axis and an extremal arc.)

35. Discuss the solution of the equation (10.15.5)

$$\rho\ddot{\varphi} = \mu \nabla^2 \varphi$$

in Δ (where ρ and μ are positive constants) if $\varphi(x, y, t)$ has the prescribed value $g(x, y)$ on β. Prove that $\varphi = \psi(x, y, t) + \chi(x, y)$, where χ is the harmonic function taking the values g on β, and ψ satisfies the equation

$$\rho\ddot{\psi} = \mu \nabla^2 \psi$$

and vanishes on β.

Bibliography

1. Ostwald's Klassiker der exakten Wissenschaften, Englemann, Leipzig, 1894, Nos. 46 and 47. (No. 46 contains original papers by Johann Bernoulli, Jacob Bernoulli, and Euler; No. 47 contains original papers by Lagrange, Legendre, and Jacobi.)
2. Bliss, G. A., *Calculus of Variations*, Mathematical Association of America, 1925; reprinted 1944.
3. Bliss, G. A., *Lectures on the Calculus of Variations*, University of Chicago Press, 1946. (This book contains an extensive bibliography for the problem of Bolza.)
4. Bolza, O., *Vorlesungen über Variationsrechnung*, Teubner, 1909; reprinted by K. F. Koehler's Antiquarium, Leipzig, 1933.
5. Carathéodory, C., *Variationsrechnung und partielle Differentialgleichungen erster Ordnung*, Teubner, 1935.
6. Courant, R. and Hilbert, D., *Methoden der Mathematischen Physik, erster Band*, Julius Springer, Berlin, 1924. English edition, *Methods of Mathematical Physics*, Vol. I, Interscience Publishers, New York, 1953.
7. Courant, R., *Dirichlet's Principle, Conformal Mapping, and Minimal Surfaces*, Interscience Publishers, New York, 1950.
8. Goursat, E., *Cours d'Analyse Mathématique*, Vol. III, Chapter XXXIV, 5th Edition, Gauthier-Villars, 1956.
9. Marston Morse, *The Calculus of Variations in the Large*, American Mathematical Society, New York, 1934.
10. Tonelli, L., *Fondamenti di Calcolo delle Variazioni*, Bologna, Vol. I, 1921, Vol. II, 1923.
11. Weinstock, R., *Calculus of Variations*, McGraw-Hill Book Company New York, 1952.

Index